D0883885

FROM ROLLO
TO
TOM SAWYER

And Other Papers

From ROLLO *to* TOM SAWYER

AND OTHER PAPERS

by
Alice M. Jordan

Decorations by Nora S. Unwin

1948

THE HORN BOOK INC., BOSTON

TO

My Mother

*T*hese brief chapters on a few of the nineteenth century writers of books for children make no claim to be more than footnotes to that complete history of American children's books, greatly needed and as yet unwritten.

The paper from which the book takes its title was the first Caroline M. Hewins Lecture, read at Swampscott, Massachusetts, October 18, 1947. Six of the other chapters have appeared at various times in the "Horn Book" which has graciously allowed them to be reprinted with some revision.

Permission to quote from the following is here acknowledged with appreciation: Charles D. Abbott's "Howard Pyle. A Chronicle" (Harper and Brothers); Samuel Crothers' "Miss Muffet's Christmas Party" (Houghton Mifflin Company); Robert Morss Lovett's "Boy's Reading Fifty Years Ago" ("New Republic"); and Howard Pyle's "The Merry Adventures of Robin Hood," Thomas Nelson Page's "Two Little Confederates" and Frances Hodgson Burnett's "The Little Princess" (all Charles Scribner's Sons).

To Harriet Swift, of the Rare Books Department of the Boston Public Library, my cordial thanks are due for her help in securing material on early American publications.

Most of all, I owe a debt of continuing gratitude to Bertha Mahony Miller for her constant sympathy and understanding over the years. Without her unfailing confidence and encouragement "From Rollo to Tom Sawyer and Other Papers" would never have been finished.

A. M. J.

Cambridge
September, 1948

CONTENTS

INTRODUCTORY

I

NY STUDY, like the present, of nineteenth century writers for American children requires at least a brief glance at the book production of earlier years. For while the desirability of juvenile books to meet American needs did not make itself felt before the second quarter of the nineteenth century, there was no lack of activity in behalf of young American readers. A survey of the work of native presses may well be entered upon by reference to the distinguished volume entitled *Early American Children's Books*, describing the famous collection assembled by Dr. A. S. W. Rosenbach, of Philadelphia. In this exhaustive catalogue eight hundred juvenile books, published in the United States between 1682 and 1836, are listed and annotated. The basis of the information contained in the present chapter rests mainly upon an examination of *Early American Children's Books* (Southworth Press).

The nucleus of the collection was the varied stock of Jacob Johnson, a Quaker publisher who did a flourishing business in Philadelphia in the late eighteenth century and continuing into the nineteenth when Moses Polock, then a clerk in the office, acquired it. Although books published in Philadelphia naturally outnumber in the catalogue those from any other one place, it is surprising to learn how extensive the production of children's books really was in the first two hundred years of the English settlement of America.

Nor were the printers and publishers confined to the cities on the seaboard. Before the year 1836 we find that a market had arisen for the publishing output of fifteen states. In New York alone nineteen towns had connections with the publishing business. As a group, New England was in the lead. All her larger communities could show one or more printers who included children's books on their lists. Fourteen towns in Massachusetts and ten in Connecticut made their names known in this way. Isaiah Thomas at Boston and Worcester, Hugh Gaine at New York, John and Sidney Babcock at Hartford and New Haven, William Charles, printer and engraver of Philadelphia—all these are names associated with memorable work. Not a few publishers maintained branch houses. Isaiah Thomas controlled at one time sixteen presses, seven of them in Worcester, as well as bookstores in five states. If such abundance had been attended by a corresponding flow of creative ability, children's literature would have been rich indeed. But we look in vain for titles that have endured to become a part of children's reading today. With a few exceptions of books not written for children they have vanished, save as they are preserved here and there in special libraries.

The period before the Revolution has been called "the dreariest and most sterile in the entire history of American literature." As James Truslow Adams points out, it is the intellectual and aesthetic part of life that suffers in pioneer days.

Until the beginning of the nineteenth century the center for the publication of children's books was in Boston, where the Puritan element took the lead. Shadowed by the "terrible reality of invisible things," life was presented to Puritan children on both sides of the ocean as a hard and cruel bondage from which an early death was to be counted a joyful escape. To understand the depressing popularity of children's books overborne by thoughts of the grave, it is necessary to realize the Puritan's concern with a future life which completely dwarfed all sense of proportion. As we turn the pages of one of the most widely read books of the era, the severity of the prevailing influence makes itself felt in full strength. The book is called *A Token for Children*. It is by James Janeway, a famous English divine whose creed was a harsh and cruel one with no room in it for love and forgiveness. His noted book, printed in England and reprinted many times in America, is devoted to the condemnation of worldly pleasures and to the praise of the life and death of remarkably pious young children. The Boston bookseller, John Usher, imported thirty copies of the *Token* in one shipment.

Perhaps to show that American children were not to be outdone by English ones in piety, Cotton Mather added to the reprinted edition similar life histories of New England infants whose early deaths showed remarkable instances of religious convictions.

If *A Token for Children* and similar books were favorite gifts to the little colonials, John Cotton's *Spiritual Milk for Babes* was a favorite catechism. Like nearly all the others this book was of English origin, but it seems to belong especially to America because its author, the Reverend John Cotton, was the most renowned preacher in both Bostons as well as the most influential Puritan in the whole history of New England. Besides, the Massachusetts reprint bore the name *Spiritual Milk for Boston Babes in Either England*.

From its first appearance his catechism went through many editions and was revived for use in Sunday schools little more than a hundred years ago. It also became a part of a far more important book, *The New-England Primer*. The roots of this famous little book go far back to the Latin "Book of Hours," later called "The Prymer." There were many primers written in Latin, or in English and Latin, varying in form in the different dioceses, called "The Prymer after the use of Salisbury," or of York or Bangor, etc., according to the diocese in which it was prepared and used. Such a primer has been termed the "Lay Folks Prayer

Book," being really a primary—hence primer—manual of church service. The inclusion of the alphabet in many primers of the sixteenth and seventeenth centuries gave the name to first books for children. After 1600 the main purpose of the primer became educational.

To this class belonged *The New-England Primer*, rightly called "The Little Bible of New England." Sold first by Benjamin Harris at the London Coffee House in Boston, it went through many editions and was widely used for a period of one hundred and fifty years. From its small, ill-printed pages children learned to read, learned, too, from its shortened version of the Westminster Catechism what they were to think on matters of religion. The crude woodcuts with which it was illustrated must have put it into the picture book class, often the only book of its kind in a houseful of children. No wonder that its rhymed alphabet so adorned was early and easily memorized. Familiar and unaltered through many editions the lines ran,

> "In Adam's fall
> We sinnéd all."

But the variations in the couplets for later letters in the alphabet are multiplied by the changing state of relations with the mother country. Moreover, the other contents, too, differ in editions. After a while appeared the four lines used as an evening prayer by generations of children,

> "Now I lay me down to sleep,
> I pray the Lord my soul to keep.
> If I should die before I wake
> I pray the Lord my soul to take."

Later on the gentle "Cradle Hymn" and others by Isaac Watts were included.

At a time when the doctrines of fear and retribution so generally prevailed, it is a relief to find a man whose piety was tempered by gentleness and serenity, as was that of Isaac Watts. His name was a household word in New England. His hymnbook, from which the Psalms, often converted into doggerel and labored verse, were sung in all the churches, contained at least a half dozen majestic songs found in every hymnbook today. A young English clergyman without wife or child, he composed for the small daughters of his friend, Sir Thomas Abney, the volume of *Divine and Moral Songs* which became immediately popular in the colonies. Published in England in 1715, it ran through one hundred editions before the middle of the century. Altogether more than six hundred editions have been identified. Here appeared the still familiar lines, "How doth the little busy bee improve each shining hour," and "Let dogs delight to bark and bite."

Two books of great literature, unqualifiedly approved for children, the early colonists had in their often meager libraries. In the King James Bible they were the possessors of a rich store of varied writings which more than filled the place held today by fiction and poetry and history. Joseph and his Brethren, Samson and the Philistines, David and Goliath, Daniel in the Lions' Den—all these were wonderful stories for the boys and girls who heard them read over and over in the meetinghouses and at home. *Pilgrim's Progress*, too, was a book of wide popularity, one of the small group of great classics not written for children but taken over by them wholeheartedly. Simply by its contrast to the stern school of gloomy writing it was bound to appear a stirring tale of adventure and romance. A well-known passage in Benjamin Franklin's *Autobiography* records his pleasure in Bunyan. Franklin was a great reader and not at all satisfied with the religious books open to him. From Plutarch's *Lives* he drew much satisfaction, but he regretted in later years that he had in boyhood so few books to satisfy his thirst for knowledge. But if the supply was limited it was yet quite as good and quite as abundant as that available to children in England. Moreover, shortly before the Revolution the new era in children's books in both countries had set in with the kindly outflow from John Newbery's bookshop in St. Paul's Churchyard.

As the Puritan age passed, the element of entertainment appeared in chapbook form, to be had for a few pennies apiece. Franklin mentions his purchase of a considerable collection of chapbooks, but he does not mention names. We know, however, that Perrault's fairy tales, Cinderella,

Blue Beard, and the rest, as well as separate stories from the Arabian Nights, were sold in the little paper-covered leaflets that were the first form for books of amusement. *Robinson Crusoe*, published by Hugh Gaine in New York in 1774, was in chapbook format. Although abridged it yet told the adventures of the renowned hero on his uninhabited island. Dr. Rosenbach believes this may have been a Newbery reprint, as Hugh Gaine was not unlike John Newbery in that he, too, sold patent medicines and printed attractive toy books.

Anna Green Winslow, the Boston schoolgirl of Revolutionary days, noted in her *Diary* her New Year's Gift of 1772, the Bible, *Pilgrim's Progress, Gulliver's Travels* and the *History of Joseph Andrews*, abreviated [sic]. She also borrowed three of Cousin Charles' books, *The Puzzling-Cap, The Female Orators* and the *History of Gaffer* [Goody] *Two Shoes*. Plainly these were all fresh from London, as *Goody Two Shoes* and *The Puzzling-Cap* were not reprinted in America until a later date. The fashion to abridge adult novels to make them suitable for children had arisen. *Pamela, Clarissa Harlowe, Tom Jones, Gulliver's Travels* were all printed by Newbery among his little books greatly reduced in size for younger readers. Of the group, *Gulliver* alone has survived in the favor of those who buy books for boys and girls.

Goody Two Shoes, the most celebrated of John Newbery's inventions, was reprinted in Worcester by Isaiah Thomas, the first American printer not content with taking English books as they were. Practically everything he transplanted was altered to suit the American setting. Nor did Thomas seem to have any compunctions in making whatever changes seemed desirable, nor in adopting another man's work as his own. His life was an interesting one. He was a Boston boy, apprenticed at six years of age to Zechariah Fowle, a printer for whom he worked eleven years. When later he had secured his own establishment he became so obnoxious to the British forces in Boston by reason of his patriotic paper, *The Massachusetts Spy*, that the town became too hot for him. A few nights before the Battle of Lexington he packed up his presses and types and sent them across the Charles River and thence to Worcester. After the battle, in which he took part, he went to Worcester and resumed his printing.

The name of Isaiah Thomas will always be closely associated in literary history with that of John Newbery, whom he copied sedulously. All the Newbery successes were appropriated by Thomas, who was quick to give them a patriotic appeal by turning allusions to royalty into references to governors and Congress. The history of early children's books in Boston bears a close relation to the political situation in the Revolutionary period. John Mein— who opened the first Boston circulating library, advertised in 1765 as containing ten thousand volumes—was an importer of little books from Newbery's famous stock for children. Such books as *Giles Gingerbread* and *The Famous Tommy*

Thumb's Little Story-Book were sold at his "London Book Store." When the Non-Importation Agreement made English books for children unpopular in the years just prior to the Revolution, John Mein was marked as a loyalist and returned to England.

With the importation and imitation of Newbery books the tide of little books of amusement swept in. The titles are characteristic of the time: *Be Merry and Wise; or the Cream of the Jests and the Marrow of Maxims For the Conduct of Life. Published for the Use of all good Little Boys and Girls.* By Tommy Trapwit, Esq.; *The History of Giles Gingerbread, a little boy who lived upon Learning; The Wisdom of Crop the Conjuror; Nurse Truelove's New-Year's Gift.* Besides introducing *Goody Two Shoes* in an American edition, Isaiah Thomas naturalized *Mother Goose's Melody: or Sonnets for the Cradle,* in which he made a few changes though following Newbery's edition in the main.

On the whole, children could now procure a fairly varied supply of reading, if they had money for the purchase, and the price was generally low. There were the collections of riddles of which *The Puzzling-Cap* is an example. Always a favorite source of entertainment, such books are perhaps to be counted as games rather than as literature.

Then from the old French fairy tale Thomas produced a play, "The Beauty and the Monster," which appears something of an innovation. However, it was probably intended more to facilitate reading than for acting. More attention, too, was given to instruction about the animal kingdom. In *Jacky Dandy's Delight: or, the History of Birds and Beasts* we find numerous woodcuts accompanied by verses which usually point a moral.

> "The Bear in coldest climate lives,
> Screen'd by his shaggy hair;
> But boys may cold and hunger dread
> Who naught for learning care."

No doubt such was the small volume that pleased Dicky Lee some years earlier when he wrote to his cousin, George Washington, that his father had brought him two pretty books full of pictures. "They have pictures of dogs and cats and tigers and elefants and ever so many pretty things," wrote Dicky.

Still the writers hid themselves in anonymity. Charley Columbus was responsible for one title, Tom Trip for another containing the same descriptions with different woodcuts.

Hugh Gaine and Isaiah Thomas brought over from England the illustrations by the Bewicks, which were not only far superior to what had been seen, but were also to prove the source of inspiration to an American artist of distinction. The work of Alexander Anderson, called "the father of woodcutting in America," is accounted nearly, if not quite, as good as the best woodcuts of Thomas Bewick. In the field of illustration alone, American work for children surpassed that done in England during the same period. From the press of William Charles at Philadelphia there was issued a series of square books with plain and colored engravings of great charm. The colors were frequently put on by children, each set down with a brush to engage in an occupation far more like play than work. Of course, the colored books cost more than the plain ones. We remember Robert Louis Stevenson's essay at a much later time, on the superior merits of "tuppence colored" over "a penny plain."

By the beginning of the nineteenth century there was no lack of books of amusement and instruction, but there was small indication of originality. All follow English models, if they are not actually the work of English writers.

American producers were very faithful copyists, even in the matter of crying their wares. Newbery's rhymed advertisements were duplicated many times. Mahlon Day, the New York printer, proved especially ingenious in keeping his name before the youthful public by a variety of flourishes. A typical quatrain reads:

> "Some children for cakes are inclined,
>   Some buy a little barking Tray.
>   But don't forget there is food for the mind
>   In the books that are sold by M. Day."

After the sway of the strictly religious book was over the hand of the moralist was to rest heavily on books for children for many years. George the Third's long reign was drawing to a close when Maria Edgeworth began her career as a writer for children. The forces that shaped her course, the influence of Rousseau, the example of Thomas Day, her father's direction, are worthy of separate consideration. It is enough to emphasize here the importance of her contribution in dignifying writing for children. Her skill in the construction of plots, her sense of humor, her attention to lifelike detail, her ability to write well are all significant for their effect upon those who followed her. But Maria Edgeworth's crowning distinction is her power to create real children. For this alone she stands head and shoulders above her predecessors and contemporaries. With her name, realism in children's books has its beginning.

FROM ROLLO TO TOM SAWYER

II

OULD there be a wider gulf of separation between two types of book children than that between docile, earnest, literal, inquiring Rollo and mischievous, imaginative, harum-scarum, happy-go-lucky Tom? And yet this gulf was largely bridged in the fifteen years following the Civil War, that period of bad taste in architecture and house furnishings, of self-consciousness, of repressions and inhibitions. It is through consideration of the reading of New England children in the 1870's that we may trace some of the factors contributing to the greater freedom in the attitude toward children's reading. We shall discover a great fertility in the production of children's books, the first widespread awakening to the need of critical appraisal, the first wholehearted liberality toward children's tastes and interests, admitted without boundaries, without propaganda—in short, it was the beginning of a new era.

In *A Mid-Century Child and Her Books*, Caroline Hewins gives us a charming picture of the reading open to a child in a cultivated home in New England during the 1850's and sixties, when she herself was between the ages of five and fifteen. Miss Hewins counted the influence of the books that she read in those years so important that she later brought together in her library copies of as many as she could find to illustrate different phases in the history of children's books. Her early delight in the pleasures of reading, coupled with her lively remembrance of childhood tastes and native literary discernment, made her throughout life a warm champion of children and their books. Her own influence was wide and lasting, always to be felt by those who were privileged to know her personally and through those who were young when children's library work was in its infancy, an inspiration reaching far beyond her own personal circle and her own lifetime. The soundest principles of book selection for young people accepted today follow lines that Caroline Hewins laid down from the beginning of her association with the library in Hartford seventy years ago. With voice and pen she was always active in the cause of good books for children and her keen literary judgment, humor and pungent speech made her opinions highly valued by head librarians in library conferences and gatherings.

Early New England drew largely from old England the reading granted its children until well past 1850, but the children who began their association with books during the next two decades were destined to see a great change in the number of books designed in America for their special pleasure.

Those were the memorable years of the renaissance in the literary life of the six seaboard states—the golden age of American literature. If, in the 1870's, New England was declining from its pre-eminent position, many of the figures of that brilliant flowering were still living. Emerson was in retirement, it is true, but Longfellow, Whittier, Lowell and Holmes all were active with their pens. Parkman's great historical panorama was in process of unfolding. Hawthorne, with his unique imaginative powers, had not long been gone. Fathers and mothers who had felt the impact of this distinctive creative period could not fail to pass on something of a literary tradition to the children growing up in their homes. Those children accepted as an indisputable fact the importance of books in the lives of people—they had a respect for literature.

In Cambridge the little granddaughter of Jacob Abbott, later the author of *Molly Make-Believe*, averse to learning to read, yielded to the cajolery of the famous creator of the Rollo books who was summoned from Maine to see that she remained a dunce no longer. Poetry came to her straight from Longfellow who read her his most appealing verses. Then, as now, Longfellow was the children's poet, belonging as much to Maine as to Massachusetts. Children loved the

Norseland poems, *Hiawatha*, *The Building of the Ship*, *Paul Revere's Ride*, and other storytelling poems. From Whittier, too, came pictures of scenes familiar to country children, the schoolhouse by the road, the silence and wonder of a snow-storm on a farm buried deep in drifts, the chores of old-fashioned farmers' boys.

At Gardiner, in Maine, Laura Richards was reading to her children many of the books her mother, Julia Ward Howe, had put into her hands at Green Peace in South Boston. After *Mother Goose* and Lear's *Book of Nonsense*, she began to introduce a six-year-old to *A Midsummer Night's Dream*, taking first the fairy and clown parts, then filling in as the child became familiar with the lighter part. After that she went on to *As You Like It* and *Twelfth Night*. Lear's *Book of Nonsense* was published in England in 1846, and all over England children and grownups rocked with glee over the inconsequence of his taking rhymes. Walter De La Mare says that Lear Limericks are very different from "mere limericks." Those were fortunate American children who did not miss this nonsense in childhood. Mrs. Richards fed much poetry to her children, especially songs, ballads and heroic verse, for she herself would rather read poetry than eat her dinner any day. And the poetry dearest to her was the ringing kind "with bells and trumpets."

Other mothers delighted to read poetry to their children. There were excellent anthologies with poetry classified into groups—Poems of Home and Childhood, Poems of Sentiment, Poems of Patriotism, and so on. There were, too, the *Lays of Ancient Rome, Marmion, Ivry, Lord Ullin's Daughter,* Byron's sonorous lines,

"The Assyrian came down like a wolf on the fold
And his cohorts were gleaming with purple and gold."

Of the collections for younger children, Whittier's *Child Life* satisfied gentle moods.

Little children could have the fine edition of *Mother Goose* containing music and admirably illustrated by H. L. Stephens. They had *John Gilpin*, with Caldecott's unsurpassed pictures, and Walter Crane's *Baby's Opera;* they had *Struwwelpeter*, which they never took seriously; they had *The Nursery* with its large type and simple stories. Though the name suggests an English household, this monthly magazine for the youngest was a dearly loved American periodical.

Within New England homes the favorites of an older generation stood on the shelves to tempt exploring eyes and minds, the Waverley Novels, with *Ivanhoe* and *The Talisman* affording vigorous substance for plays of knights and tournaments; Dickens, who had lately died, was full of odd characters to quote and imitate, but he could not be acted in the barn on a rainy day; Cooper, ah, there was plenty of theater for long Saturdays in the woods! His heroes were both of the sea and of the forest. Whether under the name of Leatherstocking, Deerslayer, Pathfinder, or Hawkeye, brave Natty Bumppo was always the ideal hunter and frontiersman, lean and sinewy, keen of eye, wise in the ways of Indians, long enduring, yet gentle and considerate, an American to the core. His deeds made wilderness life alluring, for Indian warfare was not too remote from young people in the 1870's.

History reading was held in high esteem in New England, from the days when Abigail Adams wrote to her husband in Washington, in the midst of the Revolutionary War:

> "I have taken a very great fondness for reading Rollins' Ancient History since you left me. I am determined to go through with it, if possible in these my days of solitude. I find great pleasure and entertainment from it and I have persuaded Johnny to read me a page or two every day, and hope he will from his desire to oblige me, entertain a fondness for it."

Johnny (John Quincy Adams) was then seven years old.

A boy of the 1870's, with a true love of books and ease in reading, was not daunted by the size or length of a history, for if it ran to three volumes he need not make so many trips to the circulating library to take out Motley's *Dutch Republic* or *John of Barneveld*, full of glowing adventure and splendid heroes, or Prescott's brilliant *Conquests*.

Closer in point of time and closer in significance, as well as easier reading, was *The Boys of '76* by Charles Carleton Coffin. For did not the Revolutionary War begin right here at home with General Gage and the Boston boys, the Sons of

Liberty, Lexington, Concord and Bunker Hill? Fierce and uncompromising was the anti-British sentiment aroused by this exciting book. Carleton's *Winning His Way* and his four volumes relating to the campaigns of the Army of the Republic made exciting reading, too, but were not so popular as *The Boys of '76*. The Civil War was not much farther away from children in the seventies than World War II is from children now. Written in the heat of conflict and passion, all these books were one-sided and prejudiced.

Along the New England seaboard, from which ships sailed forth over the Seven Seas, captained by fathers, uncles and grandfathers, geography was a living thing and no part of the world too remote to be interesting. For those young readers who could enjoy travel, Lady Brassey's *Around the World in the Yacht "Sunbeam"* afforded intimate glimpses of pleasant family life on a luxury yacht of long ago. Or, if one preferred exploration, there was noble Elisha Kent's account of his search for the lost Franklin expedition in the far North, and his *Arctic Explorations* when he discovered the Humboldt glacier. Boys and girls in bookish homes read with enthusiasm Stanley's absorbing accounts of his search for Livingstone and his experience tracing the course of the mighty Congo, which were almost the fresh news of the day in the 1870's. And wildly improbable, even sensational, as Jules Verne's books then seemed, they were good for the imagination in their anticipation of twentieth-century wonders.

Among the children's books inherited from an earlier generation Jacob Abbott's red-covered Rollo books were beginning to seem old-fashioned. They had no plot, incident followed incident, and the story ended when the author was ready to stop. Jacob Abbott never intended his books to be merely storybooks; he wanted them to be useful, to give substantial instruction and cultivate the power to think. But he knew and loved children and never talked down to them. He believed in treating them with respect and in sharing life with them. For little girls there was real pleasure to be found in the Franconia stories where they could join with Malleville and Mary Bell in the fun of going blueberrying or hear the incomparable Beechnut tell about the fabulous shipwrecks and icebergs seen on his father's voyage to America.

Except for Hawthorne's *Wonder Book* and *Tanglewood Tales* there was little of the imaginative handed down and that little had its origin abroad. Everyone knew Ali Baba, Aladdin and Sindbad even when others of the Arabian Nights tales were unknown. The Grimm Brothers' collection of folklore came to England in the 1840's and thence to America; *The Rose and the Ring* was written in the next decade; so, also, *The King of the Golden River*, which Laura Richards counted a lifelong joy, most precious of all children's books. Certain of Andersen's stories were being published for the first time in *The Riverside Magazine*.

George Macdonald's lovely spiritual fairy tales, brought

over from England, were accepted in homes where a strong evangelical atmosphere was less friendly toward fairy tales in general. *The Little Lame Prince* was dearly loved in those Victorian days and its moral was never even noticed. Besides Mrs. Mulock-Craik, who wrote it, another English woman was exploring the realm of imagination. Annie Keary, who had ventured to present to English children the Norse myths in the *Heroes of Asgard*, wrote a favorite story called *Little Wanderlin* which tells how a boy who never helped anyone was taken to Mrs. Calkill's wonderful house and there was turned into an elf. He traveled through the air and under the sea on a gull's back, learning to be sorry for his selfishness and antedating the adventures of Nils by some forty years.

The most important of all imaginative stories for children, *Alice in Wonderland*, published in 1865, crossed the sea early and later took its place in the juvenile section of widely distributed lists of good books. Happy the children in whose home it was a treasure.

Once having tasted at home the joys of reading, intelligent children felt compelled to supplement the family book shelves by borrowing elsewhere. Though as yet children's reading rooms in libraries were far in the future, New England was well supplied with circulating libraries, many of them supported by public funds. Often these had age restrictions, limiting borrowers to those over sixteen years. But children used their parents' cards as they do now and there were ways of circumventing the rules.

A library report of the period records that two small girls were observed by a vigilant official carrying away five books and holding them in such a way that it was evident a very small accident would throw some of the five volumes into the gutter. And another regretfully states that, "One boy sold his father's card to another boy, who lent it to a third who lost both books and card, but the three boys came to the Library and united to pay for the books lost."

There was one widespread agency which did cater eagerly to children; it was the Sunday-school libraries commonly flourishing in city, town and village. Few personal reminiscences of childhood reading in the first three quarters of the nineteenth century fail to mention the books brought home from the church schools.

While the weight of the Puritan sabbath had been measurably lightened by the 1870's there were nevertheless many homes in New England where children were not expected, or even allowed, to read on Sunday the books they could have on any other day of the week. Moreover, conventional observance of Sunday called for decorous inactivity in the long afternoon, leaving reading the only resource of boys and girls in the stricter homes, so in spite of inward rebellion, the Sunday-school library became their mainstay. As we trace the general and extensive use of these libraries it is important to remember that in this part of the world concern for children's reading grew, in the first instance, out of the Puritan emphasis upon the religious life of the child.

It was about 1830 that the American Sunday School Union, already in existence for some six years in Philadelphia, deliberately set out to create a juvenile literature for a public inadequately supplied, they felt, with suitable reading matter. In the next thirty years they actually produced a literature, widely read and greatly effective in developing the reading habits of a large part of the American people.

Four rules were set down to be followed by writers of books acceptable for publication by this organization:

(1) The book must be clearly and absolutely of a moral and religious character. (2) It must be graded and adapted to the capacity of the growing mind of the child. (3) It must be of a high order of style and fairly good literature. (4) The book must be American and for American children.

On this last requirement the Committee pointed out that there was no need to go abroad for subjects and scenes of interest; "American statesmen and benefactors, American forests, prairies and rivers, American prospects" might surely furnish enough subjects to make profitable and interesting reading for American children.

So far as I know, this was the earliest American attempt to set up standards for writing children's books. True, the rule that the book must be of a high order of style and good literature seems early to have lapsed with the emphasis placed more upon religious character. But while the books of the early years were often controversial, the Sunday School Union itself proved desirous of eliminating all denominational emphasis and by the 1870's books that had comparatively little actual religious teaching formed an increasing percentage of the Sunday-school library collections.

Aware that every child attending Sunday school expected to take home a book, and that this book was often read by several members of the family, some of the religious leaders began to be alarmed by the indiscriminate production of these library books; one a day and all the while increasing, they said. At the same time, secular publishers became conscious of the large and growing market over the country, and determined to enter a field in which appetites were so eager.

The Sunday School Union suggested, uneasily, that churches appoint their own reading committees of persons qualified to make wise choice of books for their own parishes, for they perceived the evils of unregulated purchase. Catalogues of Sunday-school libraries of the 1860's and 1870's are largely made up of colorless titles by unknown writers whose books cannot be recognized as belonging to authentic literature for children. It is no wonder that recommendations that the libraries be discontinued were common, or that some parents looked with disapproval upon books brought home on Sundays.

But fortunately, once fully conscious of the widespread circulation of books overloaded with precocious goodness, morbid piety and sickly sentiment, certain enlightened organizations took the matter vigorously and competently in hand. One of the most influential of these societies was the Ladies' Commission of the American Unitarian Society, in Boston, whose admirable lists, published and renewed in the years preceding the opening of children's rooms, were an invaluable aid to public libraries as well as denominational ones. In these excellent lists are to be found the names of books by established English writers for children, George Macdonald, Charlotte Yonge and Mrs. Craik, as well as a selection by Dickens and Scott. Widely used, these lists did much to overcome the flood of sentimentality which flowed so plentifully in the Elsie Dinsmore books and the less tearful stories by Pansy.

When during the 1870's the public library movement began its rapid development, the Sunday-school libraries no longer filled the place they had long enjoyed, except in rural communities where their popularity continued for several decades. Legislative authority for the maintenance of libraries by public funds, given in Massachusetts in 1848, spread over the New England states rapidly, with New Hampshire enacting such a law the next year. When the American Library Association was established in 1876, the

Centennial year, New England was fully prepared to join. Boston with its six branch libraries, then, was the first city in the country to organize a library system.

In Hartford, Miss Hewins had become librarian of the Young Men's Institute which later became the Hartford Public Library. Her swift disapproval of the type of books which many children were then reading took action in the preparation of unusual reading lists; her voice in favor of discerning criticism was one of decision and leadership.

Among other librarians who felt deeply the responsibility for the eager young readers was William E. Foster of the Providence Public Library, whose early paper on coopera-tion with schools is a landmark in that field. At Quincy the library trustees were deeply concerned with the subject, and papers by Charles Francis Adams and Josiah Quincy are sound reading today.

Meanwhile, the new freedom from the bonds of didacti-cism had brought on, here and abroad, the tide of adven-turous fiction in which American writers proved to be highly prolific. Properly, this type of literature might be said to start with *Robinson Crusoe*, which has held its place all through the years, although it has in its original form a full share of religious passages. This was the first real book of the Connecticut Yankee, Governor Wilbur L. Cross, a country boy of the 1870's, who puzzled over the difficult passages in the uncut version, believing every word from cover to cover.

Next to Fenimore Cooper's books, Daniel P. Thompson's *Green Mountain Boys* had long held an honorable place in New England homes and libraries and was read by men and boys with a taste for stories from history. A truthful picture of pioneer days, it was written out of a lively sense of the Vermont struggle to keep its boundaries free from New York claimants and British oppression. Thompson's tales of Revolutionary heroes drew from the memories of those who had known the men and it was more truly a novel than a book written especially for young people.

Four Englishmen were in the forefront in establishing a pattern for adventurous fiction primarily for adults but also read by boys, at least twenty years before our period: Marryat, Kingston, Ballantyne and Mayne Reid, no one of whom was an armchair traveler. Captain Marryat was the earliest. He remains for this country the only one of the four whose books are wont to appear in new editions from time to time. Marryat's books have often a strongly religious and moral tone, but *Masterman Ready*, a castaway tale, and *Children of the New Forest*, drawn from history, have genuine story interest as well. *Mr. Midshipman Easy*, written out of his own experiences in the British Navy, was also popular.

W. H. G. Kingston, too, was in the British Navy before he wrote *Peter the Whaler* and *The Three Midshipmen*. Some of his books are full of details of animal life. *In the Wilds of Africa* fascinated quite young children with its tales about elephants, lions and gorillas.

Ballantyne wrote a number of trustworthy accounts of travel in the far North where his own fortunes had carried him, and several of his books were long on the shelves of children's rooms, as were those of Paul Du Chaillu.

As for Captain Mayne Reid, some of whose adventures with American Indians really took place, he belongs in both camps, the informational and the sensational. He had run away to sea and had his fill of Indian fighting. *Afloat in the Forest*, which continued as a serial in *Our Young Folks*, contains much detailed description about South American jungles and rivers. Laura Richards has testified that all she knew of natural history she learned from Mayne Reid whose dashing heroes were her delight.

Yet he was also one of the host of writers whose books were published by the Beadles of New York, responsible for the deluge of notorious paper-covered dime novels, which every New England boy knew it was a "Major Crime" to read. Beadle's Dime Books, Munro's Ten Cent Books, and subsequent series of Civil War stories, all flourished and waxed strong in the 1870's. By 1880, the dime novel business was a thriving industry, making fortunes for the manufacturers.

Edward S. Ellis, author of the Deerfoot series even now fondly remembered by Old Boys, was another dime novel writer with as many as six pen names. He began to write when he was hardly more than a boy himself and produced altogether over a dozen series of juvenile stories, as well as several respectable histories and biographies. He was at one time even a school superintendent in New Jersey. The Deerfoot series drew their inspiration from Cooper; they were bound books and are probably best remembered of anything Ellis wrote.

Oliver Optic, who was responsible for the issue of 116 volumes, in cloth bindings, not published by Beadle but by more reputable firms, was the pen name of a Boston teacher and school principal. His books were circulated freely and long by public libraries. In the 1875 catalogue of the Cambridge Public Library seven series by Optic are listed, and other libraries agreed in naming him as among the most popular fiction authors, whose works were read by men as well as boys and girls. Some contemporary reviewers called his stories pure and ennobling, "improving the taste and elevating the mind, while at the same time they stirred the blood and warmed the heart." Yet before his death his books were ruled out of most public libraries.

One need only turn the pages of *Outward Bound*, widely read long after its publication in Boston in 1872, to realize how little true criticism there was then, so far as children's books were concerned. In breathless one-line sentences, the career of a reckless youth on a school ship with many companions is expanded through page after page, punctuated with stilted speeches. The boys stole, they drank, they gambled, they had pistols, they even read "yellow covered novels," and they conspired to mutiny against the officers. The conversation of his young ladies was absurd.

When Billy Phelps, of Hartford, Connecticut, was twelve years old in 1877, he went to the Watkinson Library to take out one of Oliver Optic's Outward Bound series. Mr. Frank Gay, the wise head of the library, asked the boy why he read so much trash. Young Phelps replied that he read it because he liked it. After Mr. Gay had suggested that the boy read Shakespeare, a suggestion promptly resented, a bargain was struck between the two. The librarian proposed that Billy read one play by Shakespeare and if he did not like it, Mr. Gay would never ask him to read another and, more than that, he would keep the lad informed of every new book by Oliver Optic as it was placed on the library shelves. This seemed fair enough and the experiment began with *Julius Caesar*, which was read with great excitement and immediately followed by fifteen or twenty more of Shakespeare's plays. That William Lyon Phelps' catholic taste continued may be gathered from an entry in his journal, two years later.

"I read the entire book of Psalms today. This morning I finished *Jean Têterol's Idea* (by Cherbuliez) and in the afternoon and evening read two books of the Gunboat series."

Harry Castlemon, pen name of Charles A. Fosdick, seems to have been slightly less well known in New England than he was in the Middle States, but there are still men who think with nostalgia of *Frank on a Gunboat* and *Frank on the Lower*

Mississippi. The author claimed that the adventures of this series and of his other books really took place; and as he had run away from home to join the Navy during the Civil War, this may be true. His further claim that he had never met with one word of criticism seems a little less credible.

The name of Horatio Alger, one of the most widely read writers of boys' stories in the whole range of American literature, is a synonym for the success story. Whether or not his *Ragged Dick* and *Phil the Fiddler* resulted in putting an end to the exploitation of boys in the New York street trades, as has been claimed, his books have actually had a wide and possibly hurtful effect upon the reading tastes of countless young people. Supposedly an educated man himself, his writing was cheap and tawdry, his characters impossible, his plots repeated endlessly. Alger vulgarized high ideals and stressed the aim of life to be material success; his values were false; his moralizing, of which there purported to be much, was insincere because his own life was sordid.

Careful mothers along the New England coast who frowned upon sensational books gave a somewhat reluctant approval to the reading of books by Elijah Kellogg—reluctant because the scenes were often rough, the English faulty. But while the characters are wooden, the conversation unnatural, the stories are straightforward and honest with an infusion of robust orthodox Christianity, but never goody-goody or insincere, and full of scorn for meanness. Elijah Kellogg was a minister, the son of a minister who had been widely known and respected, and was himself a loved figure at Harpswell near Portland. Kellogg drew upon the pioneer history of Maine soon after the Revolutionary War for his material, and his accounts of the hardships and perils of the early settlers, the dangerous hazards of fishermen, the rugged business of building a home in the unbroken forests, are authentic, deriving from his own family traditions and personal knowledge. The pictures Elijah Kellogg gives of the early fishing industry show the actual practice of the times, while the achievements of his gigantic leader, Lion Ben, were derived from legends of the deeds of valiant heroes of the Maine coast. It is the character of the writer shining through his books that makes the Elm Island and Pleasant Cove stories better than other series of the period, though as in the others, six books about the same persons tend to become rather thin.

Amid the crowd of clay figures who were moved about like puppets on the stage of Optic, Alger and Company on battlefield, shipboard or in the city streets, the figure of Tom Bailey has a lonely distinction. Yet, if you would know what boy life in New England was really like in the 1870's, you have only to turn to *The Story of a Bad Boy* for what amounts to an historical photograph. The snowball fights on Slatter's

Hill, carried out with military strategy and fury, the Fourth of July celebration when the old stagecoach was burned, the club initiation with its mysterious trappings, these were all a part of New England boyhood.

Tom Bailey, as he said himself, was not a very bad boy and there are no lurid unrealities in his narrative. Probably if events were too much like everyday life to capture the multitude, the unexaggerated happenings were so true to life that they were enjoyed. Essentially a true portrait, the book stands as the most enduring work of Thomas Bailey Aldrich, who was moved by an artistic, rather than an educational or merchandising, impulse to tell in a charming style what he knew about boys.

Tom Bailey was appreciably closer to New England boys than was Tom Brown, whose school days at Rugby were obscured by talk of fags and English class distinctions which seemed remote from American public school experience. But, of course, there were some good fights in the story.

With far more genius than was displayed by Thomas Bailey Aldrich and Thomas Hughes, Mark Twain reached back into his memories of young Sam Clemens and gave the world Tom Sawyer—no period picture but the figure of the eternal boy. Although it was written in 1876, few New England boys knew Tom Sawyer before 1880. Even then Mark Twain's riotous humor was scarcely appreciated. It was an exceptional public library where Tom Sawyer was allowed in the hands of children; and that Miss Hewins listed it among boys' books in her epoch-making book list of 1882 was one of the marks of her liberal librarianship.

While boys would seem to have fared more lavishly than their sisters in our period, the girls were by no means neglected by the publishers. Girls read boys' books then, as they do today, and it was well that they did, for even when such books were poor they were more vigorous as a whole than stories for girls. Many wholesome minded girls scorned Martha Finley's endless series about Elsie Dinsmore and set her down as the tiresome prig she was. But they often reveled in *The Lamplighter*, that amazingly popular novel of a generation earlier, which described vividly the degradation of the poorer sections of Boston as seen by hard-working Gerty. Turned out of doors in a blinding snowstorm as a child, Gerty lived to heap coals of fire upon the heads of her most unworthy acquaintances. Secretly, too, some girls luxuriated in the sentimental, self-sacrificing pages of *Tempest and Sunshine* and *St. Elmo*.

For little girls there was one beloved author whose habit of continuation took shape in four sets of six little books in a box, each bearing the name of the leading child character. Sophie May was not given to overmuch moralizing and she made a real effort to bestow individuality upon her children —Prudy, Dotty Dimple, Flaxie Frizzle and Flyaway—all pet names. The incidents in the uneventful lives of the Parlin children are those commonly found in books for little girls, accidents and misunderstandings, mischievous pranks and willful disobedience, the marriage of a favorite aunt, a visit to New York. It is hard now to grasp the reason for the widespread affection for these books until we contrast the children in them with the children of earlier stories. Then it becomes evident that Sophie May made an effort to get away from the type of impossibly exemplary children, and attempted to give personality to her children and draw them as they are, in good moods and in bad.

In an unusual article on children's books, written while Sophie May's books were being published, the sober and scholarly *North American Review*, mouthpiece of New England's most dignified literary circle, waxes enthusiastic about the author, declaring :

> "Genius comes in with Little Prudy. Compared with her all other book children are cold creations of literature only; she is the real thing."

That was the viewpoint of an adult who found quaintness and tenderness, drollery and charm in children's original sayings, in baby talk, grammatical mistakes, teasing and spoiled ways, which are often funny to grownups, but hardly the best reading for children. Here is Dotty Dimple musing: "I know I don't ought to. I'm a goin' to do wicked and get punished, but I *want* to do wicked and get punished. I've been goody till I'm all tired up."

Even boys sometimes read Sophie May's books. Robert Morss Lovett, a Boston boy of the seventies, a devotee of

J. T. Trowbridge, with a zeal for military history, one who grew up to do some writing of his own, tells of seeing the sets at a neighbor's house, in a period of starvation. Listen to his admission:

> "It was a shameful thing for one who had recently en-acted Deerslayer and the Young Engineer even to look at such books and I averted my eyes; but in the evening, with home lessons done and time heavy I bribed my sister to go across the street and borrow *Little Prudy's Captain Horace*—the military title taking off something of the curse. And once drawn in I read the whole lot—they were so small that two or three a day wasn't much—and I fell for them all, all the heroines I mean—sedate Susie and patient Prudy and dashing Dotty Dimple—my first love. Flaxie Frizzle never made a hit with me, somehow."

But it is hardly fair to credit Sophie May with only the Prudy and Dotty Dimple books. Her *Quinnebasset Girls* with others in the Quinnebasset series for older girls were natural, lifelike stories comparing favorably with similar books today.

While the younger girls were still happy with Little Prudy, a more truly American story came from the press of Roberts Brothers to remain a children's classic for eighty years—*Little Women*, with its chronicle of the March family in all their endearing reality, their fun and their cheerfulness, their sorrows and heartaches. "The press generally commends it highly, and the young folks write expressing admiration," her father, Bronson Alcott, noted proudly in his Journal. "She is among the first," he wrote, "to draw her characters from New England life and scenes, and is more successful, in my judgment, in holding fast to nature, intermingling less of foreign sentiment than any of our novelists. Her culture has been left to nature and the bias of temperament and she comes to her pen taught simply by an experience that few of her age have had the good fortune to enjoy—freedom from the trammels of school and sects."

With what good courage Louisa Alcott undertook to admit her readers into the precious home circle we know from her own words. The years have paid generous tribute to her unselfishness, for no other American story for girls has reached a wider circle, no other heroine has been so well loved as dear, honest, open-hearted Jo March, best drawn because best known by Louisa Alcott.

Boys as well as girls read this book, too. Billy Phelps confided to his journal that he thought the book spoiled by not having Jo marry Laurie. "I won't marry Jo to Laurie to please anyone," Miss Alcott had told *her* Journal.

Miss Alcott with five other books following *Little Women* during the 1870's was not the only writer whose realistic stories of American girls exemplified the new kind of writing. Even before *Little Women* was published, two books by Mrs. A. D. T. Whitney brought natural young people before the girls of New England—*A Summer in*

Leslie Goldthwaite's Life and *Faith Gartney's Girlhood*. Mrs. Whitney was a good storyteller with a sense of humor and a gift of characterization which she called readily to service. Her books had a religious tone, which made them among the best acceptable to the stricter Sunday-school library committees, where Miss Alcott's were not. She included pleasing descriptions of New England country life and activities and yielded no more than Louisa Alcott to the temptation of writing long series. Susan Coolidge, with impetuous, lovable, mischievous Katy, and Elizabeth Stuart Phelps Ward, with the Gypsy books, were long to be found on the shelves of children's rooms, each with a popular boarding school story to her credit. *Nelly's Silver Mine* by Helen Hunt Jackson opened the eyes of many girls to the mining country of Colorado.

We were still in the magazine era in the 1870's. Some of the best American magazines for adults, the *Atlantic*, *Harper's Magazine*, the *Century*, were read under the kerosene lamps all over our region, and children dipped into them frequently. It was after the close of the Civil War that a change came over the periodicals intended for children. The double columns of *Merry's Museum*, to which Louisa Alcott had sent many short stories, was abandoned and a more friendly page was introduced.

True, *The Youth's Companion*, in form more newspaper than magazine, continued to go into New England homes everywhere. It had belonged to the whole family for a generation, providing a weekly stimulus to the moral and mental life of different ages, though its original stated aim was to entertain children and insensibly instruct them, occupy leisure hours and turn them to good account, warn against the ways of transgression and allure to those of virtue and piety. As time went on the religious element became less pronounced, but always *The Youth's Companion* kept its definite view as to what was healthy and moral for children, rejecting both love-making and killings as unsuitable.

Over the years this paper contained special articles by famous men from Wilkie Collins to Kipling, its feature pages of anecdotes afforded many a hearty laugh, its serial story kept up the suspense from week to week. It was in *The Youth's Companion* that one of the earliest series of hunting and camping stories, those by Charles Asbury Stephens, held boys absorbed in the 1870's.

"Children have too much reading and the fault is not theirs but their elders," wrote Horace E. Scudder, in the first issue of *The Riverside Magazine*, in 1867. Under one of the two most discriminating editors a children's magazine has ever had, this fine periodical ran its short course of four years, marking a new age in such publications. For although he felt that there were too many books for children, Mr. Scudder wisely saw in the abundance a movement that could not be checked but could be studied and influenced, an abundance from which selection should be made under high criteria of values, set by those who cared for the growth of children's minds.

Books placed before children should not be confined to literature expressly prepared for them, said Mr. Scudder; they need have no age limit, they need not be new, and they may best be introduced by reading aloud in the home. His informal notes about reading, addressed to parents, and running through the first two years of *The Riverside Magazine*, are full of wisdom. He undertook then to arouse in children an interest in great writers, Shakespeare, Plutarch, William Blake; he called attention to new English books, printed Browning's *Pied Piper of Hamelin* with a memorable illustration, reprinted certain old ballads, all the time encouraging the foremost writers of the day to write for his magazine and the best artists to make pictures for it.

To Horace Scudder American children owed a fresh introduction to Hans Christian Andersen, for each year of the *Riverside* was enriched by one or more of his delicate fairy tales, several being written especially for American readers. Scudder's sympathy and love for children gave him a peculiar kinship with the poet artist.

The magazine was brightened, too, by Frank Stockton's playful fancy as it showed itself in that charming group of tales about the fairy youth Ting-a-ling and his friend the good giant, embroidered with the gentle humor and curious surprises that make Frank Stockton's work unique. He was to become assistant editor to Mary Mapes Dodge when *St. Nicholas* came into being, bringing to his editorial task his bubbling vivacity, his exuberant fancy and lightness of touch, combined with his sane, kindly philosophy.

Behind the ideals of *The Riverside Magazine* lies the vision of the day when children would see themselves related to a wider world than that in which they were growing up. Peter Parley and Jacob Abbott dwelt upon the odd customs of other countries. Grace Greenwood's travel papers dealt with history mainly. Only two lasting books succeeded in giving children truthful and interesting pictures of child life in other lands—Jane Andrews' *Seven Little Sisters Who Live on the Round Ball That Floats in the Air* and Mary Mapes Dodge's *Hans Brinker,* both appearing in the 1860's. While neither of these was printed in *The Riverside Magazine,* they established a pattern for it worth following in their *Ten Boys Who Lived on the Road from Long Ago to Now* and *Land of Pluck,* respectively. Chapters from Bayard Taylor's *Boys of Other Countries* showed a similar friendly warmth.

For undiluted realism Mr. Scudder presented the Bodley family when that pleasantly inquisitive household moved a few miles into the country with all the fervor of a journey across the continent. While the Bodleys seem not too distant relatives of Rollo Holiday, their travels were punctuated by selections from general literature. At their best the Bodley books were considered only tame.

The last words in the *Riverside* are a calendar entry for December 31, "The Riverside Magazine for Young People died, 1870." Mr. Scudder did not expect to edit any more magazines for young people. He was sorry to give it up, but he did not give up, as long as he lived, an abiding interest in young people and their reading.

Handed down by older brothers and sisters, *Our Young Folks* was greatly enjoyed by the children of the 1870's. Living three years longer than the *Riverside*, it held an important place in the household before it was merged in *St. Nicholas*. Under the leadership of John T. Trowbridge *Our Young Folks* was full of good things. The Peterkins first made their bow to the public in its pages and in Abby Morton Diaz' *The William Henry Letters* a country boy, away at boarding school, told the family how he was getting on. He illustrated his letters, by his own hand, showing what was happening to a natural boy and his school friends. Nor was pure nonsense lacking, for "The Owl and the Pussy-Cat" and "The Duck and the Kangaroo" came to New England children through *Our Young Folks.*

Mr. Trowbridge brought to his editorship a genuine wish to give boys and girls only what would interest them rather than instruct. Out of his own boyhood in central New York he called up the memory of life along the Erie Canal, creating a real boy character in Jack Hazard. With his loved dog Lion, Jack became a favorite whose adventures were chronicled through several years of *Our Young Folks* and were continued in the early numbers of *St. Nicholas*. One piece of writing by Mr. Trowbridge stands out as a reminder of the interval that separates the machine age from the 1870's when typewriters were curiosities, telephones an unrealized dream, automobiles and airplanes like wonders from Jules Verne. This is the famous story poem, "Darius Green and His Flying Machine," with its humorous account of a boy's backyard experiment, written in country dialect and ending,

> "Wal, I like flyin' well enough,
> He said; but it ain't sich a thunderin' sight
> O' fun in it when ye come to light."

While with the advent of *St. Nicholas* the leadership in publishing for children passed out of New England into New York, the New England writers were well represented among its contributors and the new magazine was distributed all over the country, and overseas as well, bringing pleasure and enlightenment to a host of constant readers. Thanks to the vision of Mary Mapes Dodge they had rich treasure. Started in 1873, as a branch of the Scribner tree, the first ten years of *St. Nicholas* are counted the most valuable in its history. Then appeared stories and poems that have long held a central place in the permanent body of American children's books.

Besides Frank Stockton, assistant editor during those years, the list of important writers is a long one. Lucretia Hale had more to tell about the Peterkins, about Elizabeth

Eliza and the problems of her piano, about Agamemnon's Career and about the little boys with their India rubber boots. There were nonsense verses by Laura Richards, "The King of the Hobbledygoblins," "Little John Bottlejohn." *Eight Cousins* and *Under the Lilacs* appeared, Susan Coolidge contributed *Eyebright*, Trowbridge sent in *The Young Surveyor*. *Boy Emigrants* was a favorite serial which grew out of Noah Brooks' own experiences when he and a friend struck out for the Far West, took up a claim in the territory of Kansas and then moved out on the overland emigrant trail to settle farther on.

Appealing to the same public as *St. Nicholas*, *Wide Awake* flourished for a number of years. It was published by Lothrop in Boston, had a fine large page and good type, but it was not so fully illustrated as *St. Nicholas*, nor was Ella Farman Pratt so gifted an editor as Mrs. Dodge.

The New England children who welcomed the mail which brought *St. Nicholas* in the 1870's made their first acquaintance with Howard Pyle in a set of animal fables; they met the Brownies in their initial adventures; they learned to like good pictures; they pored over Jack-in-the-Pulpit's wise advice, guessed the riddles, discovered the hobbies of children in distant states from their letters. Their horizons were widened, their reading tastes developed, their happiness increased by the beloved magazine which proclaimed that the new age in children's books had arrived.

"THE JUVENILE MISCELLANY" AND ITS LITERARY LADIES

III

WHEN the first number of *The Juvenile Miscellany* was drawn from the press of John Putnam, of Boston, in September, 1826, Thomas Jefferson's term as President was near its close, to be followed by that of the second of the Adamses of Massachusetts. The next eight years were to see the beginnings of modern America, not only in the growth of cities, the movement for free education, the introduction of manufactured goods, but in the signs of social reforms, temperance, woman's rights, the treatment of prisoners.

If we search for indications of these great stirrings in our first real magazine for children we shall be disappointed. And yet, perhaps, on later reflection marked evidence of humanitarian fires may be noted in the editor's stories of minority races and the physically handicapped.

Looked at today this recognized forerunner of modern periodicals for children is distinguished from its faltering predecessors by its unabashed Americanism, noticeable in the space given American history and biography and, no less, in the countless allusions to the American landscape so different from the English background of books hitherto available to children.

The stories printed in *The Juvenile Miscellany* are largely placed in New England, especially the countryside lying along the Charles or Merrimack Rivers, in the Berkshires and around Hartford. There the authors were at home, in the environment they knew best. Local pride is to be recognized, as well, in the description of the Quincy Railway, the first in the United States, built to draw blocks from the quarries for the shaft of Bunker Hill Monument.

Yet the magazine was by no means wholly provincial, for included in the contents are extracts from a journal written in 1818 enlarging upon the wonderful sights of New York and still further afield is a detailed description of the President's home in Washington. Short biographies of noted foreigners who had aided the young country, De Kalb, Kosciusko, Baron Steuben, alternate with sketches of such great national figures as Benjamin Franklin, William Penn and General Putnam and stories of the painter Benjamin West and the explorer John Ledyard. Incidents many times repeated in later publications first found a place in the pages of *The Juvenile Miscellany*.

Three numbers of the magazine are bound together in the small volume which covers the first year. Later, the numbers appear six times a year through 1836. Much of the writing in the early issues undoubtedly came from the hand of the editor herself. Hers was, unquestionably, the tale of two colonial children wandering from their home on Shawmut peninsula, soon to be called Boston, rescued and restored to their family by a kindly Indian woman. Hers, no less surely, "The Little Rebels," a play based on the now familiar episode of the Boston boys who visited General Howe's headquarters to complain of interference by British soldiers with their play on the Common. An amusing woodcut accompanies this historic scene.

In her introductory Address to the Young, printed in *The Juvenile Miscellany* for September, 1826, the editor asserts that she seldom meets a little girl, "even in the crowded streets of Boston, without thinking with anxious tenderness concerning her education, her temper and her principles." So broadened was this solicitude in her later maturity that Mrs. Child is best remembered as a philanthropist.

That Lydia Maria Francis, then in her twenty-fifth year, already the author of two successful novels, had launched a children's periodical was no secret to her friends, in spite of her modest anonymity. Lydia had always wanted to write. At the age of twelve she had the good luck to read Scott's *Waverley* and was so fascinated that she asked herself why she, too, might not become a novelist. Her daring ambition was encouraged by her older brother, whose books and conversation proved a valuable stimulus to her literary tastes.

Like the majority of American girls living in the first quarter of the nineteenth century, Miss Francis had little formal education but, thanks to her brother's books and the circle in which she was fortunately placed, she found means to satisfy an eager curiosity and thus acquire a well-stocked mind. With her innate good sense and fine intelligence, she took high place in the literary world of her day. Her father was a baker in Medford, Massachusetts, a man of solid worth with strong convictions against slavery and a genuine respect for intellectual pursuits. Two years after Lydia began her career as editor she was married to David Lee Child, a Boston lawyer who shared her zeal for literature and reform.

Called the foremost woman writer of the United States in the 1830's, Mrs. Child had a wide range of interests. Her first book, *Hobomok*, appeared anonymously when she was nineteen. Venturing into a field then untouched except for Cooper's first novel, *Hobomok* arrested the attention of readers because of its independence and enterprise in the use of a theme chosen from American history. Since imaginative writing which owed nothing to English sources was practically nonexistent in America then, this novel is generally recognized as the fruit of an article by John G. Palfrey in the *North American Review*, emphasizing the rich field offered novelists by American history.

Hobomok tells the story of an Indian youth and a daughter of Plymouth, bound together by marriage after her English lover was lost, separated on his return by the Indian's noble renunciation and subsequent disappearance. Stilted as the telling is, the book had significance by reason of the sincerity of its effort to picture the life of the colonists in a romantic and original fashion.

The reception accorded *Hobomok* led the way to other historical novels, *The Rebels*, dealing with the American Revolution and much later, *Philothea*, a tale of Greece in the age of Pericles in which a timid innocent maiden of matchless beauty moves stainlessly among the rich and worldly of her city. It must be admitted, however, that Mrs. Child's most popular work for adults was *The Frugal Housewife*, with its lessons in New England thrift, ways to save expense and waste nothing. This went into many editions. Throughout a long lifetime her pen was seldom idle, for she was always aiming to instruct her readers or to "sow some seeds for freedom, truth and humanity," always ready to champion the cause of the oppressed, the prisoner, the Negro and all persecuted races.

At the time Lydia Francis started *The Juvenile Miscellany* her work as a reformer was all in the future, her concern was simply to give pleasure and information to children. So she turned lightly from stories and plays to factual articles on coral reefs or gases, or propounded easy riddles and set home-spun puzzles. Nor would the paper truly belong to its time were the didactic element lacking. Brief dialogues appear on ethical themes, on "Keeping Promises" and "Memory," suited to youthful understanding. But while her composi-tions sometimes took a rhymed form, Whittier, her stoutest eulogist, admitted that she was no poet.

The first editor was not long dependent upon her own in-vention. Early in the history of the *Miscellany* she announced the reception of excellent contributions for which there was no room. Gradually, we find one or more initials at the foot of the contents. Mr. Child obviously lent his help from time to time and other initials are easily identified as those of well-known writers of the day.

Something of the nature of the books then approved in a well-to-do family living in a city may be gathered from a narrative entitled "Children's Books." In this story four children walking along Washington Street in Boston are discussing what they will buy with the two dollars their mother had given to each.

"'I shall go to Munroe and Francis to buy *The Pearl*,' said Mary, a tall pretty girl of fourteen, 'for it has eight beautiful engravings in it and a great many pretty stories.'"

She describes a picture and tells how the lady who signs L.H.S., in the *Miscellany*, has written a pretty piece of poetry about the flowers dressing up for a prize. She mentions *The Mirror*, and this brings out an exclamation from Alfred,

> " 'Oh, that *Mirror* was a proper pretty book. What a capital story that is about the old woman who was caught out in a snowstorm and dillydallied about till her poor children were frozen at home. I shall read all the stories that lady writes.' "

He decides to buy a little arithmetic for Henry at home, while Lucy plans to spend her two dollars for *The Juvenile Keepsake*, soon to be published by Carter and Hendee, of which she has seen some of the pictures and proof sheets at Aunt Maria's. Jane, who loves all of Peter Parley's books, resolves to buy his little *Geography*, as another gift for Henry, whose education evidently rests heavily on the minds of brother and sister. Both *The Juvenile Keepsake* and *The Pearl*, mentioned by these children, are among the Annuals receiving high praise in the *American Journal of Education* for January, 1830. Perhaps Aunt Maria wrote the reviews.

So smoothly did the *Miscellany* seem to pursue its way that the subscribers could scarcely have been prepared for the sad note of 1834, in which the editor bade a reluctant and affectionate farewell to the readers and requested writers to send no more contributions, because the magazine was about to be discontinued for lack of patronage. The reason is not far to seek. Such was Mrs. Child's intense activity in the unpopular anti-slavery cause that she had now become notorious. Barely a year had passed since the publication of her ardent "Appeal for that class of Americans called Africans," the first book against slavery to appear in America. She was numbered among the conspicuous leaders of the abolition movement. She was no longer acceptable in society and was dropped from membership in the Boston Athenaeum.

While her association with *The Juvenile Miscellany* is the principal factor entitling Lydia Maria Child to a place in the history of children's literature in the United States, she produced a number of juvenile books well liked in their day. *The Little Girl's Own Book* (1831) was one of the earliest examples of that large class of useful volumes of games and riddles, recipes and rules, designed to supply occupation for leisure hours.

In *Flowers for Children* and *New Flowers for Children* some of the favorite stories from the *Miscellany* were reprinted with an equal number of pieces written expressly for these books. The stories show affection for children combined with some understanding of their behavior. Without possessing much imagination they illustrate domestic manners and customs in New England during the first part of the nineteenth century. Titles like Little Jane, Little Mary, Little Emma, Discontented Dora, all characteristic of the period, were bound to make an appeal to young children.

It is in *Flowers for Children* and *New Flowers for Children*

that we find Mrs. Child's two most popular poems. Familiar even now are the lines beginning

> "Over the river and through the wood
> To Grandmother's house we go."

This was originally entitled "The New England Boy's Song about Thanksgiving Day." To match it there was printed later a song by a New York boy in praise of Croton water which runs in big pipes underground. These verses recount the benefits of hydrants to dogs and horses. The lines entitled "Who Stole the Bird's Nest?" by Mrs. Child were long included in collections of verse for children and still may be found in old-fashioned books.

Mrs. Child was the editor of Mrs. Tappan's collection of short stories called *Rainbows for Children*. Two quite charming stories printed there show more imagination than was commonly to be found in 1855, when they appeared. One, based on a familiar folklore theme, concerns Fianna who went around the world in search of a flask of golden water which would heal the eyes of her blind sister. Fianna traveled by turns on a whale, an ostrich and a camel among other animals, real and fabulous, all of which, the writer says, gave her an excellent opportunity to study natural history. She was carried across the Pacific by a phoenix, across the prairie by an eagle which had been summoned for her by two Indian boys. Walking and running at intervals, she rode on a deer, a buffalo and, at the end, on a railway.

Another story, "Fanny's Menagerie," tells how a little girl is surprised one rainy day by visits from the animals who had supplied material utilized in some of the treasured possessions in her room. They came to take back their gifts and little was left to Fanny after the geese had taken her pillow, the horse her mattress, the sheep her shawl, the bees the wax from her doll's head, the whale the oil in her lamp, and the elephant her ivory basket.

If Lydia Maria Child left nothing of permanent value to enrich literature for children, her work may be counted that of a pioneer who had the courage to forsake English models and write for American children in terms of their world. Breaking a pathway toward freedom from heavy-handed didacticism, her magazine was truly a beacon for others.

A fresh series of *The Juvenile Miscellany* was projected immediately after her resignation, under another editor, long a valued contributor, now willing, with Mrs. Child's friendly approval, to carry on where the first editor had laid down her task. After the change, as before, the American scene was given prominence. Early in 1835, a glowing description, accompanied by an engraved plate, did honor to the "great railroad which will in time run clear from Boston to Buffalo."

Far more diplomatic in her reforms, successful in furthering a number of worthy movements without antagonizing the public as Mrs. Child had done, Sarah Josepha Hale is inseparably associated with *Godey's Lady's Book*. As its

"Lady Editor" Mrs. Hale holds a definite position in the history of journalism in America, but her share in the promotion of children's reading was a less constructive one than that of the first editor of *The Juvenile Miscellany*. She would never have believed, however, that a certain contribution made over the initials S.J.H. in 1830 would call forth a spirited controversy, within a limited circle, one hundred years later.

America has, perhaps, never produced a set of child rhymes more widely known than the verses that tell about Mary and the lamb that followed her to school, except possibly Clement C. Moore's "Visit from St. Nicholas." There was something about Mary's pet which caught the fancy of little children and likewise the fancy of industrious makers of school readers. Was it the complete naturalness and absence of moralizing? Whatever the reason the simple quatrains were read and sung and quoted by innumerable American parents after they were printed in the *Miscellany*.

That very same year the verses found a place in Mrs. Hale's own book, *Poems for Children*. Nobody knows which was the earlier date. Little heed to sources was given in those days of unstinted borrowing, so Mary's Lamb was printed anonymously in various school readers which gave it wide distribution. Among those books was McGuffey's Second Reader, that prime favorite over a generous section of the United States where it is still fondly remembered.

Not until after 1870 was the claim made by Mrs. Mary

Sawyer that she was the heroine of this poem written by a certain John Roulston who had died some fifty years earlier.

Now it is not improbable that more than one little girl living on a farm had a teachable pet lamb who followed her to school and nobody knows how Mrs. Hale heard the story. But *Wide Awake* magazine came to her support printing, in 1879, a letter from Mrs. Hale who was then living. Her letter states unequivocally that she was truly the poet, having written these and other verses at the request of the well-known composer, Lowell Mason, for him to put to music. There would seem to be no reason to doubt Mrs. Hale's word, as the evidence is all in her favor, had not the rival author been honored by Henry Ford on a bronze tablet in Sudbury. So visitors to his New England village are prone to accept this tablet on a little red schoolhouse, moved from Sterling to Sudbury by Mr. Ford, as proof that John Roulston, not Sarah Josepha Hale, wrote the poem about Mary and her lamb.

The fourteen-year-old girl of the family mentioned earlier, who bought books on Washington Street, expressed special admiration for a poem in *The Juvenile Miscellany* about the flowers dressing up for a prize, written by the lady who signed her contributions with the letters L.H.S. The subject indicates that it was one of the host of imitations of Roscoe's *Butterfly's Ball*, so popular in England at that time. Certainly it must have had some inspiration from outside, for it was far removed from the customary style of a writer whose effusions generally carried a weighty load of morals or were edged with mourning over an early death.

The Juvenile Miscellany was, no doubt, favored in presenting to its readers the work of Lydia Huntley Sigourney, the Sweet Singer of Hartford, a writer so popular that editors and publishers vied with one another to obtain her prose and verse, paying liberally for both. Among the periodicals and annuals published during the third and fourth decades of the nineteenth century there were few from which her sentimental outpourings were missing. Gathered from different magazines some of her verses were printed in her two volumes, *Poetry for Children* and *The Child's Book.* They dripped sweetness and emotion, reflecting the taste of a great body of adults in the age of sensibility. Only rarely, if ever, could they have given pleasure to a child.

Mrs. Sigourney's own life story is one her ardent readers must have loved. Daughter of a humble Connecticut gardener, patronized by a wealthy widow to whom she devoted her early years, marrying a prosperous merchant, rising from poverty by the aid of a facile pen, sought after as a distinguished "poetess," hers is indeed a success story of full dimensions.

Meatier food for children's minds was offered by Miss Leslie, of Philadelphia, another regular contributor to the *Miscellany.* Her stories, frequently published in *Godey's Lady's Book* or *Graham's Magazine,* were enjoyed by young girls since they were bright and entertaining, but though she enlivened the contents of *The Juvenile Miscellany* with an element from outside New England, she has left no trace on children's literature. She wrote of dolls as magnificent effigies, of richly caparisoned rocking horses and of the tempting delights of the confectioner's art "that have made Philadelphia famous as the city of cakes and pies."

Eliza Leslie was the sister of Charles Leslie, the American artist who lived long abroad and painted, among other portraits, one of Sir Walter Scott for George Ticknor, of Boston. She traveled with her brother. Her stories contain descriptions of scenes in Europe and, in her own Annual, *The Violet*, they are often illustrated with engravings by artists of wide reputation. Following Mrs. Child's lead Miss Leslie edited, in 1831, the *American Girl's Book* devoted to handiwork and pastimes.

Still another important contributor had a share in making *The Juvenile Miscellany* a representative publication. The qualifications of Catharine M. Sedgwick as an author for children were based not only on her affection for her own nieces and nephews, who looked to her for much of their entertainment, but also were rooted in a childhood love of books and a long association with the best in English. An established novelist, she belonged by birth to a cultivated circle in the Berkshires where Cooper and Bryant were frequent guests and to a home where reading aloud was habitual. When Catharine Sedgwick was eight years old her father insisted that she listen quietly while he read to older members of the family from Shakespeare, Hume and other English classics.

Before becoming one of the lights of the *Miscellany* Miss Sedgwick had published *The Travellers,* her first story for children, relating the experiences of a young brother and sister on a visit to Niagara with their parents. This was followed by other books mostly about New England, truthful and unaffected. *Hope Leslie* and *Redwood* were among her most widely read books. She praised the good and virtuous, contrasted the lot of the rich man with that of the poor but honest worker and stressed the beauty of character. Following this pattern her stories for the *Miscellany* served their purpose and have been forgotten.

Interspersed with the prose and verses of these foremost writers, *The Juvenile Miscellany* gave space to the verse of prolific rhymesters like Hannah F. Gould, of Newburyport, and Anna M. Wells. It printed letters from the South where Caroline Howard Gilman had moved from her Boston home. No other early magazine for children reached so wide an audience, none commanded the assistance of so many prominent persons of that time. There is good reason for it to be counted as a landmark in American literature for children.

PETER PARLEY

IV

N a certain day in May, 1824, a young American who had been exploring the druid circle at Stonehenge and gazing reverently upon the lofty spire of Salisbury Cathedral took postchaise for a small village ten miles out of Bristol to call on a lady. He was not insensitive to the charm of the countryside, with its wide valley sloping to the Bay of Bristol, framed in the distance by the Welsh mountains, but his was not a poetic nature and the fragrance of spring in England was simply a cheerful prelude to the high moment of his grand tour.

Young Mr. Goodrich was in his early thirties at the time. Miss Hannah More, whose home at Barley Wood he was approaching as to the shrine of a divinity, was nearly eighty. Some six months earlier Mr. Goodrich had landed at Liverpool from an ocean so stormy that he thought it would be not only his first voyage but his last. Like other travelers he was to forget his unpleasant experiences after a few weeks

ashore, and to enjoy thoroughly his European pilgrimage across England and France, into Switzerland, Germany and Holland, leading up to a return to England and this crowning event, so long anticipated, now to be realized.

The orderly young man noted with approval the neat gravel walks around the vine-covered cottage under its thatched roof. As his eye followed them he discovered a monument to the great John Locke, who was born many years before in a house still to be seen in the village. It seemed to the American visitor a spot twice blessed.

The little old lady of Barley Wood was physically frail and infirm, but her mind was still active. Dressed in a dark red bombazine gown, with hair "slightly frizzed and lightly powdered," she was plainly not above a care for her personal appearance. She inquired for Mrs. Sigourney and other friends in America. Goodrich told her of the inspiration he had drawn from her books, especially from *The Shepherd of Salisbury Plain*, which seemed to him hardly inferior to the Bible narrative of Joseph and his brethren; he told how from this highly moral tale he had received his first glimpse of the joys of reading, how great a benefactor to the human race he felt her to be.

What was she really like, this woman whose writings so widely and genuinely influenced readers in the England and America of her day? Her life seems to have had two quite distinct chapters. All the latter part was devoted wholly to improving the condition of the poor and to the spread of

evangelical religion. To these ends she wrote innumerable tracts and books with simple moral lessons, extolling the virtues of honesty and piety, acceptance of one's lot, kindness, faithfulness to duty and a cheerful spirit. The child who was thankful when she remembered "What must poor people do who have no salt to their potatoes" was the daughter of the Shepherd of Salisbury Plain.

Hannah More's portrait, painted by Opie when she was much younger, shows a face of great sweetness, small regular features, fine dark eyes under a crown of abundant hair dressed high in the exaggerated style of the period. There can be no doubt that she possessed great charm in her youth.

One of the brilliant circle surrounding Dr. Johnson, she was an intimate friend of David Garrick and his attractive Viennese wife, who had given up her career as an admired dancer to marry the great actor. It was as a successful playwright and poet that Hannah More was welcomed into the intellectual society of the eighteenth century. A Blue Stocking, she was counted an ornament to the lively conversation parties attended by the Garricks, Sir Joshua Reynolds, Lady Mary Wortley Montagu, and the rest of the eminent circle. She looked up to Dr. Johnson with reverence, flattered him with admiration, and enjoyed with him a friendship similar to that bestowed upon another witty and graceful young woman, Fanny Burney.

Alas, it is only the curious, intent upon recreating the past, who would consider her writings worth attention today, for save the sincerity of their moral purpose they have little to praise. She had nothing of Fanny Burney's liveliness and wit, nothing of Maria Edgeworth's skill in plot or able delineation of character.

Although Hannah More did not write for children, many of her later books fell into their hands. Intended for the simple uneducated masses whom she hoped to elevate by means of moral tales, they had given Mr. Goodrich, of Connecticut, the germ of an idea which developed rapidly after his memorable visit to Barley Wood. Through his conversations there he was strengthened in his belief that facts could be made more interesting than fiction to children. He resolved to undertake the task of proving this by the production of suitable books containing only facts.

About three years after that visit, in 1827, there was published in Boston a little square book bearing the title, *Tales of Peter Parley about America*. It was the first use of a pen name, happily chosen and destined to become famous. It was, as well, the beginning of the flowing stream of books made in America, designed especially for the benefit of American children. When they were read at home or in the one-room schoolhouses over the country the names of familiar birds and trees, the mention of local rivers and towns gave a homely quality to the pages. These were things boys and girls had heard about.

For the next five years Peter Parley devoted himself to writing without revealing his identity, until the indefatigable

Mrs. Hale discovered and divulged the secret. Other small square volumes followed in rapid succession: *Tales of Peter Parley about Europe, Africa, Asia* and other countries, *Peter Parley's Tales about the Sun, Moon and Stars* and other books, sometimes several in a year. The thin square volumes which were Parley's *Geographies* were counted treasures of great value in remote country places. Marvelous pictures opened the world to eager eyes and revealed wonders hitherto undreamed of, Eskimo houses, caravans in the desert, strange animals like camels and elephants, never failing sources of delight to minds hungry for knowledge.

From the didactic school, then dominant in England, these books drew their full share of moralizing, but they breathed a fresh spirit of independence and complacent Americanism. As Peter Parley observes in his *Book of the United States:* "If therefore you were to visit foreign lands, you would meet with many curious manners and customs which you do not find in this country, and you would probably return satisfied that we are a plain, commonsense people, living on terms of great equality with each other, and more distinguished for general intelligence, simple manners, and a good opinion of ourselves than anything else."

The author of the Peter Parley books, Samuel Griswold Goodrich, is seldom thought of except by his chosen pseudonym. Born into a well-known Connecticut family, in 1793, he received the usual rural schooling of his time. His father was a Congregational minister in the village of Red-

field, with a farm of forty acres to be worked on week days and made productive enough to support a family. In *Recollections of a Lifetime*, the son has drawn a realistic and entertaining picture of his home and the primitive hard-working community over which his father presided. The country towns of New England in the opening years of the nineteenth century harbored many shrewd odd characters, fit subjects for humorous anecdotes or legends, and memories of these are to be found in Goodrich's *Recollections*. Then the heroes of the Revolutionary War still lived to spread their patriotic tales among the boys and girls of the village and young Samuel lent a ready ear to these fragments of American history.

Farm life had little interest for the boy who possessed both the aptitude for mechanics, so often seen in New England, and a taste for intellectual pursuits. Passing through terms of storekeeping and bookselling, he became a publisher in Hartford and in Boston, where as author and editor he was responsible for one hundred and seventy books. By wide reading he fitted himself to associate with men of affairs and became State Senator. Shortly before the upheaval of 1848, he served as Consul at Paris when some of the Parley Tales were translated into French.

Looking back at his boyhood as he grew older, Peter Parley undoubtedly read into his memories the theories on children's literature which he had evolved in a lifetime. Up to his tenth year he had read but little outside his school books and *The New-England Primer*. Perhaps his introduction to Mother Goose as late as that accounts for his thinking the rhymes merely silly and always afterward scorning them for all children. Generally regarded as unimaginative, he must have been quite the opposite as a child, since he thought "Red Riding Hood" was true and was filled with horror by the tales of "Jack the Giant-Killer" and "Bluebeard."

When he was about twelve years of age he read *Robinson Crusoe* with delight, then a translation of the *Tales of the Castle*, by Madame de Genlis, followed by Hannah More's *Moral Sketches* and *The Shepherd of Salisbury Plain*. These were the first books to rouse any enthusiasm. "I do not recollect," he says, "to have discovered before this time that books contained inexhaustible sources of instruction and amusement and all within my own reach."

Peculiar interest centers around the boyhood of this man because of its obvious bearing upon his chief claim to be remembered. Whatever his later beliefs about children's reading may have been, they were rooted in prejudices and impressions formed when he was himself a child. Because as a literal-minded boy his association with folk tales had been unhappy, he entered upon a crusade against everything fanciful or imaginative; because the little dame school at Ridgefield had neither histories nor geographies for its pupils, he multiplied their production for other schools. As he reflected upon the subject he imagined himself on the floor with children and wrote as he would have talked, working out his ideas with the design of enlarging the children's knowledge.

In the library of the elder Goodrich the boy found a considerable collection of books including folios in Latin, mostly on theological subjects, with a scattering of books in English. When once he had learned to read, Samuel dipped into a big book which happened to be in large print, reading whole pages aloud to himself, spelling out long words, fascinated by type and sound, although he could not understand a single word. This experience he later interpreted as an indication of what other children enjoyed.

The name of Peter Parley was rightfully attached to one hundred and sixteen books, but there were many more, purporting to be his, published at home and abroad far up into the nineteenth century. The Original Peter Parley, as he called himself in capitals, certainly suffered much from the pirating of his books when they were greatly in vogue. He also complained bitterly of the "spurious Parleys." At the time Peter Parley began to write for children few textbooks were to be had; history, as such, was not taught in the schools; Noah Webster's "blue-backed" speller of renown still served as reading book in New England; the comprehensive series of McGuffey readers had not yet appeared to supply literary satisfaction to other parts of the United States. As soon as the school reader idea became financially profitable the five elementary books by Goodrich competed successfully.

The diligent producer declared that his object was "to make nursery books reasonable and truthful and thus to feed the young mind upon things wholesome and pure instead of things monstrous, false and pestilent." Confident that he alone was right in his characterization of old folk tales, he fiercely defended his theories against all opponents who believed in the value of the imagination. His quarrel with Sir Henry Cole forms an amusing chapter in itself.

Old Peter Parley followed the device of taking his readers on an imaginary journey and describing the experiences they were likely to have and the kind of people they would meet. Often he told his story in the first person, interspersing anecdotes and incidents in the style later employed by the authors of the Bodley books and the *Zigzag Journeys*. His books vary in quality, but the best ones are not dull, for the writer selected his material with an understanding of children's tastes, introducing unusual happenings sure to hold attention. There were pictures, too, crudely illustrating scenes in the text and adding greatly to the popularity of the volumes. He took a hand also in the magazine business and for about twelve years *Parley's Magazine* was planned by him but edited by others because of Goodrich's serious eye trouble. Quite frankly, Goodrich admits that he had help in his large enterprises, particularly in the preparation of the histories. Among the young writers contributing to the series pompously termed *Parley's Historical Compends*, easily the most distinguished was Nathaniel Hawthorne.

Goodrich edited, too, *The Token*, notable member of the family of annuals in the period of their greatest success. Among its contributors were numbered Longfellow, Hawthorne, Oliver Wendell Holmes and other writers, then almost unknown in the world of letters ruled by Cooper, Irving and Bryant.

As American Consul in Paris soon after the middle of the nineteenth century, Samuel G. Goodrich added to his reputation abroad as well as at home, so it could have been no surprise to his countrymen when he was singled out for a new honor toward the close of his life.

It was on a platform at New Orleans that the chairman of the meeting, speaking before a large crowd gathered to pay their respects to Samuel Griswold Goodrich, greeted the distinguished guest as "a blessed benefactor to the youth of the rising generation, as one who has emphatically earned the proud and endearing appellation 'L'Ami des Enfants.'" On this great occasion there were speakers from more than one country where the name of Peter Parley was highly regarded. A gentleman from Greece declared that Peter Parley's works had found a welcome in that classic land, another from England bore witness to the admiration they aroused all over Great Britain, while it was common knowledge that they had been translated into French. Self-opinionated he was and inherently prosaic, yet there is something likable about Peter Parley. He was honestly anxious to give good reading to children, but he was incapable of seeing worth in anything except the purely factual. Notwithstanding, a whole generation loved his books and found many of them amusing, gaining from them at the same time a wider view of the world and its people. For the strong influence that he had upon the development of American children's books he seems as deserving to be called "the children's friend" as was the Frenchman Arnaud Berquin.

THE CHILDREN OF
JACOB ABBOTT

V

T the famous Christmas party given to book people by Miss Muffet and the Spider, one of the favored guests according to Dr. Crothers who reported the occasion, was the youth Rollo.

"I always did like Rollo," said Miss Muffet. "I almost forget that he is a Youth sometimes. The nicest thing about him is that you always know what he means. He always tells you where he is and how he got there, without skipping anything that you ought to know. When he goes into a room, he goes through the door, opening and shutting the door just as you expected. He isn't at all like Humpty Dumpty. I don't think I ever knew two people more different."

Is anyone acquainted with Rollo except by hearsay, now? Yet for many years he was one of the best known of all the characters created by Jacob Abbott, and the first truly American child in fiction to become popular.

If it was Peter Parley who started the stream of children's books with an American setting, it was the father of the four Abbott boys who first peopled them with natural lifelike children to work and play in American surroundings. No definite person stands out in any one of Peter Parley's books, but in those of Jacob Abbott there is a whole gallery of individuals whose names were household words in many families and whose blameless adventures held and delighted more than one generation of boys and girls.

Rollo is not a "Youth" but a very little boy when we first meet him. He plants corn in his garden and two days later, since it has not come up, he replants the garden with beans; he picks up chips.

> " 'When shall I learn to work, father?' said Rollo.
>
> 'I have been thinking that it is full time, now. You are about six years old, and they say that a boy of seven years old is able to earn his living.'
>
> 'Well, father, I wish you would teach me to work. What should you do first?'
>
> 'The first lesson would be to teach you to do some common, easy work *steadily*.' "

So Mr. Holiday proceeds in the most approved fashion to inculcate his young son with one of the sound New England doctrines of his time. In the twelve small volumes dealing with Rollo's childhood he is a real boy, quarreling with Cousin James over the building of a wigwam or keeping the best fruit for himself instead of giving it to Lucy; he is not a goody-goody as it is sometimes supposed. But his ordinary childish faults are always used by his parents as texts for instruction in right behavior.

True to the theories of the didactic school, the children in the Abbott books are allowed to reap the consequences of their own choices, though the fathers and mothers are far more understanding and sympathetic than those in the English books of the period. Wise counsel and patient explanations are furnished to guide children's actions and emphasis is laid upon the old-fashioned conception of duty. Jacob Abbott believed that moral conduct must be taught like walking and talking. He felt that industry and honesty were cornerstones of character; that the "amiable and gentle qualities of the heart" might be cultivated by books like his intended principally for entertainment.

The scenes of the Rollo books, the Franconia stories, and some of the others were laid in New England, in quiet country neighborhoods where respect for authority rules. Full of the details that children love, these books had a wide influence through all the middle years of the nineteenth century. The relation of a book to its generation is best measured against the literature that precedes it rather than what comes after. To children seventy-five years ago the Abbott stories were a new type. Then the familiarity of the setting delighted, the reality of the characters charmed, the store of useful information was remembered. Older people, too, gave their wholehearted approval to books from which so much was to be learned. An unnamed writer, much closer than we are to the heyday of the Rollo books, has commented amusingly upon them in the *North American Review* for 1866:

"These works are invaluable to fathers; by keeping always one volume in advance of his oldest son, a man can stand before the household an encyclopedia of every practical art. . . . In these paths of peace the principal guide, philosopher and friend is Jonas. . . . Jonas is an admirable creation—the typical New England boy, such a boy as every one of us has been or known. Steady, sensible, sagacious, not troubled with languor or imagination, he is always a wholesome companion who neither intoxicates nor misleads. Domestic and agricultural virtues adorn his sedate career. His little barn chamber is always neat; his tools are always sharp; if he makes a box it holds together, if he digs a ditch there the water flows. He attends lyceum lectures and experimentalizes on his slate at evening touching the abstruse properties of the number nine. Jonas is American Democracy in its teens; it is Jonas who has conducted our town meetings, built our commonwealth and fought our wars."

Jonas was the first of those remarkable young people,

generally portrayed in Jacob Abbott's stories as sources of universal knowledge, looked up to and revered by the younger children. Everyone who recalls the hero worship so touchingly given by little boys and girls to those somewhat older can see a reason for the invention of these model characters. Beechnut, Mary Bell and Rainbow are all equally intelligent and are all trusted implicitly by the grownups to shoulder the responsibilities of maturity and take complete charge of the younger ones. Though still in their early teens, they never disappoint their employers and friends, are never found wanting in resourcefulness and common sense.

When Rollo was twelve years old he was taken on a European tour, described in twelve volumes, very tedious to readers of the present day. He had then become a "Youth," who traveled through the countries of Europe with the satisfied consciousness of hailing from a land far superior to those inhabited by foreigners. He cannot at this stage escape the charge of being hopelessly priggish; he has proved a fit subject for caricature.

Far more successful in bringing a native of another land to America than in taking Americans abroad, Mr. Abbott enriched children's books by creating a French boy of genuine individuality in the person of Beechnut of the Franconia stories. This Swiss boy, originally from Geneva by way of Paris and Montreal, introduces a delightfully new element into the series, for he supplements the habitual round of rural joys with his inventiveness and gay spirits.

He plans unusual games, he makes unusual toys and gives them diverting names. With his precious picture of Paris, displayed on the wall of his bedroom, he has a starting point for stories of French life that entrance his listeners. All the arts of the storyteller are his. Who, having read it, does not remember his description of the voyage to America, with the famous example of embellishment, given to Malleville and her brother Phonny?

"'Shall I tell you the story just as it was, as a sober matter of fact, or shall I embellish it?'

'I don't know what you mean by embellishing it.'

'Why,' said Beechnut, 'not telling exactly what is true, but inventing something to add to it to make it interesting.'

'I want to have it true,' said Malleville, 'and interesting, too.'

'But sometimes,' replied Beechnut, 'interesting things don't happen; and in such cases, if we should only relate what actually does happen the story would be likely to be dull.'

'I think you had better embellish the story a little,' said Phonny; 'just a little, you know.'"

Then what a grand story of shipwreck and iceberg follows. Jacob Abbott was never afraid of using unfamiliar words in his stories if they expressed the meaning.

By most readers the Franconia stories are counted the

liveliest and most engaging of the Abbott books. Any child reading them today will receive a vivid impression of the pleasures of blueberrying and sleigh riding; he will learn about woodcutting and bear hunts; he will travel over mountain roads or sit before an open fire and roast apples on a string. Mostly vanished joys, to be sure, yet their very strangeness holds a kind of fascination.

With the Rainbow and Lucky series still another sober and industrious lad of fourteen is introduced to the reader. Rainbow is a colored boy whose methods of dealing with others are similar to those of Jonas and Beechnut, and so of their creator, Mr. Abbott. Lucky is a horse with an adequate amount of sense. Where did all the large assortment of curious names originate? In the account of Rainbow's journey on the ill-fated mountain stage alone, we meet Handie and Triggett, Jex and Hitover and Tolie; only the girls are called by such common names as Ruth and Melinda and Ann.

During the years from 1832 to 1879, this father of the story series, as he may properly be called, brought out fully two hundred books for young people, few of which reached the popularity of his major series. His method did not demand that he choose only short and easy words or write down to children's understanding. Instead, he used the words best suited to express his meaning, regardless of length, trusting that the young reader would ask his mother if he did not get the sense.

Together with his brother, John S. C. Abbott, author of a long biography of Napoleon, Jacob produced the little red histories, fondly regarded for many years. Through them even older people became aware of famous kings and queens who played important parts in the life of great nations. Among others, Abraham Lincoln made warm acknowledgment of the debt he owed these books.

If the vein seems all but exhausted in the thin quarto volumes appearing as Harper's Story Books, each month for several years, an occasional gleam here and there rewards the seeker, as in *Timboo and Joliba; or, The Art of Being Useful.* Timboo was an olive-skinned boy, born of a savage mother on an island in the South Seas. We are not informed by what strange circumstance he becomes a sailor and arrives in New York, bringing his parrot, Joliba, with him. Faint copy of Beechnut, as he is, he immediately begins to be useful, sleeping in a hogshead and doing chores for the Cheveril family, but his best good deed, after teaching himself to read, was the instruction of Fanny Cheveril, aged five. Fanny did not like to go to school because she had nothing to do there, except sit still on a bench until it was her turn to go forward to the teacher to read. In Timboo's opinion, "The two reasons why children are sent to school are, first, that they may learn to read and write, and secondly, to get rid of their noise and the trouble they make at home." Just for the light it throws upon the school situation, this is an instructive story.

Education, indeed, was the supreme interest of the author. All his ideas on the subject were forward-looking, growing out of his deep respect for children as individuals. Both in the home and in the school, Jacob Abbott worked for a closer understanding, and an equalizing relationship between the teacher and the taught. One of the innovations when he was principal of the Mount Vernon School for Girls, in Boston, was the introduction of self-government and the honor system. In a day when corporal punishment was the rule in schools and in families, Mr. Abbott's *Gentle Measures in the Management and Training of the Young* did much to bring about a more wholesome attitude in the upbringing of children.

With his own children he was quick to commend, and firm when it was necessary to control them. Sharing intimately the lives of his motherless boys, he, with an inborn sympathy, gained an insight into child nature in general. What country boy could fail to appreciate and enjoy the significance of this advice in the "Code Barbarian," sent by Jacob Abbott from New York, in a newspaper letter to his boys in Maine:

"When you come in from sliding leave your sled in the yard upon the snow.

It will rust the irons a little and may prevent its going too fast when you go out to slide next time. You may save breaking your neck by this means.

If you lose your knife or anything it is a convenient plan to tell some boy that you lent it to him one day and you have not seen it since."

Possibly, in spite of the remoteness of the leisurely days when there was time to teach children to handle tools and do chores, there are still elements in the best of the Abbott books that are worth the consideration of those who have to do with boys and girls.

SUSAN WARNER AND HER
"WIDE, WIDE WORLD"
VI

TWO years after its publication in 1850 in two plump volumes, *The Wide, Wide World*, that famous story so dear to Mid-Victorian girlhood both in England and America, had reached its thirteenth edition. The charm has not yet wholly vanished from the recital of Ellen Montgomery's sorrows. Those who, reading widely among the letters and biographies of our grandmothers, chance upon more than one allusion to young ladies who sat in cold rooms and wept over *The Wide, Wide World*, may justly wonder where the charm lay. Perhaps only by reading this old-fashioned, sentimental story can we arrive at the answer, for which few in these crowded days, overfull of shorter books, have patience to search.

Just as Peter Parley introduced the authentic American scene into children's books and Jacob Abbott peopled it with real children, so Susan Warner seems to have been the first writer to combine for girls in their teens American characters with the national background.

As we look back to the other books written for girls during the first half of the nineteenth century we are obliged to turn again to England to find any that have left a mark. Susan Warner read the books of Mrs. Sherwood and Maria Edgeworth in her childhood and Miss Edgeworth's little girls must have been her only models worthy the name. There is, in the visit to the New York shops taken by Ellen Montgomery before parting with her mother, a faint echo of Rosamond's well-known shopping expedition when she bought the purple jar. But with a difference. It is for a Bible, one not too large, nor yet with too fine print, that Ellen is seeking. A strongly religious note pervades every production of the author of *The Wide, Wide World*.

The Warner sisters grew up in the atmosphere of books, with a father who read Boswell's *Life of Johnson* aloud to his daughters and awaited with them each new novel by Scott as it was issued. Susan was born in 1819 and lived all her life among the scenes she has chosen to draw under the pen name of Elizabeth Wetherell.

The Wide, Wide World was her first book, begun at the suggestion of an aunt and named by Anna Warner, her adoring younger sister. Written mainly at Constitution Island, three hundred yards off West Point in the Hudson River, and read to the family for approval, the book was not quick to find a publisher. Mr. Warner himself undertook to market it and one disappointment followed another until it came into the hands of George P. Putnam, who gave it serious consideration. Mr. Putnam, in grave doubt as to its availability, turned the manuscript over to his mother to read and from her came the verdict: "If you never publish another book you should publish this." Later events proved the soundness of her judgment, as *The Wide, Wide World* became immediately popular. It was reprinted many times, large numbers were sold in England and it was translated into several other languages.

Perhaps it may not be far wrong to call this story the first important example of the Sunday-school book type. Characteristic of the group is an atmosphere of fervent evangelism, overlaid with sentimentality, both religious and secular. As time went on such books took on a tone of self-righteousness in addition to their other qualities, and became altogether very distasteful to many sincere persons of the orthodox faith. "Too emotional for children," a London review of 1853 pronounced Susan Warner's famous book. Yet the *Edinburgh Witness* asserted that the author "has few equals and no superiors on either side of the Atlantic," and the *New York Times* stoutly declared that "one book like this is not produced in an age."

A state of copious tearfulness is inseparably connected with *The Wide, Wide World* in the memory of many readers. And no wonder. A few of the different phrases used to express Ellen's grief may be selected at random, yielding these expressions of sorrow:

"Ellen sat down and began to cry." (Ellen) "burst into tears." (Ellen) "threw herself on the floor in an agony of grief"; "quivering from head to foot with convulsive sobs"; "burst into one of those uncontrollable agonies of weeping"; "tears of mingled sweet and bitter were poured out fast"; "hiding her face in her hands"; "tears wet upon her cheek"; "tears fell like rain."

The theme is a favorite one. In Ellen Montgomery we have youth and innocence subjected to the hard knocks by which a callous world is apt to buffet children deprived of the natural protection of their parents and more or less at the mercy of the indifferent. Aunt Fortune was a singularly hardhearted guardian, especially in the matter of appropriating Ellen's letters without letting her see them. She is vividly described in the book.

In spite of her ready tears, however, the little girl has real personality and her grief over separation from her beloved mother, her longing for letters and her pathetic loneliness in the crude farming community touched the hearts of young and old. Her childish confidence was constantly winning friends. Among others there was the old gentleman who helped her buy a merino dress before leaving New York, who made her a present of a good warm winter hood and a brace of woodcock; there was the gentleman on the Hudson River boat who talked to her about the comforts of religion;

there was Mr. Van Brunt, the friendly Dutch farmer; there were Alice and John Humphreys, and Nancy, the naughty girl. One of the best portraits in the book is that of the jovial Mr. Van Brunt. Ellen's arrival at her aunt's home in his oxcart makes a delightful picture of a way of travel, strange enough to readers of the present day.

A strange, new world Ellen found it on Aunt Fortune's farm. Life there was more rigorous than that of her own home. When Ellen rose in the morning, the following day, she was bidden to go to bathe at a wooden tub fed by water flowing in wooden troughs from the spring; her white stockings splashed in the mud of the marsh were promptly dyed slate color; city ways must be laid aside.

Except for short glimpses of New York the setting of *The Wide, Wide World* and of *Queechy*, Miss Warner's very successful second book, is the home of her grandfather, just west of the Massachusetts border. Both books are undoubtedly based on many of the experiences of her own girlhood. Certainly the difficult adjustments between conditions of affluence and of poverty, described in both books, are the result of a kindred situation in the circumstances of the Warner family. Like the household in *Queechy*, Susan knew what it was to give up the amenities of the city and adapt herself to a society that seemed rude and restricted. The old news carrier with snuff-colored coat, broad-brimmed hat and tin trumpet was to her an arresting figure, as expressive of the countryside as the bees for pork chopping, corn husk-

ing and apple paring or the donation party for the new minister, all of which she describes with zest and humor.

Her love for the woods and fields of Canaan, for its farm-
lands, its old houses, the sawmill and the stream that turned
it and for Queechy Lake itself is apparent on many pages.
All the outdoor world with its infinite variety of sunset and
moonlight, snowstorms and sunny days was a source of
joy and inspiration which she could not keep out of her
books.

A larger stage is set for the characters in *Queechy* than for
those in *The Wide, Wide World;* indeed, it might be called
a novel were it not that to the Warner sisters the name con-
noted something worldly and dangerous. Their point of
view is reflected in the promise not to read novels, exacted
from Ellen Montgomery by Mr. John, when that insuf-
ferable prig and pedant leaves her in Scotland with her fine
relations. Fleda, the heroine of *Queechy*, is an orphan who
early in the book loses her closest of kin, the grandfather in
whom her whole world centers. Though less tearful than
Ellen, she shows her delicate sensibilities by the inevitable
headache following any strain upon her emotions. She is a
child of sunshine, however, swift to see the right thing, wise
to meet every emergency, considerate and self-sacrificing,
constant in her Christian faith. But these qualities are not
enough. Her ideals of what is true and beautiful in character
and in nature are matched not only by her happy and cheerful temperament, but equally by her unfailing competence

in practical affairs. We meet her at eleven years old as her watchful eyes are traveling disapprovingly over the old mare's rope-bound harness with a determination to have it adequately repaired. Whenever provisions ran a little short it was Fleda, even at this age, who could toss up a delicious omelette. Until her twentieth year, when the book leaves her, she never falters in doing the right thing, never fails to win the approbation of old and young for her matchless loveliness and simplicity.

With her wide acquaintance among the West Point cadets it is singular that the young men in Miss Warner's books are so stilted and unreal. Far more natural and lifelike are many of those who have minor parts. While the author states that only the cat in *The Wide, Wide World* is a portrait, we can hardly believe that she had not met with the originals of the independent "hired help," of whom Barby is an admirable example, else she could not have written of them with such sympathy and discernment.

But it is in the naïve and illuminating pictures of society in New York and the surrounding country nearly one hundred years ago that readers of *Queechy* may still find entertainment. This was the New York of Dickens' *American Notes*, where finery was flaunted on the streets on which barefoot little girls swept the crossings and ragged boys sold matches, where the street cries of oystermen and chimney sweeps could still be heard. Fleda and her friends dress in fine embroidered muslins for evening levees in elegant drawing rooms to engage in earnest conversations with young men about the true sphere of woman, or to display their skill in worsted work before admiring eyes. Fleda herself is distinctly bookish in her tastes, even contributing essays and poems to newspapers and magazines. When she is in town visiting her great-uncle, the library is a favorite haunt. She shows herself able to quote from Shakespeare and Burke, or to repeat Bryant's poems if occasion requires; but to her, the Bible is the most precious book.

During the years the Warners lived on Constitution Island Susan was actively employed in writing, though none of her later stories attained the popularity of the two earliest. Taking a series name from her most admired heroine she brought out Ellen Montgomery's Book Shelf, which had formerly a certain vogue, especially in Sunday-school libraries. One of these books, intended for quite young children, deserves not to be wholly forgotten because of its engaging picture of a pair of happy little sisters in town and country life. As *Mr. Rutherford's Children* is attributed to "The Authors of *The Wide, Wide World*," it seems certain that Anna had a share in its writing. The two children, Sybil and Chryssa, are seen in a normal setting with affectionate and understanding elders, enjoying a protected, wholesome childhood. From their winter stay at a famous hotel in New York, we get an agreeable picture of the way in which well-to-do families in the great city educated and diverted their children in the middle years of the last century.

It was unquestionably rare at that time for an American writer of children's books to have so genuine a background of both city and country environment. The Warners had moved in generous and cultivated circles in New York before the loss of their property made it necessary to retrench by retiring to the country. On the other hand, even in the days of prosperity, their summers were spent among simple folk where it was but natural that an appreciative observer, like Miss Susan, should note contrasts and differences peculiar to rural surroundings. And since, in 1840, more than one-fourth of the people of the United States were engaged in agriculture, the great popularity of her stories may be the better understood.

As their years advanced it is pleasant to think of the old Revolutionary house on Constitution Island where Miss Susan and Miss Anna dwelt for many years, the older sister until her death in 1885, the younger living until 1915 and with her other occupations there writing a life of her sister Susan. Both were buried with military honors in the Government cemetery at West Point. The West Point boys found in the house on the island a welcome escape from the restraints of Academy limits, for the ladies were kind and hospitable. Their friendship was of a lasting quality, and followed the young soldiers into the world with years of faithful correspondence.

One of the cadets has left a becoming portrait of Susan Warner as she sat in a big chair in the orchard on Sunday afternoons surrounded by boys on the grass, while she talked on some religious subject, earnestly and with no cant or sectarianism. After her talk came the treat to which they had looked forward for a week, tea and homemade ginger-bread. "She looked," he said, "like a print from *Godey's Lady's Book*. She always wore silk dresses of a small flowered pattern made with voluminous skirts of wonderful stiffness and rustle, and small, close-fitting bodices. A rich Paisley shawl was always around her shoulders, and a broad black velvet ribbon was bound around her hair."

So she should, indubitably, have looked and we may leave Miss Susan, confident for once that the actor fits the part.

THE DAWN OF IMAGINATION IN AMERICAN BOOKS FOR CHILDREN

VII

OOK in any authoritative reading list for children and you will find *A Wonder-Book* and *Tanglewood Tales* holding high place among retellings from the Greek myths. They have been named in such lists for many years now, kept alive by children's deep affection, always coming freshly to a new generation, to whom they are as dear as they were to Caroline Hewins, a child of the mid-century, who found *A Wonder-Book* on her pillow when she opened her eyes on the morning of her seventh birthday. "The dear green *Wonder-Book* with the Hammatt Billings pictures of the group of children on Tanglewood porch."

Not far from one hundred years ago, while American children's books were still cast in the matter-of-fact world set by Peter Parley and Jacob Abbott, Hawthorne wrote to his publisher, from his home in Lenox, announcing his intention of writing, within the next six weeks, a book of stories from Greek mythology, to which he proposed to give a romantic rather than a classical turn. That was in May, 1851. *A Wonder-Book* was finished and the Preface written on the fifteenth of July of that year. In presenting these myths to children, Hawthorne allowed his imagination to range over the bare elements of the immortal stories and clothe them in warm, intimate details that appeal to a child's mind. He was at no pains to keep their classical aspect; on the contrary, he deliberately shed it, believing that to embroider these myths with his own idealistic fancy was legitimate, in no way affecting their essential spirit. So, Hawthorne thought, the ancient poets themselves had dealt with the stories handed down from a still earlier world. He anticipated the critics who have not approved of this freedom, making his defense in the Prefaces to the books, where he claims that the old legends cannot be injured by certain changes in form, as they are the common property of mankind.

The two books together retell, in modern language, a dozen of the great stories from classic authors—six in each volume. In *A Wonder-Book* the thread of framing story is an integral part of the book with the student storyteller, surrounded by his circle of story lovers, responsible for the rendering of each myth. This first collection of Greek myths seems, indeed, a wonder book, so different is it in playful fancy and charm of style from all other books written for children in the first half of the nineteenth century. Hawthorne's earlier work for children had included his contributions to Peter Parley's publications, often innocent and ethereal, and the childlike narratives of early New England history, contained in *Grandfather's Chair* and *Biographical Stories*, published by Elizabeth Peabody, sister of Sophia, Hawthorne's wife. They show his romantic nature and his sympathy with children and foreshadow his Greek fairy tales.

Greek mythology, far from being a remote choice of subject for a child's book in the mid-nineteenth century, was a natural world for Hawthorne's imagination to roam when he decided to allow himself a pleasant relaxation from more strenuous literary tasks. Massachusetts had been strongly influenced by the Greek revival, following the close of the War of 1812, strengthened there by the ardor of local scholars and hero-worshippers. Books, lectures and classic sculpture united to focus attention upon Greek literature and mythology, and the Hawthorne children were not the only ones to feel the irresistible fascination of the old stories. Only, with them, the association was closer because the household possessed many copies of John Flaxman's graceful designs drawn for his outlines of the *Iliad* and the *Odyssey*, and carefully traced by Mrs. Hawthorne who loved them.

One questions whether there is any other author whose books for children show a greater contrast to those intended for adult readers. If we compare *The Scarlet Letter*, the novel just completed, from which Hawthorne took flight to a lighter mood, with the Greek fairy tales, the difference is marked, indeed. The fresh, sunny atmosphere of *A Wonder-Book* gives added weight to his family's belief that he was at his happiest in these months at Lenox. He had left his irksome post at the Salem Custom House and had finished his work on his greatest novel. Now he was a new man, giving himself to his children, sharing with them their games and pleasures, accompanying them on walks and climbs among the beautiful Berkshire hills. With them he was a gay and playful comrade, far other than the man so often termed gloomy by his contemporaries.

Tanglewood, where the Hawthornes lived for rather less than two years, was a red story-and-a-half farmhouse on the lonely road from Stockbridge to Lenox, in the heart of the Berkshires. When Hawthorne walked with his children in the woods and across the fields, delighting in the beauty of the landscape, sensitive to the changing seasons, he rejoiced in his freedom. Amidst these surroundings the narrative binding together the Greek fairy tales has its setting.

The Introductions to the stories are all tuned to the special place where each story was supposed to be told, with the color and feeling of country days from autumn to late spring. The warmth and haze of an Indian summer morning hover over the telling of "The Gorgon's Head," when the children, with their flower names, were gathered around Eustace Bright on the porch at Tanglewood. At noon, the party were eating their lunch in a dell at Shadow Brook after a forenoon's fun in nutting, and here they listened to the young student's version of "The Golden Touch." Just before Christmas, as a heavy snow was falling, the college boy, home for the holidays, kept the Tanglewood children absorbed in the playroom over Pandora's troubles, while the next day, in "a magnificent palace of snow," he told about the "Three Golden Apples." It was in Maytime that the series was finished on the hilltop, with "The Miraculous Pitcher" and "The Chimaera."

Some of Hawthorne's most delightful descriptive writing is to be found in these Introductions. His eyes, always responsive to beauty, noted how the morning mists filled the valley and hid the tops of the encircling mountains, how the bright yellow leaves sprinkled golden sunshine over the brook, how the fluttering snowflakes mantled the trees and frozen lake in dazzling white. He knew the little brook in all its aspects, rushing merrily along over the stones or tinkling under its icy banks of snow. His, too, was the sure knowledge of a New England spring with its cherished wild flowers breaking the cold ground—arbutus and violets, columbine and "that sociablest of flowers, the little Houstonia," for which he evidently felt a special affection.

As the children climbed the hillside in the spring and looked far to the west, they saw a range of blue mountains which, Eustace Bright told them, were the Catskills. "Among those misty hills, he said, was a spot where some

old Dutchmen were playing an everlasting game of nine-pins, and where an idle fellow, whose name was Rip Van Winkle, had fallen asleep, and slept twenty years at a stretch." When the children begged for that story, Eustace replied that the story "had been told once already, and better than it ever could be told again; and that nobody would have a right to alter a word of it until it should have grown as old as 'The Gorgon's Head,' and 'The Three Golden Apples,' and the rest of those miraculous legends."

Tanglewood Tales were written at Wayside, in Concord. Hawthorne mentioned the date of their completion, March 9, 1853, in his *American Notebooks*, together with the order of their writing: "The Pomegranate Seeds," "The Minotaur," "The Golden Fleece," "The Dragon's Teeth," "Circe's Palace," "The Pygmies." This is not the arrangement in the published book, as it now appears. To these later tales there is but one Introduction, when Eustace Bright, now a college senior, turns over to the editor his "wild stories from the classic myths," which in his own estimation were better chosen and better handled than those of *A Wonder-Book.* Whether or not this is true, countless numbers of English-reading children have been grateful these many years that Hawthorne opened for them the gateway to Greek mythology through these matchless stories.

Less than a generation ago, children in New England still read with pleasure *The Last of the Huggermuggers* and *Kobboltozo,* two fanciful tales written a year or two after *Tangle-*

wood Tales appeared. Unlike Hawthorne's stories, they derived nothing from the Greek classics, but perhaps it may be thought that the author's imagination drew a little upon *Gulliver's Travels*. When the two stories, written in Paris by Christopher P. Cranch, in 1855-1856, were sent to friends in Boston for publication, they were counted a decided success.

Both books have to do with the fabulous experiences of a young sailor, Jacket or Jacky, who was shipwrecked in the East Indies, not far from Java. On the island where he and a few companions were cast up, everything was of enormous size, for here lived two giants, the Huggermuggers, last of their race. Little Jacket, sleeping in a huge sea shell, was picked up by one of the giants, who desired the shell as a present for his wife, without seeing its unusual occupant. Thenceforward, the story flows on over Jacket's adventures with the giants, who proved to be a good and kindly pair, lonely in their large house because they had no companions except a race of dwarfs, and glad to make friends with the castaways. An exploring trip afforded many strange sights on the island and brought acquaintance with the colony of dwarfs, with which the second book, *Kobboltozo*, is concerned. *The Last of the Huggermuggers* ends too sadly for children, as Mrs. Huggermugger dies and her lonely mate, taken off the island by Jacket in a Yankee ship, does not survive the voyage to America.

Kobboltozo is an account of a second visit to the island,

when Jacky learns what happened there after he and the giants had gone. There was one malicious dwarf, named Kobboltozo, whose jealous nature had actually caused the end of the race of giants. He and his companions were eager to grow big and inherit the island and Kobboltozo had succeeded in learning a part of the secret of becoming great. This lay in eating a magic shellfish to be found on the shore. Since no one knew which was the right shellfish among the different varieties, the dwarfs spent their time sampling many kinds, with the result that most of them became smaller and vanished away. Kobboltozo was found by Jacket in a cave, still eating oysters and no larger than he ever was.

This is a livelier story than *The Last of the Huggermuggers*. It has more humor and some delightful descriptions of the wonderful caves where gnomes tended their forges, where lived the witch and the Mer-king. Illustrated by **Mr. Cranch** with pencil drawings, similar to those of Thackeray, there is not a little charm in the allegory, possibly better appreciated by adults than by children. It was the Mer-king who sang an interpretive song.

> "Not in the Ocean deep and clear,
>   Not on the Land so broad and fair,
>   Not in the regions of boundless Air,
>   Not in the Fire's burning sphere—
>   'Tis not here—'tis not there.

Ye may seek it everywhere.
He that is a dwarf in spirit
Never shall the isle inherit.
Hearts that grow 'mid daily cares
Grow to greatness unawares;
Noble souls alone may know
How the giants live and grow."

Christopher Pearse Cranch was a versatile and gifted American who shared with Hawthorne some of the ideals of the transcendentalists, like him finding congenial friends in the community at Brook Farm, in the 1840's. Handsome and graceful, with an agreeable singing voice and easy facility at the piano and with the flute, Cranch was always a welcome guest. He had an eye for caricature, too, and did not hesitate to make fun in his cartoons of such a dignified friend as Emerson, though with the utmost good nature. Too variously gifted, possibly too indolent, to become distinguished in any field, Christopher Cranch wrote several volumes of poetry and painted many pictures, but little of his work in either field has lasted. Years of travel and residence abroad in Italy, France and England brought him in touch with the Brownings and Thackeray and their circles. His own four children liked the giant and dwarf stories, but wept over the end of the Huggermuggers.

Cranch's friends urged him to continue writing books for children, for they felt he could improve upon what he had done. W. W. Story, the sculptor, begged him to put his energies into his writing and lighten it with more fun and gaiety. "If you can," he writes, "let it hold a double story, an internal one and an external one, as Andersen's do, so that the wiseacres shall like it as well as the children. Read 'The Little Tin Soldier,' 'The Ugly Duckling' and 'The Emperor's New Clothes.' You *can* do this and you *must*." James Russell Lowell and George William Curtis bestowed their approval upon his rare faculty of invention, but neither was wholly satisfied with their friend's achievement. For, in spite of his poet's feeling and artist's eye, all this good advice could not make a Hans Christian Andersen out of Christopher Cranch.

ELIJAH KELLOGG AND THE
ELM ISLAND BOYS

VIII

SIX miles off the Maine coast "broad off at sea" lay Elm Island, home of Lion Ben and Charlie Bell, cradle of the "Ark" and the "Hardscrabble," mecca for the Young Ship Builders and Boy Farmers. Heavily wooded with spruce, interspersed with fir and hemlock, at one end there was a grove of elm trees which gave the small island its name. There were maples enough to form a good sugar bush and a famous beech tree in which the herons nested. From the rockbound shores high cliffs rose up at intervals and one ran down to a quiet cove, safe harbor for boats, with a spring-nourished brook where frostfish and smelts came in, where wild geese, brant, sea ducks and other game birds settled in the fresh water.

Here, and on the neighboring mainland, the enterprises described in the Elm Island and Pleasant Cove series took place, those names beloved by hundreds of boys in the last quarter of the nineteenth century. The action of the stories and the attendant living conditions date back to the years just after the Revolutionary War, before the great days of shipbuilding in Maine, when the people on the coast were mostly pioneers, fishermen, farmers and small boatbuilders.

Lion Ben of Elm Island was the first book in the series. Young Ben Rhines, who gave up a sailor's life on the urgent plea of the girl he was to marry, is the central figure of the Elm Island stories. He had nothing but his hands and his narrow ax when he started to make a home for his Sally, whom he brought to the island in a squall of wind to the log cabin he had built in the woods. He hoped to pay for the island, which he had bought on credit, by cutting and selling masts and spars and other valuable lumber.

Stalwart is the fitting word for Lion Ben. A giant in stature with strength to match, it was nothing for him to pick up a canoe and "heave" it on shore like a bundle of chips, while with equal ease he could toss over his head any bully or braggart who crossed his path. With all his strength and hardihood this young man could be kind and gentle and his integrity was above reproach. Indeed, Ben and Sally "resembled in solidity the granite of their native soil." The younger boys to whom Ben was a hero, who looked to him for leadership, were his young relatives and the sons of the neighbors.

Industry and hard work tamed the wilderness for them,

ingenuity and energy turned every natural resource to good account. Fish from the sea and abundant wild fowl at their door provided the main food staples, supplemented in time by the produce from their garden. Turnips were the first vegetable crop planted.

Little by little the home place grew. Equipment needed for carrying on was fashioned mostly by hand labor. The loom that Sally wanted for weaving her homespun was made by Charlie Bell, the capable waif who blew in from Halifax and was adopted by Ben and Sally. The feathers for her pillows she plucked from the wild geese brought down by Ben's sure aim. Sally's carefully tended garden held the fragrant herbs she had brought from her mother's home, used as remedies in old New England, tansy, coltsfoot, wormwood, saffron, lovage and peppermint.

Since his tall trees held the best promise of advancing his fortunes, Lion Ben seems to have had an unusually intelligent grasp of the principles of conservation in contrast to methods followed by more grasping settlers. For Ben loved his island and did not want to strip it, "diminishing the fertility of the soil, exposing it to tempests, drying up the springs and defacing its beauty," so he cut economically and cleared only so much of the island as was needed for tillage.

Hewing spars from the straightest of his trees, Lion Ben bound them together and rafted them along the Maine coast on a voyage which ended at Long Wharf in Boston, where he netted enough to pay half the initial debt for his island.

Encouraged by this success, the ingenious settler planned a more daring project which is the subject of *The Ark of Elm Island*. In order to market his lumber without the aid of middlemen, he built a remarkable craft for a longer voyage. She was constructed of logs, made buoyant by casks, protected by the partial framework of a vessel and rigged as a fore-and-aft schooner. With a whimsical touch which is but seldom apparent in the chronicles of Elm Island, this curious vessel was named the "Ark," because, like Noah's boat of old, she carried a mixed cargo.

Captained by Ben's father, the "Ark" was manned by neighbors' boys and sailed to Cuba, where she was broken up and sold profitably. With the proceeds of the sale a brig was bought, loaded with molasses, coffee and sugar, and brought back to Boston.

Molasses was a desirable import in those days and it was by no means all turned into New England rum. Always desirable for cooking, it was sometimes the only sweetener to be found to satisfy the taste of the heavy toilers of the sea and shore. Every fishing boat carried twelve gallons of "long sweetening." No lumber camp would be without it.

The account of the "Ark's" arrival in Boston afforded an opportunity to set forth to rural readers the impression made on country boys by the sights of a large city, where one might even be invited to the home of a well-to-do merchant with whom the Captain could do business selling the cargo and even the brig herself. And the boys had money in their pockets, too, with which to pay for presents for the womenfolk at home, a shawl perhaps, or even a brooch. For the "Ark" not only took herself to market, but carried, as well, ventures by the crew including livestock, pigs and hens. It was in the handling of this mixed cargo in an uneasy sea that some of the dangers and accidents occurred which provided excitement and suspense on the voyage.

Absorbing as these details of pioneer industry are, the boys who loved the stories probably enjoyed as much some of the commoner episodes, like the country wrestling matches in which one can be sure Lion Ben will come out on top, though the struggle may be stiff. Or, perhaps, they liked better the thrilling fight in earnest with the piratical crew who brought Charlie Bell to the island, or maybe the hunting yarns of Uncle Isaac who could, and did, outrun more than one bull moose in the Maine woods.

Enough authentic matter is contained in *The Fisher Boys of Pleasant Cove* for it to be counted an historical picture of the fishing business of the Maine coast in the eighteenth and early nineteenth centuries. This unvarnished tale of the risks and hazards endured by Andrew Colcord recounts the experiences that were likely to befall men while "going over the Bay," to Fundy or Chaleur, to fish within a short distance of shore, sometimes in the track of ships inward or outward bound.

Boys who read the story learned that "going over the Bay" signified the practice of fishing near enough shore to come quickly into harbor with the catch, as distinguished from the practice followed by fishermen who made longer trips, salted their fish, and did not come home until they had used all their salt and "made their fare." They learned also, from this book, about the various fishing banks, about owners and outfitters and the rules for sharing the catch.

Each of the six books in the Elm Island series has a central theme of character-building import. *The Boy Farmers of Elm Island* stresses the importance of being ready to lend your neighbors a hand whenever there is need, as there so often was need in the sparsely settled regions where these pioneers dwelt.

One truth is implicit in all these stories, that character develops rapidly under pressure and the spur of necessity. No hint of an expectation of easy success or quickly gained riches enters into any of Kellogg's books. Endurance, self-sacrifice, pluck and upright living, the dignity of work, the worth of a plain man are emphasized in all his stories, told in the Maine vernacular and with a thoroughgoing knowledge of fishing, farming and boatbuilding. If the characters do not always come to life, if their conversations are frequently stiff and unnatural, their adventures have the ring of truthfulness.

Three series of Kellogg's books, six volumes in each, are to be found in *Books for the Young* by Caroline Hewins.

Besides Elm Island stories and the Pleasant Cove series, she listed the Forest Glen series among the books on North American travel and adventure. The Forest Glen series, of which the best known book is *Wolf Run*, is laid in a frontier settlement in western Pennsylvania, not far from Braddock's old battlefield. The books are mainly concerned with Indian warfare over the disputed territory claimed alike by the province of Pennsylvania and the Indians of the locality, Mohawks and Delawares.

The first, and by all odds the best, though not the most popular of Elijah Kellogg's books, is *Good Old Times; or Grandfather's Struggles for a Homestead*. Announced in the prospectus of *Our Young Folks*, for 1867, as the leading story of the year, it gives a vivid picture of American customs and manners a century earlier. From the frontier experiences of his own great-grandfather, Hugh McLellan, among the first settlers in Gorham, Kellogg drew the material for a detailed story of life in Maine before the Revolution, when conditions were primitive and toilsome.

Early settlers then found their most lucrative employment in mast hauling. Regal pines towered in the forests. Every sound straight tree over thirty-six inches in diameter was marked by the broad arrow of the king, to be felled and taken to the coast by ox teams.

Good Old Times holds the fascination of other books which show how Americans managed in pioneer settlements before the industrial age, when eight-foot sticks blazed on a farmer's hearth of an evening, with a dish of apples temptingly standing between the andirons. Such inviting details as the pleasures of picking blueberries in abundance and gathering beechnuts and acorns make the times seem good, indeed, but the grimmer side comes to light with the description of the old blockhouse at Gorham and the garrisons against Indian raids.

Widely known and widely loved in New England, Elijah Kellogg, the man who wrote these books, was well qualified to speak with authority about farmers, fishermen and sailors, for he had not only lived among them, but had also tried a hand at all three occupations. In his boyhood customs had not changed greatly from those described in the Elm Island and Pleasant Cove books.

There were two Elijah Kelloggs. The father had been a drummer boy with the minutemen in 1775, had fought at Bunker Hill and Ticonderoga and had shared the privations of Valley Forge. After the Revolutionary War he went to Dartmouth College, became a minister and preached many years in Portland. He was greatly beloved and greatly influential along the Maine coast, especially in his missionary days when he had finished his settled pastorate and journeyed to the eastward speaking to the people along the way. Parson Kellogg had, by inheritance, a freedom-loving spirit and an uncompromising Puritanism.

Young Elijah, born in 1813, drew a similar inheritance of sturdy independence from his mother also, granddaughter of the Gorham pioneer, Hugh McLellan. The small city of Portland was too narrow for the boy's activities and he ran away to sea at thirteen, to spend three years before the mast in Maine sailing vessels. After the urge for roving wore itself off, Elijah came ashore for a turn at farming and it was then that he realized that he needed an education. This meant preparation at the famous old Academy at Gorham, and earning the money for entering Bowdoin College, from which he graduated in 1840, going from there to Andover to study for the ministry.

Cruising around Casco Bay while he was still a college student, Kellogg discovered the long narrow neck of land which, with forty near-by islands, comprised the parish of Harpswell. The boy, whom the sea had called very early, fell under the spell of the seagirt village, returning there for every possible vacation and identifying himself with the kind of life that went on there. The shipbuilders, fishermen and retired sailors who lived in the township liked this friendly young man as much as he liked them, and before Elijah had graduated from Bowdoin he had promised to return there as preacher. Trusting in his good faith, the men of Harpswell built for him a church where his memory is still fondly cherished as a graceful orator and a devoted pastor.

When he finished his theological training, Elijah Kellogg went back to Harpswell to become pastor of the church for a salary of three hundred dollars, and though interrupting his service to act as Chaplain of the Sailors' Home in Boston, he never severed his connection with Harpswell and its citizens.

His twenty-nine books, written in Boston, have on some of their title pages a note to the effect that he was the author of "Spartacus to the Gladiators," an identification that gave him great prestige in the days when rhetorical exercises were a part of all college programs. For this speech became a tested favorite for prize declamations and was seldom absent from collections of oratorical writing compiled for school contests. Dozens of boys have stood on platforms in assembly halls and mouthed the opening words, written and spoken by a young theological student:

> "Ye call me chief, and ye do well to call him chief who, for twelve long years, has met upon the arena every shape of man or beast the broad empire of Rome could furnish, and who never yet has lowered his arm."

Now there is nothing apparent in the mere facts of Elijah Kellogg's life, nor in his books, that would account for the high esteem in which his name has been held at Bowdoin College and at other spots along the coast of Maine. The reason must be sought in the nature of the man himself. He was loved for his quick sympathies, his kindness and generosity, his fearlessness for the right, his otherworldliness.

All his life, too, Elijah Kellogg had a strong element of the mischief-loving boy with a keen sense of fun. He kept the ready wit which came to his aid in early years and caused him to lay the blame for his being late to school on the frogs, which had screamed K'logg K'logg, so insistently, that he felt obliged to turn back to see what they wanted.

Many stories are told of his personal courage, strength and self-reliance, the qualities he sought to arouse in his boys. Tradition gives the name of Elijah Kellogg as that of the first man to climb the spire of the college chapel to place the president's hat atop it. It was more than forty years before another daring Maine boy matched the reckless deed and put his class flag there.

The books that Kellogg wrote were prompted by a desire to help boys live upright lives. They never emphasize the making of money, though a practical regard for a decent living is not lacking. While he was at Harpswell it was a common practice for the college authorities to send him students who had to be "rusticated," to make up deficiencies in their academic work. They learned to study there and to revere his wise advice. Thus he became dear to thousands of boys and a college president was moved to write with all earnestness, "It will be a sad day for Bowdoin College if there shall ever be a generation of students who know not Elijah Kellogg."

HORACE E. SCUDDER, CRITIC AND EDITOR

IX

T is counted almost an axiom that a sound foundation of comparative values is essential for an intelligent approach to book selection for children. Best of all is to know good books at first hand, by reading them in childhood, thus carving a scale for measuring the ever-growing mass of current publications. For those are the precious reading years when one learns to know the difference between a real hero and a sham superman. Was Matthew Arnold right in his famous dictum that criticism is "a disinterested endeavor to learn and propagate the best that is known and thought in the world," and does this rule apply to those who discuss children's books? There were those who thought so in the nineteenth century, before there were children's librarians or children's book editors in publishing houses.

In the twenty-five years from 1870-1895 the two dominating influences affecting for good the production of children's literature in America were the *St. Nicholas* magazine, under the editorship of Mary Mapes Dodge in New York, and the editorial work of Horace E. Scudder in Boston. Believing that books for children should be judged by the same standards of criticism that govern the consideration of general literature, both Mrs. Dodge and Mr. Scudder made certain demands upon their contributors. Each had tireless energy and finely balanced judgment. So they set themselves to the task of providing boys and girls with reading that was worthy of their intelligence in the hope that young people would thus learn to distinguish the good from the bad for themselves.

Horace E. Scudder was a New Englander, the youngest son in a family of seven children, boys all but one. He was generously endowed with a strong sense of spiritual values, a love of music and art, and a discerning literary taste. During his years at college the Greek poets were his great delight and all through life he read from the Greek Testament every day. When he graduated from Williams College at twenty years of age he held the determination to pursue a literary career of some kind, though as yet he did not see his course plainly. His first published work grew out of his friendship for children. A little handful of fanciful stories written in that exquisite handwriting which he retained all his life, illustrated by himself and tied with ribbons, remains as witness of the pains he took to give enjoyment to his younger friends. These early stories show the tender sympathy Mr. Scudder always had with child life. They are permeated by a spirit of kinship with the imaginary world so real to children and to those older persons who have been blessed with an inborn gift of mysticism.

There was little sound criticism of children's books in the late sixties, so when Mr. Scudder introduced a series of articles on "Books for Young People" into a children's magazine which he had planned, it was a true innovation. *The Riverside Magazine*, whose brief existence of four years (1867-1870) was marked by this unusual feature, was his first venture as an editor. His editorials written to introduce the subject of children's reading and express his views on the parents' responsibility for making a right choice are full of meat. "What is it to a child," he asks, "whether a book was first published in hot haste this Christmas or has lain on the counters for a year, and is now, maybe, rather dull in cloth beside its new companions, though then it was thought brilliant enough? We may as well discard at once all such unnecessary considerations as when a book was published, or where it was published, and come right at the gist of the matter and ask if it is *good*,—good in itself and adapted to the reader for whom we are buying it."

And again, "We shall pay no very close attention to the line which divides books written for the young from books written for the old, but making a survey of literature, single out those writings which are worth giving to a child and for an acquaintance with which he will always hold us in grateful remembrance."

It was a delightful monthly, *The Riverside Magazine for Young People*. Think of looking forward to reading every month or so a new story by Hans Christian Andersen never before published! For several of these made their first appearance through the pages of *The Riverside Magazine*, and were later printed in Denmark. Altogether seventeen stories by Andersen came out in the *Riverside* in the course of its four years. There was much good poetry, too, ballads and famous verse as well as stories by some of the best writers of the day. But in the care bestowed upon the illustrations *The Riverside Magazine* struck a wholly new note for its time. To obtain pictures that he considered worthy of putting before children, Mr. Scudder searched far and wide. The measure of his success is indicated by the list of illustrations for 1867, which includes the names of John La Farge, Thomas Nast, Winslow Homer, E. B. Bensell, H. L. Stephens and F. O. C. Darley. "I did my best," said he in speaking of this feature, "to obtain pictures of child life from painters who were not mere professional book illustrators. It was only now and then that I was able to obtain any simple, unaffected design, showing an understanding of a child's figure and face." A few years after *The Riverside Magazine* ceased publication some of its valued contributors became closely connected with *St. Nicholas*, started by Mary

Mapes Dodge in 1873. Mr. Scudder was warmly interested in its development and was content to have it in his home for his daughter to read with her Andersen and Grimm, Mrs. Ewing and George Macdonald.

As a member of the house of Hurd and Houghton, the predecessors of the Houghton Mifflin Company, a connection established in 1872, Mr. Scudder had still greater opportunity to emphasize the importance of children's reading. About this time he was writing for the *New York Tribune*: "This distinction between books for children and books for their elders, so purely a creation of the last hundred years, ought to be abolished in our schools, and the better lesson taught of the common inheritance held by children with their parents in the great literature of the nation and parent country. If it is objected that this is impossible, that children cannot understand classic English literature, we reply—try them and see."

The idea of the "Riverside Literature Series for Young People" began to take shape in his mind. The impulse toward this series of whole works instead of fragments for the use of schools came from his dissatisfaction with the old-fashioned school readers. These, he felt, contained many scraps, sometimes from excellent sources but very seldom of the first quality. Mr. Scudder's theory was that anything in English and American literature which lives by virtue of its common acceptance may safely be made a part of the school curriculum. But he wanted reading to be a joy and not a task. The right kind of reading should be chosen "to stimulate interest, rouse the imagination and fix the attention, reading at the same time healthy and sound and which shall lead to better things in the future." In this series of worthwhile literature designed largely for use in schools the format and the low cost played important parts. Each regular number in paper covers cost but fifteen cents and was of a size to go easily into pockets for reading at leisure. Longfellow's "Evangeline" was the first poem selected for the series, a natural choice at that period. But later numbers went farther and put a great store of English as well as American classics within the reach of young people with slender resources. Unquestionably, the "Riverside Literature Series" has been a great influence in the forming of taste and appreciation in countless young people, in school and out.

What were the children's books published by the Houghton Mifflin Company during the years when Mr. Scudder was its literary adviser? Sarah Orne Jewett, who had written for *The Riverside Magazine*, brought them *Betty Leicester*. Eliza Orne White's first stories for children, *When Molly Was Six* and *A Little Girl of Long Ago*, belong to those years. There were books by Joel Chandler Harris and Mrs. A. D. T. Whitney, Whittier's lovely anthology, *Child Life*, and many others. Especially important were the two volumes of Hans Christian Andersen's work which Mr. Scudder regarded so highly that he studied Danish himself in order to be assured

of the integrity of the translation. For years now these books have been considered the most complete and satisfactory, in point of text, published in this country.

Faithful adherence to the best version of a traditional work was his fixed principle. In this, Scudder sets an example for other editors of the old folk tales and fables. His splendid collection, *The Children's Book*, published in 1881, has never been equaled in comprehensiveness and authenticity. Miss Hewins said of it, "A child who has it for a companion knows the best that has been written in English for children." *The Children's Book* is, in truth, a triumph of editorial integrity and wisdom, as rewarding in a family of children now, if it can be obtained, as it was in the closing decades of the nineteenth century.

Without anywhere putting it into words, the editor arranged this treasury of good literature in a rising scale of difficulty, so a child may find his own level, unhampered by grade restrictions, if drawn to a particular story. A round dozen sections are spread over the large generous pages, starting with a considerable collection of easy fables from Aesop, since John Locke's day a classic for beginners. "The Book of Wonders," which comes next, contains favorite nursery tales, Chicken-Licken, the Three Bears, and Rumpelstilzchen among them, followed by Cinderella, Dick Whittington, Puss in Boots.

Four sections in different parts of the book present well-chosen poetry, lyrics, storytelling poems and ballads.

There is a representative selection of Andersen's tales under his name, so a child may identify the author with his work; another group brings together the best-liked stories from the *Arabian Nights;* elsewhere the most important parts of *A Voyage to Lilliput* and the *Travels of Baron Munchausen* widen familiarity with imaginative books. Mr. Scudder did not omit a few old-fashioned didactic stories with morals, like "Eyes and No Eyes," and *The Children's Book* ends with four great tales from the Greek.

With the exception of his life of Washington, still recognized as among the best of the one-volume lives of Washington, the creative work that Mr. Scudder intended for children has not lived. His volumes of fanciful stories, graceful in style and sympathetic though they are, make little appeal to the modern child. The doings of the active Bodley family have had their day of popularity and been superseded by other fashions in travel books. Yet, on fresh examination the eight volumes will be found to contain much information often amusingly imparted. They admit also ballads and legends and short stories from history which might even now be read to young children profitably. But perhaps Horace Scudder's original work is best represented for our purpose in the collection of addresses given as a Lowell Institute course in 1882 and published later under the title, *Childhood in Literature and Art.* This group of addresses dedicated to his daughter shows Mr. Scudder at his best. Because he loved his subject he wrote with enthusiasm and charm. They bear the marks of a scholar's wide research among classical writers and of an equally wide study of mediaeval art. To choose the changing aspects of child life as revealed in literature from Homer to Wordsworth for discussion in such a course of lectures is sufficient proof of the importance he placed upon it. Extensive reading and the thought of many years lie behind these essays. They are enriched by many allusions, many touching extracts, such as the tender passage in Homer where Hector takes leave of Andromache and little Astyanax. Following child life through these pages brings us in contact with famous works of art. Two chapters at the end of the book hold a special appeal. These are the chapter on Hans Christian Andersen and the one on "Childhood in American Literary Art." In the last there is much wise and discriminating comment upon Hawthorne's work and on later tendencies in children's books. But in his appreciation of Andersen's art Mr. Scudder greatly served his time. No one else in America has done so much to show the ingenuity and wit, the play of imagination, the form and grace of Andersen's delicate fairy tales. Even a factual minded person might be drawn to read Andersen by this glowing introduction.

As author and editor Mr. Scudder touched various fields and left a considerable number of works dealing with American history and biography as well as essays in keen literary criticism. But we cannot help feeling that he would wish to be remembered not so much for these or for his years as editor of *The Atlantic Monthly*, but rather, as he is, for his fundamental part in the establishment of a sane attitude toward children's books and reading.

"OUR YOUNG FOLKS": ITS EDITORS AND AUTHORS

X

OR about ten years after the close of the Civil War boys and girls from reading families waited each month at post offices and country stores for the mail to bring them *Our Young Folks*. Launched from the same ways as *The Atlantic Monthly*, it sailed into many of the same homes where its elder sister was welcomed. First of the modern type of magazines for boys and girls, *Our Young Folks* made its appearance in gay orange paper covers with the names of its editors surrounding a well-clad Minerva complacently seated on the front. Dr. Oliver Wendell Holmes, who had named *The Atlantic Monthly*, wanted its young counterpart to be called *Atlantic Lighter*, but that may have seemed too flippant to the publishers, for the name chosen was more sedate and conventional if less lively.

There had been, to be sure, other magazines for children.

Besides *The Juvenile Miscellany*, early in the century, there were *Parley's Magazine, Merry's Museum, The Schoolmate* and a sprinkling of others, some of a Sunday-school nature; there was the indispensable *Youth's Companion*. But *Our Young Folks* was cut to a different pattern. Its publication marked the beginning of a new era in writing for boys and girls, when reading for recreation was accepted as right and desirable without the ulterior motive of satisfying a thirst for information.

Never was a magazine more auspiciously started. Like *The Atlantic Monthly* it had the interest of the foremost writers of the time. To the editorial board of their new periodical Ticknor and Fields called three persons, all with established reputations in literary circles, John T. Trowbridge, Gail Hamilton and Lucy Larcom. They brought to it high ideals of the possibilities of a good magazine for boys and girls. "It should be made to distance all competitors in value as it does in patronage," said Miss Larcom, when its financial success had become assured.

Most famous among the contributors of the initial number of January, 1865, was Harriet Beecher Stowe, the best-known woman writer in the country, then at the height of her popularity. Her story of "Hum, the Son of Buz," was given place of honor. Throughout the years she continued to write articles for *Our Young Folks;* in fact, practically everything that Mrs. Stowe intended for boys and girls was published originally in this magazine. *Little Pussy*

Willow, later brought out as a book, was one of the first of the country heroines to show a languid city miss the pleasures of healthful living. Theodore Roosevelt has recorded in his *Autobiography* how much he admired this demure and sensible heroine when he met her in the pages of *Our Young Folks*. Two serial stories from the hands of favorite writers for boys were continued through the twelve issues of 1865, one by Mayne Reid, *Afloat in the Forest*, typical adventure tale of that prolific writer; the other *Winning His Way*, signed "Carleton," pen name of Charles Carleton Coffin, noted war correspondent of the North. There were a story by Louisa Alcott, poems written by Lowell and Longfellow, and over the initials, "C. T.," Celia Thaxter's exquisite "Sandpiper" was given to the world.

Of the three editors it was probably John T. Trowbridge who contributed most largely to the pages of *Our Young Folks* as long as it lived, writing at times under assumed names as well as his own. Born in a log house in a clearing in the forest which then covered Genesee County, New York, Trowbridge early showed a love of nature and an absorbing interest in literature. By the time he was thirteen he was writing verses while eagerly gathering up a knowledge of books of various kinds. These tastes later brought him in contact with men of letters in New York and led him finally to Boston where he became associated with the group of writers for *The Atlantic Monthly*, an association which continued until his death.

Before his appointment as editor of *Our Young Folks*, Mr. Trowbridge had written several successful novels, *Neighbor Jackwood*, *Cudjo's Cave* and *The Three Scouts*, all colored by the problems of slavery and war. When he began to write for boys, he brought to the undertaking the practiced hand of an experienced author and a name familiar to readers of the best magazines of the day. *Our Young Folks* was secure of a feature of unquestioned popularity when *Jack Hazard and His Fortunes* appeared as a leading serial. From the memory of his own early life on the banks of the Erie Canal, Trowbridge drew the background for this story of real boy character. The gaunt horses, the muddy towpath, the clumsy scow were all familiar sights to him and he made them vivid to his readers. Jack Hazard, "the ragged little driver with a whip in one hand and a piece of bread-and-molasses in the other," calls forth our sympathy as he makes his escape with his one friend, the dog Lion, from his brutal father and the rough occupants of the canal boat. Countless boys have followed Jack's fortunes through the five books which comprise the Jack Hazard series. Besides these Mr. Trowbridge produced other books, some of which were first published in *St. Nicholas*.

Lucy Larcom invested the editorial board with good taste, genuine sympathy with childhood, and a strong moral sentiment which frequently expressed itself in her articles and poems. In *A New England Girlhood*, she wrote an enduring autobiography, introducing a remarkable group of young women who lived in the days when industrial problems were less complicated than they are now. Almost every month *Our Young Folks* contained a ballad or poem or prose sketch by this gentle lady, the friend of Whittier, collaborator with him in his two anthologies, *Child Life in Poetry* and *Child Life in Prose*. Through these admirable collections in their plain green covers many children have owed their introduction to "The Ugly Duckling" and "The Story Without an End," to "The Owl and the Pussy-Cat" and many an other poem and story whose inclusion showed Miss Larcom's genuine talent for selection. She was never quite happy signing her own name and preferred using initials, for while alliteration in pen names was the fashion of the day she did not care for it. The name of Lucy Larcom, its bearer felt, seemed like the adopted signatures of some of her contemporaries, "Minnie Myrtle," "Fanny Forrester" and "Grace Greenwood."

Gail Hamilton, the editor whose name appears in the second place on the early covers of *Our Young Folks*, was a member of the anti-slavery party in whose interests she wielded a sharp and vigorous pen. Her essays and papers for the general reader were accounted witty and she had a considerable circle of admirers, but her gifts to literature for children had no real importance. Mary Abigail Dodge, of Hamilton, Massachusetts, was the designation from which her pseudonym was derived. Disagreements with her publishers, Ticknor and Fields, brought about a severance of the relationship after a few years and her name was dropped from the cover, leaving Mr. Trowbridge and Miss Larcom to carry on alone.

Our Young Folks was less than a year old when its publishers developed their plan for still a third magazine and invited to their pleasant editorial rooms overlooking Boston Common a young man from New York who used to say in after life: "Though I am not genuine Boston, I am Boston-plated." Thomas Bailey Aldrich then became editor of *Every Saturday*, an eclectic weekly which drew largely from foreign periodicals. In October, 1868, "Marjorie's Almanac," a graceful little poem with real child interest, marked Mr. Aldrich's first appearance in *Our Young Folks*. The next year the inimitable *Story of a Bad Boy* was carried as a serial.

The Story of a Bad Boy stands as a landmark among American books for boys and girls. We count it as one of our unquestioned classics and venture to say that it will outlast everything else that Aldrich wrote. For felicity of style and clear-sighted interpretation of boy life it is unsurpassed. Written mainly at Portsmouth, the Rivermouth of Tom Bailey's boyhood, it was finished in a house on Pinckney Street, in Boston, passing naturally from there to the office of *Our Young Folks*. If it is idealized autobiography it yet possesses a universal appeal. Even the inevitable changes worked by time on the pastimes and manners of each new generation do not take away the reality of certain unforgettable incidents of the story. Every boy can enter with sympathy into Tom's sensations on that memorable Fourth of July when, his friends having scattered, Tom Bailey was faced with the empty glasses for twelve sixpenny ice creams, "strawberry and verneller mixed." And combined with all the humor and fun in which the book abounds, there is still that touch of sadness said to be inseparable from perfect art, as on the memorable pages which tell about little Binny Wallace drifting out to sea.

It must have been a particularly gratifying moment for the editors of this magazine for young people when they were able to announce the name of Charles Dickens among their authors. *Holiday Romance*, best known to us now by the story called "The Magic Fishbone," was issued in four installments in 1868, just after the novelist's American visit. In book form and with Bedford's delicious illustrations, the engaging tale of the Princess Alicia, her impecunious papa and her fairy godmother, still continues to tickle the fancy of humor-loving American children. In the same volume, too, Lucretia P. Hale introduced the Peterkin family to an appreciative audience of old and young, and William Henry's letters to his grandmother were produced, a packet at a time, from the desk of Mrs. Diaz. Between the orange covers there was plenty of laughter that year. Who can wonder that Theodore Roosevelt, looking back at those halcyon days, declared that there never was such a magazine? With the names of Whittier and Lowell and Longfellow, with Bayard Taylor's chapters on the *Boys of Other*

Countries, Mrs. Whitney's *We Girls*, Dr. Isaac Hayes's *Cast Away in the Cold*, and many other notable numbers to be found in the index, such a claim has its merits.

All that a good modern magazine can offer had been included. For their day the illustrations were worthy of the text, representative work of such artists as Winslow Homer, John Gilbert and H. L. Stephens. Special departments for correspondence and puzzles had a place, but in one respect a great and significant difference between these old periodicals and those now published may be noticed—advertisements are entirely absent from their pages. It was a time when magazines could live for a while on their subscription lists alone.

Nine years seems a short life for a publication so successful and so well loved. When the time came, as it did in 1874, for *Our Young Folks* to take leave of its first home, it was not from any failure in popularity or prestige, it was only one more example of the insecurity of business undertakings. So the fine young monthly was sold to Scribner's in New York, and became the foundation of its still more famous successor, *St. Nicholas*, under the direction of Mary Mapes Dodge, a truly great editor.

GOOD OLD "ST. NICHOLAS"
AND ITS CONTEMPORARIES

XI

TANDING side by side in a row on the shelves of fortunate children's libraries is a line of large red books, stamped generously in black and gold. Perhaps they may be considered too precious for careless handling, but the knowing child who likes to make discoveries in books has already claimed them as a treasure house of riches. They are the bound volumes of the monthly magazine, *St. Nicholas*, in the days of its prime. Within these red covers lies the very kernel of American books for children, published during a period of more than thirty years.

Now and then, when readers who were young in the nineties get together, you may hear them talk of the glorious days when *St. Nicholas* flourished, bringing out, month by month, all their favorite stories. And some there are whose memories go still further back, who can remember what it was like to wait impatiently for the latest chapter of "Donald and Dorothy," or the whimsical travels of "Davy and the Goblin." They speak of it with affection. "There never was a magazine like it," they say.

So, too, thought the readers of *Our Young Folks*, or *The Riverside Magazine*, about the periodical they had learned to love. But *St. Nicholas* was, indeed, different. There is a lighthearted quality, a gaiety in its appearance which could not have been achieved in the earlier magazines. Children who never knew it in the days of its publication find its bound volumes as satisfying reading as newer books, as modern in the spirit of its contents. Behind the making of such a magazine there had to be a creative personality. To think of the great days of *St. Nicholas* is to think of Mary Mapes Dodge, its first editor.

From a girlhood home presided over by a father who combined scholarship and a scientist's inquiring mind with the gift of storyteller, she drew a spacious background of association with books and people. There were always guests in that home, guests representing New York's circle of literary men and illustrious artists, whose talk threw off sparks to kindle the thoughts and ambitions of an eager girl. Her warm and buoyant nature which surrounded her with friends gave her, too, a deep respect for children and an understanding of their interests. This was further strengthened by her close companionship with her two young sons. It was for them she had written *Hans Brinker* in 1865.

Mary Mapes Dodge was already conducting a successful juvenile department in *Hearth and Home*, a New York weekly edited by Edward Eggleston, when she was asked to undertake the editorship of a magazine devoted entirely to children. It was projected by the owners of *Scribner's Monthly*, then in its third year, and destined to become later the *Century Magazine*.

The early seventies was an arid time for children's books, no less than for literature in general, save for the small group of New England writers. Parents were worried, too, over the prevalence of "dime novels," but a sufficient body of suitable literature for children was not yet in sight. It took vision to see a future for a new magazine which should aim to please children rather than their elders, a bright and gay magazine, with many pictures by the foremost artists. Roswell Smith had that vision. Mrs. Dodge once said that the success of *St. Nicholas* rested in large measure upon the generosity of its founder. As one of the owners of *Scribner's Monthly*, he wanted to enlarge the company's influence, for he believed it was possible to make such a magazine more attractive than any hitherto published. On Mrs. Dodge's acceptance of the post of editor, its inception depended.

Scribner's Monthly, for July, 1873, contains an unsigned article on "Children's Magazines," expressing some fresh and constructive ideas, as pertinent now as they were seventy years ago. The article is significant because these views, held by Mary Mapes Dodge, show what lay behind her leadership for more than three decades in the production of a literature for children. "The children's magazine must not be a milk-and-water variety of the periodical for adults. In fact, it needs to be stronger, truer, bolder, more uncompromising than the other," she said. The publisher's announcements echoed these words. There must be entertainment, no less than information; the spirit of laughter would be evoked; there would be "no sermonizing, no wearisome spinning out of facts, no rattling of the dry bones of history," while all priggishness was condemned.

Heralded by such sane and inviting pledges, the first issue of *St. Nicholas* appeared in November, 1873, opening with a letter from the editor, giving the reasons that lay behind the choice of the name for the new magazine. That happy inspiration linked *St. Nicholas* forever with New York and its patron saint.

Assisting Mrs. Dodge was Frank Stockton, who had previously worked with her on *Hearth and Home*. He was to serve as Associate Editor of *St. Nicholas* for seven years. During those years, and afterward, his short stories were a notable feature, gladdening the pages of *St. Nicholas* for many issues with their inimitable turns of fancy, delicious sense of humor and gentle philosophy, always kindly, but never dull. They were phrased, too, in a charming style. John T. Trowbridge joined the staff in the first year, though with a heavy heart, since his own well-loved paper had been sold by its Boston owners and merged in the new magazine.

He did not know, when he planned his last number of *Our Young Folks*, that this was to happen, and his card in an early *St. Nicholas* has a natural note of sadness. "That I do not mourn the loss of our little favorite, I will not pretend," he said. "It filled its place and it is gone; and we believe from its grave violets will spring to blossom amid the leaves of a more beautiful and beloved successor." His connection with *St. Nicholas* lasted until 1916. Officially, Horace E. Scudder had no place in the *St. Nicholas* organization, yet as a congenial and trusted authority he was often consulted by the editor. Not only were his experiences in editing the short-lived *Riverside Magazine* of value to her, but the two friends were in complete agreement on the essentials of children's literature, a field where their joint influence was profound.

Mrs. Dodge wanted the new periodical to be a beautiful production and a playground as well. She brought to her post not only unusual literary discrimination but a joyous spirit, radiating enthusiasm and energy, calling out the best and most sincere writing from her authors, making them eager to win her approval, often tempting them into new fields. Her own contributions were more numerous than anyone guessed. While the initials, M. M. D., were a familiar sight at the foot of verses and articles, she also masqueraded each month as Jack-in-the-Pulpit and The Little Schoolma'am, through whose voices she could express editorial opinions and give sensible advice. Occasionally, at other times, she hid her identity in the name of Joel Stacy.

The seventies were made memorable by the work of many well-known personages. Poems by Bryant and Whittier, Celia Thaxter and Lucy Larcom indicate the interest taken by writers of established reputation. Month by month, Louisa Alcott's *Eight Cousins* and *Under the Lilacs* invited constant readers. The popular serials by Trowbridge, *Fast Friends* and *The Young Surveyor*, and Noah Brooks' *The Boy Emigrants* captured the boys who perceived the authenticity of backgrounds based on personal adventure. T. B. Aldrich, Lucretia P. Hale, Sarah Orne Jewett, Susan Coolidge and Laura E. Richards were frequent contributors during the decade. Articles on astronomy by R. A. Proctor and on bird life by Olive Thorne Miller fostered scientific tastes, not then nourished by school programs. Howard Pyle's name first appears as author-illustrator of a fairy tale in November, 1877. Later his fine books, *Otto of the Silver Hand* and *The Story of King Arthur*, came out as installments in *St. Nicholas* with his own distinguished pictures.

The eighties carried on many of the same authors, adding for boy adventure long stories by W. O. Stoddard. Mrs. Dodge's *Donald and Dorothy*, Frances Courtenay Baylor's *Juan and Juanita*, Harris' *Daddy Jake the Runaway* and Baldwin's *Northern Myths*, all belong to that period. It was in 1885-1886 that *Little Lord Fauntleroy*, most famous of all *St. Nicholas* children, took the country by storm. Frances Hodgson Burnett did not consider herself a writer for children, but she was willing to try her hand at the request of Mary Mapes

Dodge. With the appearance of *Little Lord Fauntleroy*, a great surprise was in store for editor and author alike. Pictured by Reginald Birch, the courtly little hero, with his velvet suit, lace collar and forgiving spirit, became unbelievably famous. Though never a favorite with boys, his story was translated into several other languages, and after he took the stage in the person of nine-year-old Elsie Leslie, he won the hearts of countless theater audiences.

The high point of *St. Nicholas* in the nineties was John Bennett's classic story of the reign of Queen Elizabeth, careful in historical detail and full of action, about the strolling players and the boy with the golden voice, *Master Skylark*. *Lady Jane* was another serial greatly enjoyed during those years. It was a New Orleans story, by Mrs. C. V. Jamison, one of the first of the mystery tales and felt by girls to be very exciting.

Pleasure in the *St. Nicholas* contents was greatly enhanced by the wealth of pictures from the hands of distinguished illustrators of the day, or, infrequently, by reproductions from famous paintings. "The pictures must have the greatest variety consistent with simplicity, beauty and unity. They should be heartily conceived and well executed, and they must be suggestive, attractive, and epigrammatic." The choice was varied enough to include such diverse examples as Delaroche's touching "Children of Edward IV in the Tower" and Arthur Rackham's ivory-toned drawings for Mother Goose. The names of F. S. Church, George Wharton Edwards and Joseph Pennell may all be found in files of *St. Nicholas*. For fun, there were E. B. Bensell's spirited illustrations for Frank Stockton's stories, J. G. Francis' *Cheerful Cats*, and the forerunner of the Brownies from the hand of Palmer Cox. They are held as fondly in memory as the stories.

Through articles in the volumes of *St. Nicholas* can be traced the changing American scene of the late nineteenth century, the effect of inventions and industrial development, the shifting of emphasis in social life. We can follow the rising tide of the school story, seen first in 1882 with Eggleston's *The Hoosier School-boy;* eight years later with the introduction of athletics in Allen French's *Junior Cup;* reaching its full-fledged state by emphasizing sport, in Barbour's *Crimson Sweater*, in 1906. Dan Beard's widely popular papers on handicraft and camping were abreast of the times in the eighties; equally modern in 1906 was Tudor Jenks' account of flying machines, advanced by 1910 to an article on "Boys and the Air-Ship" by Francis Arnold Collins.

The Departments claimed full measure of attention from children of different tastes. For young children, the early numbers carried a simple story in large type which could be easily read by beginners. The Letter Box brought correspondents to children in country homes, the Bird-Defenders encouraged humanitarian efforts, the Agassiz Association stimulated observation in the field of science long before the public school curriculums included more than physiology.

In 1899, St. Nicholas League, directed for ten years by Albert Bigelow Paine, began its promotion of the arts by distribution of medals and honorable mention, and by printing original work of a sufficiently meritorious standard.

In its happy days *St. Nicholas* went everywhere. Its subscribers were scattered through cities and towns, on distant ranches and isolated farms from one end of the American continent to the other. English-reading children in many other lands welcomed it. Young Rudyard Kipling used to read it and, years after, wrote some of the Jungle Book stories for its pages because of the pleasure given Mrs. Dodge by one of his Indian animal tales. A story in the bound volume of *St. Nicholas* for 1884, picked up in the Oakland Public Library, so gripped Jack London, a boy of sixteen, that he determined to give up his life as a tough young "water rat" and offer his services to the state fish patrol. He made good in that service and was proud to have his story, "The Cruise of the Dazzler," published in the magazine in 1902.

Edna St. Vincent Millay, as a girl in Rockland, Maine, read *St. Nicholas* and joined the League, in whose columns her early poems appeared repeatedly, with honorable mention. About the same time, too, *St. Nicholas* went to a lonely farmhouse in New Hampshire, bringing heartening approval of the boyish drawings of young Robert E. Jones, whose talents have burgeoned forth in stage design.

After the death of Mary Mapes Dodge in 1905, the task of editing *St. Nicholas* was assumed by William Fayal Clarke, who had worked with her from its beginning. Mr. Clarke continued as editor until 1927. It seems to be a hard fact, recognized in the publishing world, that a magazine for children is seldom, if ever, self-sustaining. In 1930, the Century Company sold *St. Nicholas* away from New York, but the decline of the old magazine could not be arrested, and its last days are best forgotten.

St. Nicholas was only five years old when another renowned New York publishing house decided to add to its monthly and weekly periodicals for adults one designed especially for children. Nor could it have been surprising at the time that Harper and Brothers took such a step, for of all the American publishers this was the one with a lengthy roll of authors who had for years given particular attention to writing for children.

A prospectus circulated in the fall of 1879 announces: "We shall begin next month the publication of an illustrated journal of amusement and instruction, to be called *Harper's Young People.*" For twenty years, this lively magazine held an important place in the hearts of American boys and girls, rivaling *St. Nicholas* in the opinion of some readers. Although it was a weekly the subscription price was only a dollar and a half a year, and the standard of writing was high. The aim of the sponsors was to "stimulate and satisfy the intelligent curiosity of boys and girls," by the inclusion of factual articles on nature, art and travel, with stories to gratify the imagination and with plenty of fun.

Placed side by side with the first issue of *St. Nicholas* the new magazine suffers by comparison as the print is fine and the format cheap. Later, these faults were corrected, the size of the paper was doubled and eventually the name changed to *Harper's Round Table*.

Kirk Munroe was the first editor of *Harper's Young People*, serving in that capacity for three years and writing for the magazine as long as it lasted. He had roved far over the United States, had been a surveyor in the West, knew Custer and Buffalo Bill. *The Flamingo Feather*, one of the best of his Indian stories, concerned the Seminoles of Florida. *Derrick Sterling* was about a boy in the mines, one of the earliest children's books about an industry. Munroe's stories were immensely popular, but as they were often carelessly written they have not survived.

Another favorite and prolific writer whose serials often appeared in *Harper's Young People* was James Otis (Kaler). Only one of his books merits recalling. *Toby Tyler*, foremost for decades among stories about the circus, has qualities that have kept it alive, appearing from time to time with new pictures, for over sixty years. Toby Tyler, who had run away from home allured by the glittering splendor of a traveling circus, was realistically drawn. In the ten uncomfortable weeks the boy spent with the big top his dearest friend was Mr. Stubbs with his little brown hands and expressive face, the compassionate clutch of his paw, the wise look in his grave eyes. Countless children have been able to believe with Toby that the aged monkey knew what was said to him and might even talk if he tried. Over Mr. Stubbs' moving fate genuine tears have been shed, yet the story never lapses into sentimentality.

Many of the *St. Nicholas* authors wrote also for *Harper's Young People* and many of the same illustrators were to be found working for both magazines. Howard Pyle turned to *Harper's Young People* when he found his first outlet overstocked with his fables. *The Merry Adventures of Robin Hood* was published there, but the few pictures then used were not included in the finished volume. As *Harper's Young People* gained in good looks, approval of it as a "noble storehouse of good reading" grew apace and, like *St. Nicholas*, it had its English edition.

The third periodical for boys and girls, flourishing in the 1880's, was *Wide Awake*, published in Boston by the Lothrop Company. Keyed for the same public as the other two magazines, it had its devoted followers throughout the course of its life (1875-1893). *Wide Awake* was designed somewhat in the likeness of *St. Nicholas*, similar in size with many pictures, and pages in large print for the youngest readers. Early volumes drew occasionally from English sources and George Macdonald's lovely *Double Story* was serialized the first year.

All three of these periodicals were analyzed in *Reading for the Young*, that fine list of books and magazine articles begun by John F. Sargent in 1886 and continued by his sisters.

Probably the most warmly cherished books growing out of *Wide Awake* are Margaret Sidney's Pepper books, beginning with *Five Little Peppers and How They Grew*. Unfortunately the series was continued too long and suffered after the first three volumes from declining vigor. The Peppers were a large and happy family abounding with high spirits and hearty activity, but with small material assets, so they were obliged to manage carefully and "make things do." Their problems are not unlike those of the March family of an earlier generation.

THE GOLDEN AGE

XII

ECHOES from the Didactic Era were passing away when *Books for the Young* was published in 1882. Caroline Hewins' reading list says almost as much by its omissions as by its inclusions. No Peter Parleys are to be found in it, no Sunday-school stories, sentimentality has disappeared.

The decade of the 1880's, preceded by the quickening effect of the Centennial four years earlier, was a brilliant period in American children's literature. Seeds planted by the great editors were coming to fullness in this period, burgeoning into a more mature and just appraisal of the "juvenile" as an honorable contribution to literature which could no longer be ignored. The children's field shared in the changes affecting books in general—the greater consciousness of national life, the trend toward more realistic fiction. At the same time there was a flowing tide of imaginative power.

Realistic fiction continued to thrive under the hands of the

New England group of women writers, whose healthy tales of normal home life had begun in the seventies, or earlier. Louisa Alcott's *Under the Lilacs* and *Jack and Jill,* though written within the shadow of her mother's death and that of "Amy," showed little of the sadness their author was hiding. Susan Coolidge (Sarah Chauncey Woolsey), an adopted New Englander, added to her honest, unaffected *Katy* books; Mary P. Wells Smith pictured the freedom of farm life in the *Jolly Good Times* stories. To satisfy boys' tastes Trowbridge, Brooks and Stoddard still carried on. But for the surge of fine books of the imagination, with one exception, we must look beyond the borders of New England.

Where the three books by Thomas Bulfinch had long stood alone with Hawthorne's Greek fairy tales to introduce boys and girls to classic myths, James Baldwin, an educator from the Wabash country, and Sidney Lanier, a poet of the South, now retold the heroic legends for young people in books that have become classics.

There were few books in the Friends Community when James Baldwin was growing up in Indiana, a backwoods boy who thought the log cabin in which he was born was the center of the world. Yet the pleasantest memories of his early years were associated with his tiny library, and his first and lasting ambition was to write books himself. When the time came to do so in earnest, he did not turn to the scenes of his boyhood for inspiration, as did Edward Eggleston who was writing at the same time, describing with fidelity and humor the rough manners of a small country neighborhood in *The Hoosier School-boy*. Instead, Baldwin recalled his own tastes when he hungered for reading and so wrote of a dragon slayer and a splendid hero.

The Story of Siegfried and *The Story of Roland* have not been superseded by later versions of these old tales. For the *Siegfried*, Baldwin drew from the Eddas and the Nibelung-enlied, changing and recasting these and other renderings of the ancient myths so as to embody the inherent qualities of poetic literature in the childhood of the world. For the *Roland*, he blended fact and fiction as they were set down by "song writers and poets of five centuries and as many languages." Through both books blow the winds of adventure, daring and loyalties to spread the fires of youthful aspiration.

Sidney Lanier, in *The Boy's King Arthur*, followed closely the history of the brave world of romance as it was set forth by Sir Thomas Malory. When Lanier felt that the old chronicler's words were too archaic to be easily understood, he added a modern equivalent in brackets, but he did this sparingly so that the style is not injured. Interest in the lofty ideals of knighthood had been nourished in the poet's southern boyhood, when deeds of valor and chivalry kindled his own imagination. Over the years *The Boy's King Arthur* has passed along these high ideals to the young manhood of many ardent boys.

In the very center of the Golden Age stands the name of Howard Pyle. Four matchless books of his creating belong in the harvest of the 1880's, two more in the nineties, followed within fifteen years by the four great volumes of the Arthurian cycle. And in each of these books there was the perfect harmony between written words and pictures which comes only as the rare gift of twofold talent.

"My ambition in days gone by," wrote Howard Pyle, "was to write a really notable adult book, but now I am glad that I have made literary friends of the children rather than older folk. In one's mature years one forgets the books that one reads, but the stories of childhood leave an indelible impression, and their author always has a niche in the temple of memory from which the image is never cast out to be thrown into the rubbish heap of things that are outgrown and outlived."

Best loved, and judged the most perfect of Pyle's work, is the *Robin Hood*, still fresh in its appeal, still merry and unspoiled, still full of the outdoor world which urgently calls young hearts to the greenwood. It was the book longest growing in the heart of Howard Pyle. He had been writing animal fables for *St. Nicholas* for several years, as a young man's first literary ventures in New York, but, insistently, his mind turned back to the old English ballads which his mother had read to him in his Delaware boyhood. He had loved Percy's *Reliques of Ancient English Poetry* then; he felt the stories would be loved by other boys and girls.

The time was ripe in 1883 for *The Merry Adventures of*

Robin Hood. Sidney Lanier and James Baldwin had introduced heroes from legend and romance whose deeds,
touched with the miraculous, were on an exalted scale; they
were knights of the first rank in the kingdom, always in
deadly earnest. In contrast, Robin Hood was neither noble
nor an aristocrat, and the handful of ballads recounting his
deeds have been retold in lighthearted mirth. All is blithe
in England —

> "at the dawn of day in the merry May-time when hedge-
> rows are green and flowers bedeck the meadows; daisies
> pied and yellow cuckoo buds and fair primroses all along
> the briery hedges; when apple buds blossom and sweet
> birds sing, the lark at dawn of day, the throstle cock and
> cuckoo; when lads and lassies look upon each other with
> sweet thoughts; when busy housewives spread their linen
> to bleach upon the green grass."

In word pictures such as these, the stage was set for the
tales of the Great Fair at Nottingham, for Robin's bout with
the tall stranger, for Little John's feats at the shooting match,
for the shouts of laughter over the mishaps of the luckless
Sheriff of Nottingham, for the entrance of the "proudest of
the Plantagenets." Scudder's *Children's Book* had contained
several of the Robin Hood ballads. Now, through successive numbers of *Harper's Young People*, fortunate children
were meeting the outlaw band, clothed in Lincoln green, in
the Forest of Sherwood or in the fields of barley and corn in

Nottinghamshire. When the book with its superb illustrations was published it met with applause that has grown rather than diminished with the years, inspiring the tribute of a third generation who count this book first favorite in their libraries.

Robin Hood was a young man's book, written when Howard Pyle was thirty years old. From his pleasure in writing it and from his readers' pleasure, the author discovered his ability to write acceptably for children and went on to elaborate themes from the old fairy tales in *Pepper and Salt* and *The Wonder Clock*, first published in *Harper's Young People*. Adorned with drawings and decorations, these two books have a vitality that constantly wakens a response from the children and satisfies their sense of fun. The beauty of line in the pictures has been all but lost in recent printings from worn plates.

Master of the short story at a time when this form of fiction was the fashion, Frank Stockton discovered early that writing meant more to him than the art of engraving for which he had been trained. Starting with *The Riverside Magazine* and continuing in *St. Nicholas*, this vivacious, ingenious man drew upon his inexhaustible imagination to produce one amusing story after another, combining the most incongruous happenings with a fine literary touch, distinctly the writer's own. Fun and philosophy are so cunningly united in them that, while Stockton's stories are ostensibly for children, they have a nearly comparable attraction for those who are older. Never localized, anything might come to pass in the world of Frank Stockton. His stories came from a sunny nature with a wit that left no barb or sting.

All sorts of odd characters people these fanciful tales. Besides the Floating Prince, there is the naïve old Bee-man who kept a beehive in his pocket so that he could be sure of having something to eat wherever he went; there is the Queen who was a collector of buttonholes and had an unpopular Museum; there is the Jolly-cum-pop who liked hunting; there is the Reformed Pirate, knitting so quietly in his rocking chair, and there are countless others who deserve to be remembered. They are just as pleasant to read about now as they were in the 1880's.

While Stockton had been turning out his lighthearted fairy tales for nearly two decades before *Davy and the Goblin* delighted *St. Nicholas* readers (1885), its author Charles Carryl derived in no way from the older American. Rather, the inspiration of this Boston father who told his own children about Davy's adventures came from Lewis Carroll, of Oxford, England. What happened on a stormy Christmas Eve, after eight-year-old Davy had been reading *Alice in Wonderland*, has touches suggesting that Davy's Believing Voyage could scarcely have been undertaken except for someone's acquaintance with scenes down the rabbit hole or in the Looking Glass country. This is frankly admitted on the first page.

Far from being an imitation, however, *Davy and the Goblin* is a kind of companion piece which proves specially attractive to little boys. They accept confidingly Davy's encounters with the Cockalorum, the Butterscotchmen, the Forty Thieves, Sindbad and Robinson Crusoe when he travels with the Goblin, riding through the air over strange lands on the big Dutch clock with sponge cakes as cushions. If Lewis Carroll's wisdom and philosophy are lacking, still there is good nonsense sprinkled with mouth-filling words and such capital verse as the chronicles of the Walloping Window-Blind and the Piccadilly Daisy which fall trippingly from the tongue.

From Charles Carryl came also *The Admiral's Caravan*, published in *St. Nicholas* in 1892.

Three more important characters appeared in children's literature early in the 1880's, Brer Rabbit, Brer Fox and Uncle Remus. Is there anyone who can forget the story of "The Wonderful Tar-Baby," with Brer Rabbit "pacin' down de road—lipperty-clipperty, clipperty-lipperty—dez ez sassy ez a jay bird," while Brer Fox, "he lay low"?

Georgia had already made entrance into the widening arena of children's books with Lanier's *Boy's King Arthur;* this was a lighter note. South and North received it with undisguised enjoyment. Lovable old Uncle Remus was a type fast disappearing, but in those who had been young in the South he revived intimate childhood memories of old folks from whom girls and boys had heard just such animal stories as those told by Uncle Remus. They saw themselves reflected in "Miss Sally's little boy," without a name. Northern children, who had never known such a relationship, made fascinating discoveries about plantation life and reveled in the humor of the tales.

Here was a cast of animals who talked and acted like real people. Yet they were not like the Toad and the Mole in "Thumbelina," not quite like Alice's Rabbit, not at all like Aesop's Beasts who were never content unless pointing a Moral. Together with personality, here were present mischievousness, a shrewd philosophy, a dramatic triumph of helplessness, a kinship between animals and humans.

Joel Chandler Harris turned for his sources to the familiar folk tales of the Southern Negro and he created in Uncle Remus the memorable portrait of a born storyteller with a faithfulness that could hardly have been achieved at a later period. Simple and serious, patient and devoted, sympathetic with children because he was himself childlike, sharing with his listeners a vivid concern in the animals' doings, he was quick to draw comparisons between animals and "fokes," and he was constantly mindful of the little boy's duty toward his family traditions.

The young Georgia editor was surprised by the acclaim which met *Uncle Remus: His Songs and His Sayings*, when it was given book form in 1880. He was even amused when learned journals discussed it as an important contribution to folklore. Folklore the stories are, as Harris knew perfectly well, but he had not printed these tales for their scholarly value and had chosen only those best suited for entertainment through the art of a natural storyteller. Much has been written about the Uncle Remus stories, their humor, their African origin, their expression of the imagination of a race which chose the most harmless of animals to be victor by its wits. Mr. Harris was only glad that he had made children happy. Fifteen years after its first appearance *Uncle Remus: His Songs and His Sayings* was reissued with the inimitable and perfect pictures by A. B. Frost who brought fresh vitality to Brer Rabbit, Brer Fox and the other animals. All attempts to retell the tales without the authentic dialect have been a failure.

Out of the South a few years later came another book in which an old Negro has a place. The Virginia gentleman, who called back memories of his boyhood to write a wartime story untouched by bitterness, had a background unlike that of Joel Chandler Harris, but his Old Balla was as true a part of the household as Uncle Remus was of Miss Sally's.

Thomas Nelson Page was writing romantic stories for adults when the idea of *Two Little Confederates* formed in his mind. He wanted to bring about a better understanding between North and South and his generous book does just that. Full of the charm of a vanished time, this home life story rests upon actual conditions surrounding his own Virginia home during the Civil War. The opening chapter of *Two Little Confederates* describes Oakland where Willy and Frank lived:

> "It was not a handsome place as modern ideas go, but down in Old Virginia where the standard was different from the later one, it passed in old times as one of the best places in all that region."

The future Ambassador to Italy was eight years old and his brother younger when the war began. Their father had earnestly hoped for peace but like so many others went with his state when it seceded. Troops from both sides passed through and around Oakland and the two boys saw soldiers often in the four years before Appomattox. They came to experience acutely the hardships and griefs of invasion, for the story is practically autobiographic and Mr. Page had good reason to know what Willy did and how he felt. Abundant humor is to be found in *Two Little Confederates*, sadness, suspense and the salt of charity and common humanity in its good writing. As the first book to give American children living far from the scenes of battle an idea of what it might mean to be in the path of war, it was a revelation, yet the temper is very different from the partisan stories of the Revolutionary War.

Aside from stories about Indians, not always trustworthy, American authors for young people had seldom tried their hand at writing historical fiction. In *Books for the Young* the names of British writers in this class, Sir Walter Scott,

Charlotte M. Yonge and George A. Henty, are more conspicuous than those of any American except Cooper. But that very year *The Prince and the Pauper* had appeared, and Miss Hewins was quick to include the title in her reading list.

Whatever librarians and mothers of that time thought about placing *Tom Sawyer* in the hands of children, they never doubted that Mark Twain had written a real children's book which might wholeheartedly be accepted for boys. *The Prince and the Pauper* with its plot of the exchange of places between Tom Canty and the Boy King Edward VI brought into the open for children the gulf between the palaces of royalty and the dwellings of the poor in the days of the Tudors — not a very likely plot perhaps, but one into which boys and girls could enter with sympathy. Mark Twain, the democrat, with his hatred of shams and false values, had thrown a bright light on injustices and inequalities little perceived by American children in their restricted study of history at school.

And again, it was Howard Pyle whose literary skill and feeling for the past strengthened children's literature by another distinguished book. He had been steeping himself, ever since his *Robin Hood*, in medieval manners and deeds, and *Otto of the Silver Hand* was the result. It brought the Middle Ages to life for boys and girls, not only of the eighties and nineties, but of years to come. Otto's affecting story, with its shadow of tragedy, embraces the days of the robber barons in Germany.

Here are all the trappings of a feudal stronghold in the dark and ancient castle of Drachenfels, with its drawbridge and portcullis, its men of arms and weapons of war. Here at the White Cross on the Hill is displayed a no less true aspect of the age in the sunny old monastery gardens. In both places, against harsh and cruel customs or self-denying charity, we see the slender form of little Otto whose endurance and noble spirit are brought into bold relief by the creative imagination of Howard Pyle. A few more years brought Myles Falworth as vitally to the fore in *Men of Iron*, one of the best medieval tales we have. These two, with John Bennett's *Master Skylark*, make a rewarding heritage of historical fiction from the nineteenth century.

Secure of a permanent place in English literature, Mark Twain's third book about a boy is claimed by every age. To bar *Adventures of Huckleberry Finn* from a list of children's classics now is as unthinkable as it would have been to include it in the year of its publication (1885). In all the range of our fiction, said Joel Chandler Harris, "there is no more wholesome book than *Huckleberry Finn*. It is history, it is romance, it is life. Here we behold human characters stripped of all tiresome details; we see people growing and living; we laugh at their humor, share their griefs and in the midst of it all, behold, we are taught the lesson of honesty, justice and mercy."

Little Lord Fauntleroy ran in *St. Nicholas* as a serial in 1885, and its progress in popularity was swift and overwhelming.

Mrs. Burnett idealized in it her own relationship with one of her boys, and it pleased more parents than did *Huckleberry Finn*. Frances Hodgson Burnett was nothing if not romantic. She did not care so much about realism, she wished that fairies would "come in fashion again," and she liked to be considered a fairy herself. Her *Sara Crewe* is the veritable Cinderella type of story that children love. One short significant conversation in this book, when Sara is helping Ermengarde, a dull schoolmate, with her history lesson, illustrates entertainingly Mrs. Burnett's feeling for the part imagination plays in the lives of certain children.

" 'It sounds nicer than it seems in the book' [Ermengarde] would say. 'I never cared about Mary Queen of Scots, before, and I always hated the French Revolution, but you make it seem like a story.' 'It is a story,' Sara would answer. 'They are all stories. Everything is a story—everything in this world. You are a story—I am a story—Miss Minchin is a story. You can make a story out of anything.' 'I can't,' said Ermengarde."

It was inevitable that Laura Richards should write books. Everything about her bringing up, her associations in childhood and early youth, all pointed that way. Besides, she had children of her own to listen to and applaud her inventions. Her nonsense verses inspired by Edward Lear whose limericks she had always known began early in the magazines, long before Lear had died, an old man; but her first complete book, *Five Mice in a Mouse-trap*, came out in 1880. Now, with these stories for the youngest, she was fairly launched on a lifetime of employing her abilities as children's author.

Other books of easy reading followed. *Four Feet, Two Feet, and No Feet* she wrote only in part, editing the rest to help little children explore the animal world. Then, in the same decade she started the Hildegarde books, and for the next fifteen years Mrs. Richards devoted her time to writing for young girls. In after days she was often critical of these early volumes, wishing she could rewrite them. Yet, notwithstanding their obvious faults, the Hildegarde series gave pleasure to hundreds of girls, also inciting in them an ambition to read the books and poems that Hildegarde liked.

About this time, too, a pioneer kindergartner in California, Kate Smith, not yet Kate Douglas Wiggin, was composing two books to further a Cause. *The Birds' Christmas Carol* and *The Story of Patsy*, written in San Francisco and bound in paper, were both sold for the benefit of the Free Kindergartens and were not intended for publication. Little did the young teacher dream that her Christmas story would one day be translated into French, Swedish, German and Japanese; that scenes from it would be dramatized and become highly esteemed for amateur production. Christmas after Christmas, since the eighties, this appealing story has called forth a warmth of affection for friendly little Carol and ripples of laughter over the vision of the Ruggleses making preparation for their Dinner Party, in which we catch a foreshadowing of the creation of *Rebecca of Sunnybrook Farm*.

Looking back at the animated procession of American girls moving through the books of the last quarter of the nineteenth century, the figure of Betty Leicester stands out in the front rank. Sarah Orne Jewett, to whom we owe her, wrote no other full-length book for girls, but her short stories had been printed in young people's magazines constantly after their appearance in the *Riverside* and older girls had become acquainted with her exquisite cameos in published collections and in the pages of *The Atlantic Monthly*. Some of them knew the delicate touch with which the lovely story of Sylvia, in *A White Heron*, had been etched.

Betty Leicester begins and ends with a journey. Tideshead, where Betty Leicester visited with her great-aunts, becomes a real place before the summer is over. So do the new friends she made there and the old ones who grew dearer seem real under Miss Jewett's skillful hand. Without excitement, without the accessories of modern invention, she weaves interest and charm into the story of an uneventful summer when a fifteen-year-old girl learned to live with other people and to know herself.

The Golden Age was further characterized by interest in books about wild life and the outdoor world. *St. Nicholas* nourished this awakening through the Agassiz Association, and Olive Thorne Miller followed her *Little Folks in Feathers and Fur* with studies about bird life. Then, too, the flood of books on how to make and do things was inaugurated by Dan Beard in *The American Boys' Handybook*. All in all, it was a great period for children's books in America, vitalized by a force which overflowed into the nineties sorely in need of it, for by the turn of the century the flame was burning low.

There was to be a full quarter of a century of marking time, but in this Golden Age were the seeds of that new flowering of children's books which opened in 1920. The decade of the 1880's saw the awakening to the richness of folklore, felt the inspiration drawn from classic hero tales, experienced the leavening of humor and fantasy. The field was being prepared for the influences, dimly discerned by the far-sighted, of those invigorating currents of literature brought to bear by many people coming from other lands to America. But as the nineteenth century closed, it could not be known what great wealth of art and color and life the newcomers would bring to American children's books.

CONFRONTATIONS

Con

frontations

A SCIENTIST'S SEARCH FOR ALIEN CONTACT

Jacques Vallee

BALLANTINE BOOKS · NEW YORK

Copyright © 1990 by Jacques Vallee
Maps and diagrams copyright © 1990 by Random House, Inc.

Library of Congress Cataloging-in-Publication Data

Vallee, Jacques.
Confrontations : a scientist's search for alien contact /
Jacques Vallee. — 1st ed.
p.   cm.
ISBN: 0-345-36453-8
1. Unidentified flying objects   I. Title.
TL789.V3353   1990
001.9′42—dc20   89-91790
                                                  CIP

Manufactured in the United States of America
Designed by Ann Gold
Maps and diagrams rendered by Patrick O'Brien
First Edition: April 1990

10 9 8 7 6 5 4 3 2 1

This book is dedicated to Aimé Michel,
who thirty years ago inspired me to
search beyond the superficial appearances
of reality and who taught me to
"shake the pear tree" of science.

Contents

CONTENTS

Illustrations appear following page 146

Acknowledgments

Progress in any research field requires the opportunity to draw upon the thoughts and the support of many people. This is especially true when the research topic lies beyond the recognized boundary of conventional science. In this work I have benefited from a rich network of friends and colleagues who have generously agreed to exchange ideas and data with me over many years. They are too numerous for all their names to be mentioned here; many of them wish to remain anonymous for personal or professional reasons. Among those I can publicly acknowledge, I owe a special debt of gratitude to the following persons and groups:

—To my colleagues in scientific and business circles who have encouraged me in this research, notably Dr. Peter Sturrock at Stanford University, Dr. Harold Puthoff at the Institute for Advanced Studies at Austin, Dr. Richard Haines at NASA and San Jose State University, Dr. Ed May and Dr. Charles Rosen at SRI International, Steve Millard at METRICOM, Dr. Douglas Price-Williams at UCLA, Dr. Keith Harary at the Institute for Advanced Psychology, Dr.

Claude Poher and Jean-Jacques Velasco at CNES, Dr. Pierre Guerin at Institut d'Astrophysique, Dr. Arthur Hastings at the Institute for Transpersonal Psychology, Professor Flavio Lago in Rio de Janeiro, Professor Agobar Oliveira at the University of Fortaleza, Dr. Richard Niemtzow at Brooks Air Force Base, William T. Powers at Northwestern University, and Fred Beckman at the University of Chicago; to members of the International Forensic Association in the United States and in Brazil; and to other specialists, notably in the law enforcement field and in the medical sciences, who understandably prefer to keep their names away from the UFO controversy.

—To those members of the UFO research community who have worked tirelessly to elucidate this phenomenon and have encouraged me to express my views, even when those opinions contradicted some of their favorite theories. I especially treasure warm and informative exchanges with Mimi Hynek, Gordon Creighton, John Keel, Jenny Randles, Pierre Lagrange, Bertrand Meheust, Whitley Strieber, Hilary Evans, Antonio Ribera, Salvatore Freixedo, Carlos Ortíz de la Huerta, Fabio Zerpa, Michel Figuet, Alexander Kazantsev, Dennis Stacy, Linda Strand, Robert Girard, Monica Williams, and Sir John Whitmore.

—To those who have helped me directly or indirectly in specific problems of case investigations and in my research on the wider documentation of the phenomenon, notably Richard Sigismond, Bill Murphy, Stanley Ferguson, Tom Adams, Bruce Scott, Ted Phillips, Tom Gates, Tina Choate, Brian Myers, Jean-François Boedec, Eve Berni, Bill Calvert, Enrique Castillo, Jim McCampbell, the late Ed and Jeanie Mills, Carlos and Ricardo Vilchez, Irene Granchi, Linda Howe, Adalberto Ujvari, Mark Uriarte, John Williams, and Daniel Rebisso Giese.

—To all the witnesses of the phenomena described in this volume who have had the courage to come forward with their observations and have trusted me with the details of their experience.

—To the memory of pioneers of UFO research who are no longer with us: Dr. J. Allen Hynek, Dr. Olavo Fontes, Jim and Coral Lorenzen, Dr. James McDonald, Donald Keyhoe and Charles Bowen, whose steps we are endlessly retracing.

—To Ned Leavitt at William Morris and to my editor, Joe Blades, at Ballantine, whose guidance made the publication of this work possible.

—To Emery Reiff, who had the patience to decipher and process the manuscript for this book.

—And, of course, to Janine, to my mother, and to my children, who have valiantly survived the vagaries of life with an investigator of the elusive and bizarre phenomena described here.

CONFRONTATIONS

Prologue

On a beautiful, clear day in late April 1980, I found myself climbing a steep hill across the bay from the city of Rio de Janeiro to locate the spot where Brazil's most dramatic UFO event had occurred. It was a case in which two men had been found dead in circumstances the police had never been able to explain. It was widely believed that they had died while awaiting a signal from the sky, possibly communication from a UFO.

If such an event could be validated, we might get closer to a proof of the reality of UFOs. At the same time, however, many of our ideas about the phenomenon would have to be drastically revised. Gone would be the gentle visitors, the scientific explorers, the mischievous aliens that fill the pages of UFO books. Gone, too, the shining presences and the angelic visions of the "New Age." At a minimum we would have to enlarge the scope of our hypotheses. A more complex and dangerous picture would emerge.

Unfortunately, everything I knew about the case had come to me secondhand through the UFO rumor mill or through the media, a notoriously unreliable source in Latin America.[1] The only way to learn more about the precise circumstances of the event was to fly to Rio and climb that hill.

With me were my wife, Janine, and a small party of investigators: Saulo Soares de Souza, a detective from Rio police headquarters who specializes in long-term follow-up of unsolved cases; Mario Dias, a journalist; Alberto Dirma, a press photographer; a local French teacher who was kind enough to serve as my interpreter; and the first adult who had seen the bodies that August day in 1966, when a group of boys came running to his house. He had accompanied them to the police station at the foot of the hill, where they described their grisly find to the officer in charge, Oscar Nunes.

The hill is located in the Rio suburb of Niterói and is called Morro do Vintem, literally *the hill of the penny coin*. It is overgrown with short trees and bushes with long, bladelike leaves. As we stepped from rock to rock along the path that snakes its way up the hill, the landscape changed—from the houses, the bungalows, the cars of Niterói's streets, to a busy tangle of shacks crowded with curious children who run everywhere in Brazil. Higher still were vacant, rusty spots on the mountain and grassy areas where lovers or smugglers meet, where kids chase birds, where strange deals are made.

The police, we were told, are wary of the area. It is noteworthy that on the night the bodies were discovered, Officer Nunes had decided to postpone the search until sunrise.

If the view at half-point is confused and disconcerting, the scene at the top is altogether different. It sweeps across miles of earth and ocean, encompassing one of the most glorious landscapes on earth: Niterói, Rio, the Sugarloaf, the whole bay. Often shrouded in low clouds or rain, or marred by the heavy industrial smog that hangs more and more frequently over the metropolis, the Morro do Vintem was absolutely clear when we made the climb that day. Framed by tall bushes that provided welcome shade, the site was more worthy of a travel poster than of a murder scene.

Finally we stopped at a place where the earth was almost bare, showing only grainy dirt among short grass, with a wall of wide-

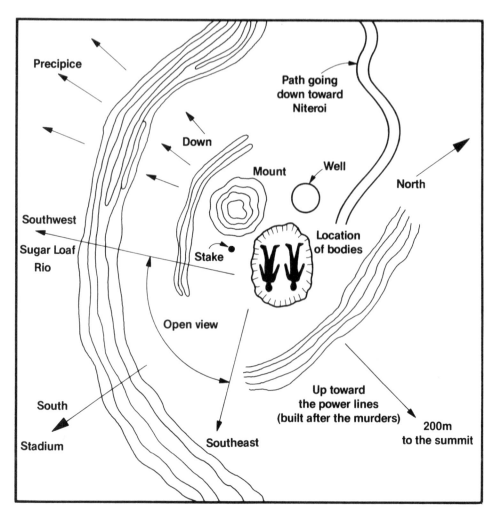

Figure 1. The scene at the Morro do Vintem

leaf bushes hiding us from direct sunlight. Detective Soares spoke and the interpreter translated: "This is where they were found."

"I don't understand how they could expect to see the sky from here," I said, "or why anybody would suggest they were waiting for some signal."

The question started a flurry of exchanges in Portuguese between Detective Soares and the short, brown-skinned man who, 14 years before, had led the police to the bodies.

"He says the bushes were a lot shorter then," the interpreter told me. "You could see the sky."

"Ask him how it happened."

The first boy to find the corpses, who was eighteen at the time, had been looking for his kite. He found the bodies dressed in neat suits and new raincoats, lying on their backs.

Nothing had been done that evening in 1966; the local police felt it was prudent to postpone any efforts until the next day. At daybreak, however, the official party of officers and fire fighters climbed the steep trail, reached the spot, and discovered that the boy had not lied to them. One of the strangest investigations in the records of the Brazilian police had just begun. It would go through three distinct phases.

The first phase was straightforward, routine detective work.

The investigators found no blood, no signs of any violence at the site. The two corpses were lying peacefully side by side. Next to them were crude metal masks as well as slips of paper covered with notes. One of these notes contained elementary electrical formulas. Also found was a crushed piece of aluminized blue and white paper, some cellophane soaked in a chemical substance, and a handkerchief with the initials AMS.

The skin of the corpses had a pinkish color and showed possible burns, but decomposition had progressed to the point where such a finding was not significant. Indeed, the coroner, Astor de Melo, soon concluded that death was by natural causes (cardiac arrest) and closed the file. His examination of the bowels had revealed no poison. The men had died sometime between Tuesday, August 16, and Saturday, August 20.

The identity of the victims was soon established. They were electronics technicians Miguel José Viana, 34, married and the father of several young children, and Manuel Pereira da Cruz, 32, also married. Both lived in the town of Campos where they were well-known, respected citizens. Both specialized in putting up local TV transmitters and repeaters. Miguel had 157,000 cruzeiros in a plastic bag inside his clothing. Manuel had only 4,000 cruzeiros.

The police were able to reconstruct the movements of the men between the morning of Wednesday, August 17, and the time when they took their position on the hilltop. They had departed Campos at 9:00 A.M. by bus to Niterói, leaving word that they intended to go to São Paulo to buy a car and electronic equipment. They were said to have 3 million cruzeiros (about $1,000) with them.

Their bus reached Niterói at 2:00 P.M. It was raining. They purchased identical raincoats for 9,400 cruzeiros. At a bar on Marques de Parana Street they bought a bottle of mineral water and kept the receipt. At about 3:15 P.M. they set off on foot up the path to the Morro do Vintem, where they were observed about 5:00 P.M. It was the last time they were seen alive.

Unhappy with the stated cause of death, the man in charge of security for the state of Rio, Col. Eduardo de Cento Pfeil, held a review meeting with police delegate José Venancio Béttencourt and an electronics technician. The next day he contacted Toledo Pizza, director of the Coroners Institute. Dr. Alberto Farah was asked to conduct a second autopsy. The viscera were removed and analyzed. The pathologist also looked for possible injection sites in the bodies, but the second autopsy revealed nothing new.

On the basis of these facts the police examined a number of hypotheses. Could robbery have been a motive for the crime? A large sum of money seemed to have disappeared between the time Miguel and Manuel left Campos with nearly 3 million cruzeiros and the time they were found dead. But this hypothesis did not explain the manner of death and the absence of a struggle.

Were the men spies? The Morro do Vintem is a strategic spot from which the entire area can be surveyed. More prosaically, it would also be an ideal location for a TV repeater, the type of electronic installation in which the two men specialized. The absence of any violence, again, seemed to exclude espionage and foul play.

Were the men smugglers? Currency regulations make foreign electronic equipment difficult to obtain in Brazil. But it was hard to reconcile these scenarios with the manner of death. If they had been found with knives in their stomachs, in an isolated spot in an area of Niterói that was known to harbor all kinds of borderline activities, the case would have attracted little notice. Why would a murderer leave so many mysterious clues: the notes, the mask, the handkerchief?

"Did you pursue other hypotheses?" I asked Detective Soares.

"We thought it might be a case of a homosexual suicide pact," he said. "The spot is known to be a rendezvous point for gays from the neighborhood. But there was no evidence of this, either in the victims' lives or in the manner they died. Every line of investigation ran into the same brick wall: no sign of violence, no poison in the digestive system, no clues to the manner of death."

When these details became known in Brazil, the police were deluged with calls from the public in the Niterói area and the case entered its second phase.

One of the first callers was a society matron, Gracinda Barbosa Coutinho de Souza. She told Officer Béttencourt that as she was driving along Alameda São Boaventura in Fonseca with three of her children on Wednesday evening, her daughter Denise, then seven, told her to look up in the sky over the Morro do Vintem. She saw an oval object, orange in color, with a line of fire around its edges, "sending out rays in all directions," while it hovered over the hill. She had time to stop the car and to observe it carefully as it rose and fell vertically for three or four minutes, giving off a well-defined "blue ray." When she got home she told her husband, a member of the Rio Stock Exchange, about the sighting. He drove back to the site but saw nothing unusual.

This observation was soon confirmed by a large number of witnesses who called police independently to report they had seen an orange-colored, egg-shaped object giving off blue rays over the Morro do Vintem, adding that they had not reported it at the time for fear of the ridicule that attaches to UFO cases. All reports placed the object in the vicinity of the victims near the estimated time of death. Thus, the investigators were forced to direct their attention to some of the details of the scene that had seemed irrelevant at first.

There was, for example, the matter of the lead masks. Were they intended to shield the eyes of the victims from some form of radiation? The police found similar masks in a workshop in Miguel José Viana's home, along with remnants of the lead that had been used. Also found was a book on "scientific spiritualism" with underlined passages regarding spirits, intense luminosity, and masks. Miguel's sister was interrogated. She disclosed that he had spoken to her of a "secret mission."

Also interrogated was Manuel Pereira da Cruz's widow. Her testimony indicated that the two victims were members of a "spiritualist" group, an occult society with unknown objectives. It was rumored that the group attempted to communicate with other planets. A civilian pilot named Elcio Correa da Silva was also a member of the group.

Elcio disclosed to the investigators that he had, indeed, conducted a number of "experiments" with the two victims, one in Manuel's garden in Campos, and another time on the beach at Atafona. In that experiment Elcio and another man named Valdir had witnessed a huge blast. This had taken place on June 13, 1966, two months before the tragedy in Niterói. There was an explosion, a luminous object in the sky, a blinding flash. Local fishermen stated they had seen a flying saucer fall into the sea. The explosion was so powerful that it was heard in Campos. But speculation was dampened when the families of the victims testified at the inquest: the devices used at Atafona and in Campos were only homemade bombs, they said, manufactured with pipes and wires.

The police started digging deeper into the victims' backgrounds: they had attended courses in São Paulo organized by Philips Electronics and other firms; they had purchased sophisticated equipment, yet they were not thought to be qualified to conduct scientific experiments. There were allegations that the victims maintained an illegal radio station in Glicerio, in the Macae district. And again, witnesses spoke of their interest in the paranormal. A few days before his death, Manuel is supposed to have said that he was going to attend a "final test," after which he would say whether or not he was a "believer."

Manuel's widow stated that she had witnessed a quarrel between Elcio and her husband. Under the pressure to demonstrate progress in the case, the police found it convenient to arrest Elcio on August 27. However, it was soon established that he had not left Campos on the day of the tragedy, and he had to be released.

Another curious element in the case was one of the notes found next to the corpses. It read:

> Meet at the designated spot at 4:30 P.M. At 6:30 P.M. ingest the capsules. After the effect is produced, protect half of the face with lead masks. Wait for the prearranged signal.

Were the two men expecting to be contacted by a UFO? Or were they, more prosaically, taking part in a spiritualist experiment that went wrong?

Further complication came. A civilian guard named Raulino de Mattos reported that he thought he had seen the victims get out of a jeep at the foot of the hill with two other persons who were not clearly observed. But the case bogged down again.

On August 23, the police ordered the exhumation of the bodies and a new battery of tests. This step was so unusual that it was reported in newspapers around the world, but the new analysis yielded nothing of significance.

Two years elapsed before the case was again mentioned: the Brazilian press announced that the police were now looking for a blond man who appeared to be a foreigner. He had been seen by a witness sitting behind the wheel of a jeep while talking to Miguel and Manuel near the Morro do Vintem. It was also disclosed that radiochemical experts at the Atomic Energy Institute in São Paulo had conducted a neutron activation analysis of the hair of the victims. The four elements measured—arsenic, mercury, barium, and thallium—were found at normal levels.

With that, the officer in charge of homicide cases, Romen José Vieira, closed the investigation and forwarded the dossier to the Ministry of Justice. The second phase of the lead mask case (the "in-depth analysis" phase) had just ended. It had failed to explain the facts, just as the first phase of plain detective work had.

The third phase, predictably, was characterized by wild speculation, silliness, and extreme measures born out of everyone's frustration with the unexplained deaths of Miguel and Manuel.

A group of Brazilian spiritualists claimed to be in contact with Jupiterian beings through psychic channeling. According to these messages, the deaths of the victims were an accident that resulted when "they started running forward [toward the saucer that was supposed to pick them up] before they were instructed to do so." The channel also disclosed that the Jupiterians were females, one foot taller than the average humans, with vertical mouths and four fingers on their hands. Nobody took the revelations seriously, since there was no evidence that the men had died while running.

More interesting was the confession of a man named Hamilton Bezani, who was in jail for contraband and car theft. He gave police a complicated account of his participation in the murders of Miguel and Manuel, claiming that he had been hired to kill them. He and three other underworld figures stole the money carried by their victims, took them to the hilltop, and forced them at gunpoint to swallow poison. The police stated that they were close to making other arrests in the case. But these arrests were never made, and the public was left with the dubious testimony of a prisoner who was serving a long jail sentence.[2]

Neither Bezani's confession nor the channeled revelations from

11

Jupiter had explained the specific details of the murder. A lengthy discussion we had at the home of Professor Silvio Lago, a medical doctor who had been called by the court as an expert witness on parapsychology, threw some light on the spiritualist aspects. According to Professor Lago, the victims may have been engaged in a series of séances during which a paranormal entity was supposed to manifest itself. After the experiment in Campos, and again after the explosion on Atafona Beach, Manuel had found powder at the site. He may have suspected that others, possibly including Elcio, had designed a hoax to convince him of the reality of the "entity." Yet, remarked Detective Saulo Soares, they were willing to make a third attempt at contact with the entity in question: there must have been a higher-level person who remained in the background and whose instructions they trusted—possibly the person who gave them the orders written on the note.

As we reviewed these details at the scene of the tragedy, I noted that no vegetation was growing at the place where the bodies had been found. I asked whether the location was known with precision. The witness showed me the stake that enabled him to ascertain the exact spot.

We returned to Saulo's concern that the two men had an "intellectual mentor" who manipulated the situation, a hypothesis supported by the wording of the notes.

"The expression *ingest the capsules* does not belong to the vocabulary of the victims," the detective concluded. "Similarly, *after the effect* is too sophisticated for them. The note reads like a prescription dictated by someone else."

"What do you make of the robbery hypothesis?" I asked.

The detective shrugged. "How do we know they had money with them in the first place? They never really intended to buy a car and electronics parts."

"You think that story was a cover?" I asked him.

"I spoke to a cousin of Miguel, who had tried to discourage him from taking the trip because it could not amount to any profitable business. Miguel answered: 'Buying a car isn't the real purpose of this trip. When I get back, I'll tell you whether or not I believe in spiritualism.'"

"What was the book that was found in Campos?"

"It was a general text on spiritualism, a book by Bezerra de Menezes."

Janine inquired about the workshop used by the victims in Campos.

"It was a small room," the police officer replied, "about four by three meters, where Miguel fixed TV sets. We found shelves with specialized materials, but nothing suspicious."

"What about the lead masks?" she asked.

"They had been hammered out of a lead sheet; they were obviously homemade, very crude."

I went back to Bezani's so-called confession. The detective laughed: "He was a thief who specialized in gems and typewriters. His nickname was Papinho de Anjo, which means *fast-talker*. He had already managed to escape from two jails. He was rearrested and sent to the Hippodrome in São Paulo, reputed to be very secure. He concocted this whole story in the hope that he would be transferred back to Niterói jail. Everybody knows it is easy to escape from Niterói! But he made a mistake when he confessed to the murders: he put the bodies on the wrong mountain! So he was kept at the Hippodrome, and do you know what happened? He eventually managed to escape from there!"

Getting my bearings from the wide landscape around us, I drew a map of the scene. As I was orienting the sketch, I noticed some power lines and a tall transmission tower.

"That's the facility for police communications," I was told. "It wasn't there in 1966."

"Let's go over what was found at the site once more, the exact circumstances."

The man who had first seen the corpses answered in a quiet voice. His story differed somewhat from the details printed in the newspapers: "Some boys found the bodies while looking for their kite. They came down to my house and told me about it. I sent them to the police."

"Were the bodies resting on the ground itself?" I asked.

"They were on a bed of leaves."

"What about the smell?"

"No, they were *not* smelling," he insisted. "And the bodies had not been attacked by predators."

I pointed to the sky, where a number of large, menacing black birds were circling us. "What about those?"

"They did not attack the corpses."

"What about the newspaper report that the boys had been attracted by the smell?"

"There was no smell when I got there."

We started on the long trek down to Pinto Street, where we had left our cars. It was a return journey Manuel and Miguel had never made. Yet, Saulo told us he thought the men had intended to come down again. Otherwise, why would they have kept the deposit receipt for the bottle of mineral water? He found it very strange that no vegetation was growing at the spot, fourteen years after the event. And he had no explanation for the hovering saucer.

Today my files of UFO data bulge to a barely manageable volume that occupies fourteen well-packed file cabinet drawers. They are organized by country, and the file on Brazil contains a series of original documents that were given to me shortly before his death from cancer, by a highly skilled investigator, a medical doctor named Dr. Olavo Fontés.

When Dr. Fontés visited us in Chicago in 1967 he took this bundle of case reports from his suitcase. "I want you to have these," he said. Was he already aware that he would soon die? Among the documents he presented to me were his personal reports on the lead mask case and another sighting of UFOs in the Niterói region.

The event had taken place on March 16, 1966, at 9:15 P.M., two months before the tragedy. A luminous object, elliptical in shape, was seen at an altitude of 100 feet. The witness, a fifty-four-year-old manager with an electronics firm trained as an industrial technician, drew a sketch of a series of what he called "effervescent" spheres. He observed them along with his wife, his daughter, and his future son-in-law, an official with the Bank of Brazil. The object flew over the Morro da Boa Viagem, in Niterói.

Clearly the observation of a large oval object by Mrs. de Souza was not an isolated incident in that region. Neither was the correlation between the sighting of the object and the unexplained physical and physiological effects—including those with tragic consequences for the witnesses. Yet the UFO literature is largely silent on such cases because they challenge both the skeptics and the believers in UFO reality.

The time has come to set aside the old theories, to search for fresh evidence.

Introduction

This is a book about the hopes, the experiences, and the frustrations of a scientist who has gone into the field in search of proof for the elusive claims of the paranormal; but first and foremost it is a book about truth-seeking of a very special kind—a story of my investigations into a bizarre, seductive, and often terrifying phenomenon reported by many witnesses as a contact with an alien form of intelligence.

Over the years, I confess—and indeed I take pride in the fact—that I have changed my mind about the meaning of UFO data. As a young student in France I grew up wanting to be an astronomer: I was convinced that UFOs were conventional phenomena because astronomers would report them if they were truly unknown. Once I had realized my dream of working professionally at a major observatory I found that scientists did observe unknown objects. But they reported very few, destroying in the process some of the most interesting or tantalizing data.

In those days the extraterrestrial theory of UFOs seemed to be our best bet. Although most of my professional work has been in the computer field (as a scientific programmer and later as a principal investigator for some of the networking projects of the U.S. Department of Defense), I have not forgotten the galactic statistics: I believe the probability for the existence of planetary systems similar to ours throughout the universe is overwhelming. Like many of my peers, I have been inspired by Teilhard de Chardin's gentle view of a great spiritual potential permeating the cosmos. I believe that life and consciousness are manifested on distant worlds. To establish the foundations of a future contact with them while enhancing human survival should be the primary long-term goal of our space program, the major contribution of the scientific generation to which I belong.

For the past forty years those who believe in UFOs have assumed that these objects were the product of a civilization of space travelers who were conducting a survey of the earth in pursuit of their own goals. I have found myself gradually at odds with that interpretation. In the process I have uncovered major contradictions between the extraterrestrial hypothesis (ETH) and many UFO reports, including "abduction" cases.

In my earlier works, most notably in *Dimensions*,[1] I have enumerated the difficulties of the extraterrestrial theory and the concerns raised by the abduction reports. I will not repeat the details of the argument here. Careful analysis of the reports shows that there are many more landings and "close encounters" than would be required for a survey of our planet. The reported interaction with the occupants of the objects is absurd and their overtly "scientific" experiments are crude to the point of being grotesque. The "medical examination" to which abductees are said to be subjected, often accompanied by sadistic sexual manipulation, is reminiscent of the medieval tales of encounters with demons. It makes no sense in a sophisticated or technical or biological framework: any intelligent being equipped with the scientific marvels that UFOs possess would be in a position to achieve any of these alleged scientific objectives in a shorter time and with fewer risks. Those among the scientific

17

community who have been openly skeptical of the entire UFO phenomenon (and they are in the majority) must be excused for stating that the reported contact is so absurd, and the conclusions of the believers so preposterous, that the alleged object must be an aberration (physical or psychological) in every case. And yet, the reports are there. They continue to come from reliable, well-balanced observers. And they increasingly point to the existence of a genuine technology pursuing its own hidden agenda.

Some witnesses react to the phenomenon with a feeling of awe and fulfillment: for Whitley Strieber the outcome was *communion* and *transformation*. Yet for many others I have interviewed the experience is better described as *confrontation*.

My friends in the UFO research community have been puzzled by my disappearance from the scene between 1980 and 1987. In the present book they will find the answer. In 1980 I felt that the debate for and against the reality of UFOs had reached a point of diminishing returns. I stopped reading UFO books and subscribing to specialized magazines. I stayed away from local study groups and national conferences on the subject. The same arguments were rehashed, the same cases were cited ad nauseam. It was already clear that the study of abductions was hopelessly mired in the complexities and pitfalls of the use of hypnosis in the hands of believers who were subtly—or not so subtly—influencing the outcome of the interviews they conducted. It was time for me to go back into the field in search of new information. Not for the data alone; heaven knows we have more data than we can process. So much that a complete catalogue of close encounter cases would encompass between 5,000 and 10,000 reports, depending on the criteria one used. The total number of unexplained UFO cases on record worldwide is well in excess of 100,000, yet we are fairly certain on the basis of opinion polls that only one witness in ten comes forward with a report. Faced with this deluge of data, we need appropriate methodology to classify and analyze the cases. We need a new assessment of investigative techniques and a new outlook on the phenomenon.

Once I had made the decision to place my research back into an investigative mode, some simple steps suggested themselves. I made arrangements with a few laboratories in Silicon Valley to have access to the equipment I would require. I made a list of the areas where I would need expert advice—from interview techniques to photographic interpretation, from biological analysis to forensic science. To my surprise, I found that the scientists and the executives I approached were eager to help once they became convinced that my own discretion could be trusted. I also discovered that I could expect *no* cooperation from most of the UFO believers, who were willing to help me only to the extent that my conclusions would support their preconceived idea that UFOs are extraterrestrial visitors to the earth. As one field investigator for a major U.S. group put it, his dream was to find a flying saucer and kick the tires! I was not willing to commit to this party line. The UFO phenomenon, in my view, is an opportunity to practice science with humanitarian aims. But an open mind is a prerequisite. It is not easy to achieve it. The human brain loves to jump to conclusions on the basis of insufficient data.

It turned out that working in the field alone, or with just a few discreet friends, was a blessing in disguise. I could cover more ground, investigate more cases, and learn new things faster, equipped simply with my all-terrain Chevy truck and a small group of well-connected associates, than a cumbersome organization could.

When the results started piling up, a new picture of the UFO phenomenon emerged. It was bizarre, yet consistent; well patterned, yet terribly disturbing. So disturbing, in fact, that I keep in my files some data I do not want to publish until I have verified its validity and thought through the implications. This book is only a partial selection, using the cases that have risen to a sufficient degree of maturity in my own mind.

I have borrowed my own methods from the tools of technical intelligence, which are different from those of ordinary science. In science one has no reason to suspect that the phenomena under study are the result of manipulation or deliberate bias. Here we must assume that some of the data is misleading. The cases that receive a high level of media publicity are especially suspect.

Instead, the reports I selected for follow-up came mostly from private sources: either from readers of my previous books or from researchers in the field who were aware of my new activities. I drew up a list of criteria for my investigations. I would assign the highest priority to cases that had not been reported to the media or to the major UFO groups. (I made an exception for old cases where enough time had passed so that interest in them had waned.) I stressed access to the site and to the witnesses, and I placed a high value on physical or biological data.

I have selected from my research files one hundred UFO events for detailed presentation in this book. Forty-seven of them are first-hand cases in which I met and interviewed the witnesses myself, generally at the site. These events come primarily from the United States, Brazil, France, and Argentina. *Many of them involve secondary physical and medical effects, including twelve cases of fatal injuries in which the victim typically survived less than twenty-four hours.*

In the course of my field work on UFOs I also accumulated evidence in three related domains that I consider to be outside the scope of the present book. First, I obtained much new information about cults. I am repelled by this material, yet the cultist temptation is definitely present among many witnesses and quite a few ufologists. My attempts to sound a note of alarm on this subject in an earlier book entitled *Messengers of Deception* went largely unheeded. Many ufologists even became angry at me for pointing out that a belief in extraterrestrials could be used to manipulate unsuspecting populations. Perhaps the experience of the People's Temple in Jonestown, Guyana, will have to be repeated before the full impact of cults in our society is realized. Cults are driven by irrational beliefs, and they serve a psychological purpose in their members by providing a release from the confrontation with the unknown. It is my view today—as it was when I wrote *Messengers of Deception* ten years ago—that science, by refusing to openly study the UFO phenomenon, drives many sincere witnesses into such cults. The skeptics, who flatly deny the existence of *any* unexplained phenomenon in the name of "rationalism," are among the primary contributors to the rejection of science by the public. People are not stupid and they know very well when they have seen something out of the ordinary. When a so-called expert tells them the object must have been the moon or a mirage, he is really teaching the public that science is impotent or unwilling to pursue the study of the unknown. He is contributing to the growth of irrational movements in modern society.

Another domain I have explored concerns cattle mutilations. Over a two-year period I interviewed ranchers, veterinarians, and law enforcement officials in Arkansas, Missouri, and Kansas. Today a number of the episodes I investigated are still unexplained. They may have a direct relationship to the UFO phenomenon. Because I cannot yet prove this relationship, I have decided not to burden the reader with what may be irrelevant data. But the entire subject remains very much open in my own mind, even if the UFO research community, except for a few courageous investigators, prefers to sweep it under the rug and keep it there.

The third theme untouched by this book is government intervention. In the course of my professional work I was asked twice to testify in congressional hearings on the subject of emergency management.[2] This activity helped me to better understand how governmental agencies work. Like many of my colleagues in the field, I have become convinced that the U.S. government, as well as other governments, was very much involved in the UFO business. This involvement is not limited to the kind of data collection that is the normal responsibility of intelligence agencies. It extends to the close monitoring of the UFO organizations themselves and, in some cases, to the staging of false sightings and the occasional leaking of false documents. It is not my business to interfere with such activities. The belief in extraterrestrials, like any other strong belief, is an attractive vehicle for some mind control and psychological warfare activities. I do not believe that any government has the answer to the UFO problem, although several governments must have the proof of its reality.

Once these three domains—cults, mutilations, and government activity—are excluded, we are left with what I regard as the core of the UFO problem: a mass of bewildering data coming from sincere observers who have been confronted with an unexplained source of energy affecting them in their physical environment and in their spiritual outlook.

What distinguishes this book from much of the UFO literature is that essential information was obtained (1) by the author himself, (2) from firsthand sources, and (3) at the site; furthermore, all potential lines of conventional explanation have been followed to the best of my ability.

It will take many years, and more resources and skills than one man can assemble, to solve this problem. But I offer this report on my field work as a first step on this long and exciting road.

When I returned from my first trip to Brazil, it had become clear to me that the UFO problem was much more dangerous and much more technologically complex than the literature of the field had indicated. The methods of the amateur groups and those of official investigators armed with complicated forms and statistics were practically irrelevant. What was needed was not academic research but direct, down and dirty scientific intelligence. This would mean a lot of time and travel, careful weighing of contradictory data, and years of analysis of the resulting patterns. What I did not know when I embarked on this enterprise was the depth of the impact it would make on me and the clarity of the final conclusions.

Any systematic work of scientific intelligence begins with physical data. Hence, in the first part of the book I have assembled those cases that can teach us something new about the energy and the structure that characterize the phenomenon. Part Two, which deals with the puzzling, often subtle problems of field investigation, provides a few examples of apparently routine cases that turned out to be important, and of fascinating reports that were found to have conventional explanations. In Part Three I have covered the reported impact on human witnesses, from the simple stories of sunburns and conjunctivitis to apparent exposure to a lethal force. In Part Four I have gathered what are, in my own experience, some of the most challenging cases for my fellow scientists to ponder. And in Part Five the reader will find the observations I made in 1988 when I returned to Brazil in search of evidence for the medical injuries consecutive to UFO encounters—perhaps the most significant area of investigation for the future. An appendix proposes a new definition and classification system for UFO data, and a complete case index lists sightings described in the book.

All of the cases examined in this volume were unidentified when I started studying them. Most of them are still unidentified after all the work my associates and I did. What we learned in the process has to do with the power, and also the weakness, of scientific methodology, with the limitations of technical analysis, and with the very nature of our fears and biases as scientists facing the unknown. It is a process that teaches us a new measure of humility before the universe and its bewildering potential to reveal alien forms of consciousness and, more importantly perhaps, new insights into our own. But my immediate conclusion is this: whatever else they may be, UFOs represent a technology capable of harmful actions. This observation should send us back into the field with better resources and a renewed sense of urgency.

Part One

A PARADE OF PARAMETERS

T he phenomenon of UFOs is so complex, it evokes so many archetypal images and so many dreams and conflicts; it is so powerful in its spiritual impact, that its ordinary physical manifestations are often obscured or forgotten.

As with religious miracles and other so-called paranormal events, it is easy to be swept away by the potential implications of the perceived event before one has had time to ask detailed, critical questions about the mundane reality that surrounds it. I have learned to linger on the mundane, even if by doing so I run the risk of antagonizing some of the more enthusiastic theorists.

To establish clearly that we are indeed dealing with effects that are material, energetic, and that interact in powerful ways with the

25

environment, I have assembled in the three chapters that compose Part One some of the cases from my files that address the physical characteristics of UFOs. These cases not only contain the testimony of the observers about such effects, but they also offer quantifiable parameters.

Thus, chapter 1 reviews several instances in which an energy estimate could be derived from the observations; two of them are firsthand cases, defined as instances in which I spoke with the original witness in person. Chapter 2 gathers nine cases of alleged fragments from unidentified objects. I participated directly in four of these investigations; two of the samples are in my custody, and I keep them available for further tests by qualified scientists. In chapter 3 I have presented four cases of previously unpublished UFO photographs that I obtained during trips to Latin America and which I find especially challenging. In three of these cases I visited the site and met with witnesses.

No attempt has been made here to cover all physical characteristics of the phenomenon in an exhaustive way. Such a study will have to await the time when preconceptions among the academic community can be overcome and when a well-funded, well-staffed effort (or, preferably, several independent efforts with different outlooks and different methodologies, in competition with one another) can be mounted to attack the problem. In combination with an examination of the infrared signatures of UFOs detected by spy satellites, the scientists concerned would want to investigate the vast problem of UFO traces, of car ignition failures, of gravity and electromagnetic effects, and of microwave emission effects, all of which have been partially catalogued in the past twenty-five years by dedicated private researchers.[1] Although such effects have been present in the cases I have researched, I have not made a special effort to investigate them in their own context. Instead, I offer the records of these case studies as a first step in the application of technical analysis to the UFO enigma.

1

Megawatts

On July 1, 1965, two French submarines, the *Junon* and the *Daphne*, escorted by the logistic support vessel *Rhône*, left the Toulon navy base in the Mediterranean and sailed toward Gibraltar. The ships traveled first to La Horta in the Azores, then to Norfolk, Virginia, to conduct a series of joint operations with the U.S Navy, which was engaged at the time in the recovery of a Gemini capsule near Bermuda; the French submarines escorted the aircraft carrier *Wasp*.

Later the ships went through Hurricane Betsy, whose effects they avoided by diving to three hundred meters. On the way back to France they stopped for ten days at Pointe-à-Pitre, Guadeloupe, and for one day at Saintes before reaching the island of Martinique, where they anchored in late September 1965.

It was during their layover in Fort-de-France one fine evening, by a dark sky and clear weather, that a large UFO arrived slowly and silently from the west, flew to the south, made two complete loops in the sky over the French vessels, and vanished like a rapidly extinguished light bulb.

The person who told me about this case, Michel Figuet, was at the time first *timonier* of the French fleet of the Mediterranean. This helmsman observed the arrival of the object from his position on the deck of the submarine *Junon*. He had time to go up to the conning tower, where he grabbed six pairs of binoculars and distributed them to his companions. There were three hundred witnesses, including four officers on the *Junon*, three officers on the *Daphne*, a dozen French sailors, and personnel of the weather observatory.

All witnesses aboard the *Junon*, whose bow was pointing east, saw the object as a huge ball of light or a disk on edge arriving from the west at 9:15 P.M. It was the color of a fluorescent tube, about the same luminosity as the full moon. It moved slowly, horizontally, at a distance estimated at ten kilometers south of the ships, from west to east. It left a whitish trace similar to the glow of a television screen.

When it was directly south of the ships the object dropped toward the earth, made one, two, and three complete loops, then hovered in the midst of a faint "halo."

Figuet told me that he observed the last part of this trajectory through binoculars; he was able to see two red spots under the disk. Shortly thereafter, the object vanished in the center of its glow "like a bulb turned off." The trail and the halo remained visible in the sky for a full minute.

At 9:45 P.M. the halo reappeared at the same place, and the object seemed to emerge as if switched on. It rose, made two more loops and flew away to the west, where it disappeared at 9:50 P.M.

The next day Figuet compared notes with a communications engineer who had observed the same object from the Navy fort. Together, they called the weather observatory at Fort-de-France. The man who answered the call had also observed the object. He confirmed that it was neither an aircraft, nor a rocket, nor a meteor,

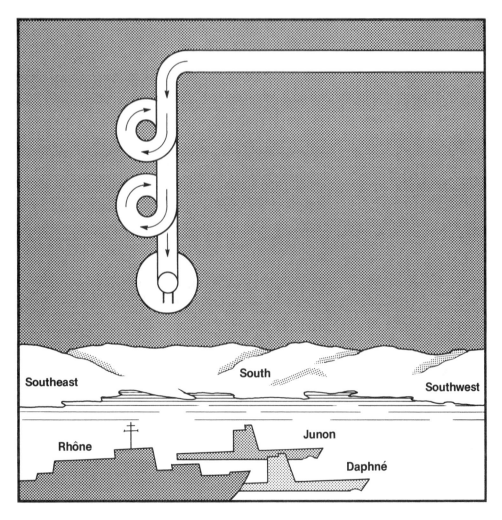

Figure 2. The harbor at Fort-de-France

nor a balloon, nor a disintegrating satellite, nor a plasma phenomenon such as globular lightning.

It is very difficult to say that such an observation never happened, or that it was a hallucination. The witnesses were competent observers who were dispersed over a wide area. They were trained in night surveillance (Michel Figuet had received particularly high marks for his ability on watch) and the sighting lasted long enough for my informant to go up to the conning tower, take the binoculars, and distribute them to other personnel.

Yet if we agree that there *was* an object, as the facts seem to dictate, then as scientists we have to face another kind of challenge. Specifically, if the object was ten kilometers away, as the witnesses estimated, then it represented a disk ninety meters in diameter, a formidable device indeed, given the remarkable maneuvers it exhibited. The entire sequence suggests control and purpose.

Furthermore, it is possible to compute the total energy output of the object based on the distance and luminosity estimates given by the witnesses. The resulting figure is 2.3 megawatts (MW).[1]

To put this number into perspective, it is useful to compare it to the energy levels of a few common devices. While the energy of a lawn mower is about three kilowatts (kW) and a car engine will range between 75 and 1,000 kW (or 1 MW), a commercial airliner will reach 50 to 150 MW; the energy of a nuclear plant is measured in thousands of megawatts.

In the above calculation, however, we have derived the energy figure solely from the amount of light emitted by the object, and only in the visible part of the spectrum, which was seen by the observers. The phenomenon may be deploying energy in other ways—in microwaves or in radio waves. If it has a material, physical structure it will require energy to overcome gravity, even if it uses extremely advanced propulsion techniques about which we can only speculate. For these reasons the figure we have computed can be regarded as a crude approximation. This note of caution should be kept in mind as we review other reliably observed cases that can give us some insight into the physics of the UFO phenomenon.

In 1988 I was able to meet once more with Michel Figuet in Brussels, at the occasion of a private European conference of UFO investigators that gathered researchers from England, France, Spain, Italy, Belgium, the Netherlands, the United States, and the Soviet Union. He confirmed the maneuvers and the appearance of the object.

An energetic man with a critical mind, which has given him something of a reputation as a "debunker" among the more enthusiastic French researchers, Figuet now lives in the south of France and clearly remembers the details of his observation. He told me he had met again with some of the crew members whose recollections of the facts were equally precise.

Another remarkable observation made near Grenoble, France, on November 5, 1976, by a senior scientist is relevant here. As in the previous case, there were multiple witnesses and the duration was long enough to allow details of the object and its trajectory to be seen and recalled. But there were two other remarkable characteristics: first, it was possible to establish the distance of the object with precision; second, the exceptional qualifications of one of the witnesses provided some physical parameters that have rarely been available in UFO cases.

I am indebted to GEPAN, the French government's official UFO investigation task force (now known as SEPRA), for communicating to me the details of the case, which I have had the opportunity to discuss with them at length prior to visiting the site in 1988. In accordance with their policies, I have changed the names of the witnesses. The official files, of course, contain full particulars and in-depth interviews with all concerned.[2]

The first witness in the chronology of this observation is a Miss M., who was watching television at her home in the town of Rives, near Grenoble. The time was 8:08 P.M. She saw a bright light outside and called her father. Both went out on the balcony and observed an intense white source crossing the sky at high speed from the northwest to the southeast, disappearing behind the mountains in the direction of Montand. The father, when interrogated by the gendarmes, stated that the light appeared to be spinning.

While these two witnesses were observing the object in Rives, a French physicist we will call Dr. Serge was driving seven miles away near Voreppe on the road that goes from Rives to Grenoble. He had just returned from Paris on a plane that landed at Grenoble airport, and he was driving to his home. Looking up, he saw a luminous disk moving in the sky. He stopped his car and got out to observe it carefully. The time was 8:10 P.M.

The disk, according to Dr. Serge, was brighter than the full moon. It was slightly flattened (with an aspect ratio of 0.9) and an angular diameter about twelve arc minutes (the full moon has an angular diameter of about thirty arc minutes). The object was white in the center and bluish-white at the periphery. It was surrounded by an intense green halo about two or three arc minutes thick.

At the beginning of the observation the disk was almost directly overhead. It flew at a constant velocity toward the east-southeast in less than eight seconds, covering approximately 1.3 degrees of arc per second.

At that point the disk *stopped*, without changing size, and hovered for three to ten seconds. Then it started again in a different direction, thirty degrees away from the previous course, at much greater speed, covering about eight degrees of arc per second and passing in front of Le Taillefer Mountain, thirty-six kilometers away. Dr. Serge lost sight of the disk when it passed *behind* Le Neron Mountain, nine kilometers away.

The whole sighting had lasted about twenty to twenty-five seconds and there was absolutely no sound at any time. The sky was clear, no wind at ground level, and the temperature was about 40°F.

Late in 1988 I drove through the area where the sighting had been made. The photographs and the drawings included in the GEPAN report do not do justice to the majesty of the site. Mountains rise on both sides of the Isère River. In places the road runs at the foot of sheer granite walls.

It is noteworthy that the investigation by GEPAN disclosed that a similar object had been seen three hours earlier about eighteen miles east of Rives, leaving a trail, and that a bright disk was seen two hours later by the civilian traffic controller in the tower of the military airport at Aulnat.

Shortly after 8:05 P.M. that same day a witness located a few kilometers near Vienne saw a slightly flattened sphere, whose light was similar to that of a very bright neon tube, with a fiery red-orange area underneath. It was about one-sixth of the diameter of the full moon and was flying very fast from the west-northwest to the east-southeast.

Given these detailed, highly competent observations, it is possible to bracket the energy and speed of the object with some reasonable numbers. From a careful reconstruction of the sighting it was estimated that the object was flying at an altitude of 1,500 to 2,500 feet, which would give it a diameter between six and twenty feet and a speed approximating one mile per second, or 3,600 miles per hour, during the second phase of its trajectory. Assuming that the disk gave off as much light as the full moon, as observed by Dr. Serge, its energy in the visible part of the spectrum was a modest 15 kW.

In the detailed interviews conducted by the UFO investigators of the French National Center for Space Studies (CNES), Dr. Serge expanded on his description of the object, noting that the halo reminded him of the color produced by the combustion of copper salts. It is also noteworthy that Dr. Serge, who serves as director of a nuclear physics laboratory, did not report the sighting to anyone and did not mention it to his colleagues. It was only when the observation by Miss M. and her father was mentioned in newspapers that he volunteered his own experience.

In addition to the reports by the gendarmes, the letters from the witnesses, and the investigations by GEPAN scientists, several of the observers were interviewed in person by a judge, a former president of the regional Court of Appeals.

During the preparation of this book I had the opportunity to discuss the data with Dr. Claude Poher, who founded the GEPAN

33

group. We met informally in a Paris cafe close to the headquarters of CNES, where he told me that the Grenoble case remained one of the most puzzling he had investigated.

CNES is located in an old corner of Paris where Les Halles, the produce market, had attracted an interesting cross section of the French population down the centuries, from alchemist Nicolas Flamel and poet Victor Hugo to the shop owners, the prostitutes, the truck drivers, and the students in search of part-time jobs. Today, the market has been moved to a suburb and the area is the home of hundreds of little shops catering to tourists. New wave fashions are found side by side with punk rock hangouts and sex shops, jewelers, and thriving garment wholesale businesses, which frequently operate on the fringes of the law. It was a strange setting for a discussion of space science.

As good as the Grenoble case was, said Poher, he did not succeed in bringing it to the attention of leading French scientists. To them it was just another UFO report, even if the main witness was one of their colleagues. They would not even take the time to meet with him to review the data because they felt UFOs had no place in a rational world.

I told him that GEPAN was ahead of its time.

To me it is not a single case that matters, but the accumulation of such cases. Many things have changed in the years that have elapsed since GEPAN investigated Dr. Serge's observation, I pointed out. The parade of extravagant fashions, the abundance of New Age books in the stores, the thousands of cartoons depicting aliens in every possible shape and form around the little cafe where we had our conference was evidence of this change. Whether traditional science likes it or not, the public long ago accepted the notion that the UFO phenomenon exists. Our task now is to select the best-documented parameters among the accumulated data and to place them before our colleagues so that research can move forward, even if we do not have all the answers we would like about the nature and the origin of the objects.

The third case we should review in this study of energy levels associated with UFOs took place near Arcachon in France on June 19, 1978, and was also investigated in depth by GEPAN. While the Grenoble case was remarkable for the convergence and the high quality of the observations, the events we are going to relate introduce another exceptional parameter: the UFO triggered the photocells that control the lights for the whole town. From the distance and the threshold level of the cell it is possible to derive another estimate of the energy of the object.[3]

The town where the sighting took place is Gujan-Mestras, and there were independent witnesses near Creon and La Reole. A local newspaper described how two frightened young men, an eighteen-year-old cook named Franck Pavia and a seventeen-year-old butcher's apprentice named Jean-Marc Guitard, knocked on the door of a baker, Mr. Varisse, who was preparing the next day's bread, at 1:30 A.M.

The teenagers had stopped on the side of the road to repair the turn signal of their car when all the lights of the town were suddenly switched off. At the same time, a powerful rumble like an earthquake made them jump. Then they saw the object. It was, by their descriptions, oval, red, surrounded with white "flames," and it flew toward them at an altitude of 11,000 feet.

At this point Jean-Marc became unable to breathe and fainted. The object then changed direction and flew away.

While telling their story to the baker (who reportedly laughed at them), both witnesses were obviously terrified, had trouble speaking, and Jean-Marc had red, teary eyes.

At approximately the same time of night a thirty-five-year-old restaurant manager named Mr. Bachere, who was driving toward Bordeaux, saw "a large orange ball, very bright" that hovered over La Reole at about 1,000 feet before disappearing. It reappeared at the same spot one minute later. Mr. Bachere's wife confirmed his observation.

Given these reports, which were transmitted by law enforcement officials to the space center in Toulouse, the GEPAN task force decided to investigate immediately: three of their scientists were at the site the very next day. They interviewed the witnesses at great length, took them to the actual location, and had them point a theodolite to the places where the object had appeared and disappeared. Finally, the witnesses were given a set of standard color samples from which they made a selection corresponding to the phenomenon they had seen.

This investigation brought to light the testimony of additional witnesses who had previously remained silent. For instance, Mr. B., a student who lived in Gujan, confirmed that he was outside when the town lights died half an hour past midnight; concurrently, he had heard a strong, low rumble that scared him. Mr. B. saw orange flashes above the pine trees, below the cloud ceiling.

While the investigators were interviewing the witnesses, several representatives from a local UFO amateur group arrived at the police station. They brandished a blurry black-and-white picture of an object allegedly seen in the same area a few months before. One of them showed the snapshot to the witnesses, declaring, "It would be very interesting to verify that it was the same UFO that had come back!"

The GEPAN investigators were able to prevail upon these ufologists to temper their enthusiasm and to postpone their own interview with the witnesses, thus avoiding the kind of contamination we constantly see when UFO observers are bombarded with leading questions by amateurs and by the media.

The series of measurements made in the field established (within the expected errors of human recall) that all the witnesses had observed the same object. There was agreement on time, duration, distance, trajectory, sound, and luminosity parameters. There were discrepancies, however, regarding the altitude and the apparent diameter of the object. One of the witnesses who gave the more consistent measures was used as the primary source for these estimates.

The manager of the town utility department was also interviewed. He showed the investigators the location of the photoelectric cells that control the street lights. Naturally, when these cells are exposed to a light that exceeds their threshold, they assume that daylight has arrived and they turn off the system. The results of the analysis bracket the distance between the cell and the UFO as 135 meters and 480 meters, or roughly between 400 and 1,500 feet. This yields an energy level between 160 kW and 5 MW.[4]

To complete this chapter I want to review a fourth case drawn from the U.S. files because it provides yet another data point on the energy range. It also gives some interesting insight into the UFO controversy and its treatment by academic scientists.

The case took place at 8:15 P.M. on December 30, 1966, in the vicinity of Haynesville, Louisiana. The witnesses are a professor of physics, Dr. G., and his family. My inquiries with the weather bureau disclose that the weather was overcast, with fog and a light drizzle, ceiling about three hundred feet, all parameters that are in agreement with the witnesses' statements. There was no thunderstorm.

In early 1967 I came across this sighting while I was systematically reviewing the files of the U.S. Air Force as an associate of Dr. J. Allen Hynek at Northwestern University, who was the scientific consultant to their UFO study known as "Project Blue Book." The report by Dr. G. and his family had not been followed up by Air Force personnel, so we decided to pursue it on our own.

Dr. G. told Dr. Hynek and me that he was driving north that night on U.S. Highway 79 between Haynesville and the Arkansas border when his wife called his attention to a red-orange glow appearing through and above the trees ahead to their left. They continued to observe it as they drove down the highway. It appeared as a luminous hemisphere, pulsating regularly, ranging from dull red to bright orange, with a period of about two seconds. There was no smoke or flame that would have been characteristic of a fire. In fact, when the car came to a point about one mile from the source of the light, it suddenly brightened to a blinding white, washing out the headlights and casting sharp shadows. This burst of light not only forced Dr. G. to shield his eyes, but it woke up his children, who had been sleeping in the back seat. After about four seconds it returned to its red-orange appearance.

Several sightings were described by other persons in the area. One witness reported that about six days before a similar bright light had been seen near the same location.

Since the University of Colorado had received funding from the U.S. Air Force in excess of $500,000 to study UFOs, I called Dr. Edward Condon's attention to this case, and a field investigation was conducted by several scientists from Boulder. I thought that Dr. Condon, a noted physicist who had been associated with the U.S. nuclear program, might take an interest in the case. In spite of a great deployment of helicopters and search parties, the investigation failed to locate the actual site. Dr. Condon concluded in his published report that the case was "of interest," and it remained as one of the many unidentified sightings in the University of Colorado project files. This fact did not stop Dr. Condon from also stating in his conclusions that the official study of the UFO phenomenon should be abandoned because no progress of knowledge could be expected from such research.

After the University of Colorado project was disbanded and after the Air Force, following its recommendations, closed down its own Blue Book, I quietly resumed my study of the case. I came in contact with a qualified investigator, Mr. W., who had also pursued his own research with Dr. G. Through them I obtained copies of the pictures taken by Barksdale Air Force planes, which had flown several infrared photographic missions over the area (plate 2). And I learned that Mr. W. and Dr. G. had pinpointed the actual site where the object had hovered.

The area in question is a clearing about thirty feet in diameter, located to the west of the railroad tracks clearly visible in the Air Force photographs. The chief dispatcher stated that no rolling equipment was within fifty miles of the location that night. The nearest high-tension power lines are about nine miles away to the west.

All the trees at the periphery of the clearing exhibited a blackening or burning of the bark in a direction pointing to the center of the area, as if they had been exposed to an intense source of radiated energy. Although I have in my possession some samples of the charred tree bark, I have not been able to find a reliable analysis laboratory that would undertake a study of it. Clearly we would like to know whether the wood was burned by light energy, direct heat, or chemical combustion. From an estimate of the energy required to produce the depth of the burn it would be possible to estimate the power of the source, assuming it was located in the center of the clearing fifteen feet away. This work has not been done.

Fortunately, there are other ways to arrive at an energy estimate, as Dr. G. realized immediately when he saw that the light from the object washed out his own headlights about ten feet ahead of the car. This enabled him to equate the intensity of the unknown object, which is given by its energy divided by the square of the distance, to the intensity of his headlights, which is given by their energy, known to be 150 watts, divided by the square of ten feet. Without inundating the reader with complicated mathematics, this gives a lower limit for the intensity of the UFO, hence its energy.[5]

In his report, Dr. Condon estimated the distance at 2,400 feet, which gave an energy of 900 MW for the UFO. A more correct estimate is given by the subsequent investigation by Dr. G. and Mr. W., since the clearing is actually located 1,800 feet from the observation point. The energy output becomes 500 MW.

This figure, which is a minimum estimate, places the object in the energy range of a small nuclear reactor. Still, we may be in the position of a person trying to estimate the power of a truck by the intensity of its headlights: the actual energy figure may be orders of magnitude beyond our calculations. It is even possible, if we follow some theories of what UFOs could be, that the light they emit is only a side effect of their propulsion mechanism, as carbon monoxide is a side effect in the exhaust of an automobile engine.

Yet we have already established one fact: UFOs are observed and described in a consistent manner by reliable, highly competent witnesses. And the information they provide can allow a dedicated group of investigators to draw certain scientific conclusions.

We are only at the beginning of this process; but it is already apparent that the UFO phenomenon is an opportunity to use science effectively. Notwithstanding the hasty conclusions of Dr. Condon, it may even be an opportunity to advance fundamental knowledge.

It is clear now that UFO reports in which qualified witnesses give consistent descriptions of the distance and light intensity of an object are not rare. From these descriptions it is possible to derive a crude approximation of the visible light energy of UFOs. The figures we obtain are in a range that would permit the phenomenon to have a harmful impact on humans.

The files of the more reliable UFO groups and the files maintained by military organizations should be searched for cases similar to the four situations given as examples above. The cases should be reinvestigated in the field whenever possible, and the energy estimates should be refined and tabulated. It is through the patient accumulation of such documented cases that the phenomenon will eventually be placed before the attention of the international scientific community—not through sensational claims by the media, not through political pressures, not through a public movement to demand that the government "reveal the truth." This work has never been done by the government or by anyone else. There is, unfortunately, no easy shortcut.

The failure of the University of Colorado to perform in a scientifically valid fashion during the Condon study from 1967 to 1969 can teach us an important lesson: it is not the amount of money expended that counts, or the notoriety of the scientists involved. It is the willingness to work in the field with imagination and diligence that match the complexity of the phenomenon itself.

In most UFO cases some of the parameters we need are missing.

We may know the luminosity but not the distance. Or we know the trajectory but not the exact time of day that would enable us to correlate the statements of independent witnesses. The burden is on us to go back, as any good scientist, any good spy, or any good cop would, and to ask more questions until the missing data emerge.

2

Liquid Sky

Over the years there have been many intriguing claims of flying disks literally raining metal from the sky. Yet these claims have not yielded tangible evidence of the reality of the objects.

Scientists interested in the UFO phenomenon have long hoped for sighting-related physical proof so well documented that it would remove most of the doubts of their colleagues. Such evidence could be analyzed in the laboratory. It might not provide a final proof of the reality of UFOs, but it would be the basis for a fruitful dialogue among the various theorists.

In the field, though, things are not so simple. The combination of a good sighting and a physical specimen is rare. And given such a specimen it is difficult to find a competent laboratory to analyze it. Not only is the cost of such an analysis significant (a few thousand dollars), but it is a complex task to determine what questions should be asked and what equipment should be used. A fascinating book could be written about the mistakes made over the years in the handling of such samples, from careless labeling to outright destruction, as was the case in the first "analysis" of a Brazilian magnesium sample in the hands of the U.S. Air Force.

A case that was brought to my attention in October 1985, and which I followed up energetically with the help of a few sympathetic colleagues, taught me about the pitfalls of physical evidence. It also taught me that after many hours of work, trips to distant laboratories, and considerable expense to use the finest in modern technology, one did not necessarily know much more than one did at the beginning.

At the time, I was in Costa Rica, where I met three respected Latin American researchers, Enrique Castillo of Venezuela, and Carlos and Ricardo Vilchez of Costa Rica. They showed me a sizable piece of a light silvery metal and, before turning it over to me for analysis, described its origin.

Two students who were walking on the campus of the University of Bogotá one rainy night in 1975 or 1976 heard a strange sound overhead. Looking up through the rain, they saw a disk swinging in the air as if in difficulty. They estimated its diameter at four meters and its altitude at 1,000 meters. While this first object seemed out of control, they observed four other disks flying to its vicinity as if to assist it. They were of the same shape and size.

It is at that point, according to the witnesses, that spouts of liquid were ejected from the central disk. The students took refuge under a tree and saw the bright liquid fall into the rainwater puddles in the street, producing a vapor. All five objects then rose and disappeared into the low rain clouds. The witnesses recovered two metal chunks, about four inches by one and one-fourth inches in size, after letting the material cool down for about ten minutes (plate 3).

The first analysis was performed in Central America by a mechanical engineer with a petroleum company. He concluded that the sample was an aluminum alloy with magnesium and tin. It was nonmagnetic and contained traces of materials that were not identified. He also stated that the metal was easy to cut and presented a very fine granulation.

43

When the sample was turned over to me by Ricardo Vilchez, I initiated a chain of evidence. Meticulous handling of physical items is required if it is to have legal validity. I therefore sealed the sample in an envelope and had Vilchez place his signature next to mine on the flap of the envelope. I carried it back to the United States, where, for the record, I summarized the case for my attorney and signed an affidavit in his office. I then placed the envelope in a secure location. The envelope was not opened until arrangements had been made with a high-technology company whose executives provided access to the tools required for a detailed investigation. They witnessed that the original signatures were present on the intact envelope before extracting the sample.

Our group noted that one side of the sample showed evidence of violent activity and bubbling, while the other side was flat, with some embedded material—possibly from the road asphalt. Next, the metal was subjected to two standard techniques of analysis, first with a scanning electron microscope (SEM), then with an instrument called a scanning ion mass spectroscope (SIMS). Since both of these techniques are often applied to the study of alleged UFO samples, it is useful to describe them in some detail.

The *scanning electron microscope* produces an X-ray fluorescence spectrum. It was applied to a small part of the sample where we had made a clean break and thus represented a typical, uncontaminated section. Microphotographs showed a cavity, possibly produced by a small gas bubble, and it is this cavity that was probed in the course of the analysis. The results of this test showed the sample to contain 93.7% aluminum, 4.8% phosphorus, 0.9% iron, and the rest in trace elements.

The metallurgical specialists performing the analysis commented that the sample had been "melted through and through" and that nothing survived of the initial structure. Its appearance, in fact, was typical of an overheat and was consistent with the blowup of a machine.

The *scanning ion mass spectroscope* test, or *Auger analysis*, explores the material by boring deeper and deeper from the surface

44

layer toward the interior. Placed in a vacuum, the sample is hit by an electron beam, and the measurements are repeated at various points for consistency.

This test surprised us because at first it showed no aluminum at all. Instead we found a surface layer of carbon, oxygen, and nitrogen. Beyond this unexplained layer we did find aluminum, as well as magnesium, potassium, sulphur, sodium, and silicium. Phosphorus and iron also showed up in trace amounts.

I provide these results in detail in the hope that some of my readers may suggest ways to refine the analysis. It left me very frustrated.

To begin with, the sample was unusual in what it did *not* contain. In particular, there was no fluoride, a normal by-product of the aluminum-refining process. The absence of heavy materials and the absence of water were equally puzzling, and the oxy-carbide layer is still unexplained.

The most useful result of this work was to refine the methodology and to force me to think through the precautions to be taken for the preservation of a chain of evidence that would stand up in court. However, I have not come to a final conclusion about the Bogotá sample. It could have come from a UFO, as the witnesses claim. But I have not been able to meet those witnesses in person, and the file that contains the initial interviews has been lost; we do not even know the exact year of the sighting. It is unlikely that we are dealing with a satellite reentry, given the testimony of the witnesses, and the composition and size of the metal piece. But we have not completely eliminated the possibility of a hoax. Can it ever be eliminated?

The history of UFOs, as determined by physical evidence, is already a lengthy one. In 1967, when Donald Hanlon and I sought to revive interest in forgotten American cases of the late nineteenth century, we published an article that shocked the conservative community of UFO researchers at the time. Our subject was the "airship" sightings of 1897. We discovered that no fewer than fourteen airships had been spotted on the single day of April 17, 1897. One sighting had taken place in the small town of Aurora, Texas. The object, it was said,

> sailed over the public square and when it reached the north part of town collided with the tower of Judge Proctor's windmill and went to pieces with a terrific explosion, scattering debris over several acres of ground, wrecking the windmill and water tank and destroying the judge's flower garden.[1]

The report went on to reveal that the pilot of the ship, who "was not an inhabitant of this world," had died in the accident:

> papers found on his person, evidently the records of his travels, are written in some unknown hieroglyphics, and cannot be deciphered. This ship was too badly wrecked to form any conclusion as to its construction or motive power. It was built of an unknown metal, resembling somewhat a mixture of aluminum and silver, and it must have weighed several tons. The town today is full of people who are viewing the wreckage and gather specimens of strange metal from the debris.

Although Hanlon and I always felt that this case was primarily of interest as a piece of early Americana and that it was probably a hoax, our article awakened interest in the 1897 wave in general and in the Aurora mystery in particular.

In 1973 I was surprised, and somewhat intrigued, by reports of several journalists embarking on new investigations at the site. Although no humanoid corpse was found, claims were made that strange metal samples had been discovered.

William Case, who published a series of articles about Aurora in the *Dallas Times-Herald*, did produce a piece of alloy that was eventually analyzed by the McDonnell Douglas Aircraft Company. It was found to consist of aluminum (about 83%) and zinc (about 16%) with possible traces of manganese and copper. The combination could originate with numerous common aluminum alloys—according to the McDonnell scientists—but not prior to 1908.

More curious is the celebrated Maury Island case. (This event occurred on June 21, 1947—three days prior to the famous sighting by the pilot Kenneth Arnold near Mount Rainier, when he described nine strange disks as "flying saucers.")

About noon on that day four men and a dog were on a boat off the coast of Tacoma, Washington.[2] The boat owner was a salvage operator named Harold Dahl. He and his companions saw six doughnut-shaped objects that hovered above the sea at an altitude of about 2,000 feet. One of the objects seemed to develop some sort of trouble, as in the Bogotá sightings, and it ejected silvery flakes resembling foil and a large quantity of material compared to "hot slag." The disk seemed to recover with the assistance of the other objects, and all flew off. Dahl returned to the harbor, reported the observation to a man named Fred Chrisman, and the latter went back to investigate. He found the shore littered with a glassy material and silver foil.

After the case was publicized a number of people took an interest in the sample, including Kenneth Arnold himself. Two Army Air Force intelligence officers from Hamilton Field near San Francisco interviewed the witnesses, collected physical evidence, and took off to return to their base. Their plane crashed near Kelso, Washington, and the officers died in the wreckage. The investigation then became a confused tangle of strange events and bizarre disappearances. Both military intelligence and the FBI concluded that the case was most likely a hoax: "Analysis of the fragments shows them to be from a Tacoma slag mill," states an FBI teletype message dated August 5, 1947. To the best of my knowledge, however, the composition of this "slag" (assuming it had in fact been analyzed) was never released. And no mention was made of the silvery material, although Kenneth Arnold, who saw it, described it as "aluminum foil."

The Maury Island incident happened long before I began my UFO research, but I did investigate a more recent report of slaglike fragments falling from the sky, and I have no doubt about the sincerity and reliability of the witnesses.

On Saturday, December 17, 1977, at 7:45 P.M. a red, luminous airborne object was observed by two residents of Council Bluffs, Iowa. This object crashed to earth in the vicinity of a dike at Big Lake Park, on the northern city limits. A bright flash was seen, followed by flames eight to ten feet high. When the witnesses reached the scene they found a large area of the dike covered with a mass of molten metal that glowed red-orange, igniting the grass in the vicinity.

Police and fire fighters arrived quickly. One law officer described the molten mass "running, boiling down the edges of the levee" over an area about four by six feet. The central portion remained warm to the touch for another two hours. The hoax hypothesis had to be eliminated; there were too many independent witnesses, eleven in all. Two of them had seen a hovering red object with lights blinking in sequence around the periphery.

Inquiries were made at Eppley Air Field and Offutt Air Force Base: no engine failure had taken place and there was no aircraft operation in the area.

The recovered residue was analyzed at the Iowa State University laboratory and at the Griffin Pipe Products Company, leading to the determination that the metal was chiefly iron with small amounts of alloying metals such as nickel and chromium. Such composition would exclude meteoritic material.

An examination of the microstructure indicated that the material was a carbon steel that was cast, subsequently reheated to about 1,000°F, and cooled, so that it resembled wrought iron.

Having failed to persuade Stanford University to conduct a new analysis of the material I had in my custody, I turned to NASA in the hope that they might allow their facilities to be used. Here I ran into a legal brick wall: NASA wanted to be released from liability if they examined the samples! In September 1978 I called the examining authorities in Council Bluffs again, and in the course of the conversation I learned a surprising fact: two similar falls had again been reported in the community, both in July 1978. A fall on

July 5 was about one mile southwest of the 1977 incident and was followed five days later by another fall.

But the Council Bluffs incident is not unique. While in Mexico in November 1978 I heard of a fall of metallic residue in the mountains near Puebla. The object was chiefly composed of iron, with 1.1% of silicium and traces of manganese, chromium, and carbon. On October 11, 1959, two witnesses in Sweden are said to have recovered a specimen that turned out to be common tungsten-carbide. Professor Peter Sturrock of Stanford University has in his custody a specimen from an object recovered by an Eskimo near Kiana, Alaska. It is silvery, light, and looks as if it had been poured in a molten state from a source close to the ground.

Two other interesting samples have come to us from Brazil. The first one was allegedly recovered on December 14, 1954, in Campinas. Numerous witnesses observed three disks in flight over the city. In a now-common pattern, one of the disks started wobbling wildly and lost altitude. The other objects followed it down and it stabilized at an altitude of three hundred feet. Suddenly, the troubled disk emitted a thin stream of silvery liquid. This material, according to independent researcher Kenneth Behrendt, was collected after cooling and subsequently analyzed by a Brazilian government laboratory. It was determined to be tin, with other metals present.

According to the late Frank Edwards, a renowned journalist, Brazilian authorities found the silvery liquid to have splattered over a wide area, including roofs, streets, sidewalks, even clothes left outside to dry.[3] An independent analysis by a private chemist, Dr. Risvaldo Maffei, revealed that the material was indeed mostly tin, but that it contained about 10% of other components.

The second Brazilian case concerns a sample at Ubatuba Beach near São Paulo. This sample first came to light in 1957, although its precise origin is still uncertain. It was studied by Dr. Olavo Fontés and was for several years under the control of Jim and Coral Lorenzen, the leaders of the Aerial Phenomena Research Organization (APRO), who conducted a careful investigation of the case. Since the death of the Lorenzens, the sample has been under study at Stanford University. According to Professor Sturrock and to Dr. Pierre Kaufmann of São Paulo, the specimen could be linked to an event that occurred as early as 1933 or 1934.

The witnesses of the Ubatuba case stated that they had seen a disk plunging toward the ocean at very high speed. Suddenly, it rose again to about a hundred feet and exploded in a shower of bright fragments. A few of these fragments fell into shallow water.

The first analysis was conducted by Dr. Luisa Barbosa at a Brazilian laboratory specializing in mineral production studies. Dr. Barbosa concluded that the sample was composed of very highly pure magnesium. Subsequent work at the University of Colorado, at Stanford, and at various specialized laboratories in France confirmed that the material was magnesium and magnesium oxide, with a very minute amount of impurities. According to Sturrock:

> After all these years, we still do not have a single reliable measurement of the actual impurities and impurity level of the Brazil magnesium. By contrast, the isotopic ratio has been measured at the California Institute of Technology and at the University of Paris at Orsay with high accuracy and with consistent results. The ratios are the same as in normal terrestrial magnesium.[4]

In 1987 Dr. Sturrock asked me to bring back from France the Ubatuba sample that had been under analysis at Orsay University. As soon as I arrived in Paris, I called the scientist who had run the tests and made an appointment to meet with him the next afternoon at a cafe near the Sorbonne.

It turned out that there was considerable political turmoil in the Quartier Latin at the time. That evening a massive student demonstration took place. Some extremist elements among the French police went on a riot of their own. Roaming the area on their motorcycles, they found an isolated student in the street behind the cafe I had foolishly selected as our rendezvous. They attacked the young man and clubbed him to death.

At the very moment the French physicist handed me the magnesium sample we found ourselves on the Boulevard Saint Michel with about 60,000 demonstrators, who had converged to protest the events of the previous night; we managed to get away before there was another clash with police. I did not relish the prospect of walking into Dr. Sturrock's office at Stanford to confess that the only remaining sample of the Ubatuba magnesium had rolled into the gutter during a close encounter of the rough kind with French riot cops.

There is a curious parallel between the Ubatuba and Campinas cases, on one hand, and the strange explosion triggered at Atafona by Manuel and Miguel, the two victims of the Niterói tragedy. All three events occurred on a Brazilian beach; all three involved rumors of a "flying saucer" exploding or plunging into the ocean; and in all cases the examination of the residue was inconclusive.

Two other cases reported in the literature mention the presence of magnesium. During the summer of 1952 a metal fragment is said to have been shot from an unidentified flying object. It was found to be "a matrix of magnesium orthosilicate," according to Frank Edwards. The Condon report states that there is no official confirmation, and the disposition of the sample is unknown.

In 1967 a collision is said to have taken place between a car and a UFO near Maumee, Ohio. The next day the driver found a small lump of metal at the site and some "fibrous" metal on the car. This fibrous sample turned out to contain 92% magnesium, according to Lorenzen and Condon.

What can we learn from all the work that has been devoted to the analysis of alleged UFO samples? Table 1 summarizes the results. Broadly speaking, the specimens come in two forms: the slag and the silvery metal. In one especially intriguing case, the Maury Island incident, both kinds of material were recovered. In other cases the investigators found either slag or silvery metal, but not both. I have not included in this survey the numerous cases of liquid, oil-like residues found at landing sites. Similarly, I have not considered the reports of manufactured objects alleged to have been recovered.

TABLE 1
Chemical Composition of Alleged UFO Samples

CASE	SLAG	SILVERY
Bogotá	None	Aluminum (94%) with Phosphorus (5%) and Iron
Aurora	None	Aluminum (83%) with Zinc
Maury Island	Results unknown	Aluminum foil?
Council Bluffs	Iron with Nickel and Chromium	None
Puebla	Iron with Silicium, Chromium, Manganese, Carbon	None
Sweden	Tungsten-Carbide	None
Kiana	None	Results unknown
Campinas	None	Tin (90%) with other components
Ubatuba	None	Magnesium, high purity
Washington	None	Magnesium
Washington	None	Magnesium (92%)

In terms of UFO propulsion, unfortunately, these pieces of data do not mean very much. Liquid metal is commonly used in high-technology equipment. I am indebted to Dr. Robert Rincheloe for bringing to my attention an article by J. R. Bumby of the engineering department at the University of Durham entitled "Superconducting Rotating Electrical Machines."[5] To minimize wear and friction in such machines, liquid metal is used as a current conductor instead of brushes. In the words of Bumby, "Each liquid metal has its own advantages and disadvantages." He goes on to categorize the most common metals used in such technology, starting with mercury, and going on to sodium-potassium and gallium-indium. Mercury and sodium-potassium are liquid at room temperature, and gallium-indium is liquid above 15.7°C.

If a superconducting rotating machine could fly, and it had some sort of breakdown, we would expect to recover either drops of mercury or various combinations of the above elements—for instance, an alloy with 76% gallium and 24% indium, or 78% potassium and 22% sodium. A look at table 1 will show the reader that nothing of the kind was ever found. On the other hand, we have not found any material unknown on earth.

In 1985 private researcher Kenneth Behrendt published a study entitled "Understanding Metal-Ejecting UFOs," in which he made the assumption that such devices could fly by generating "an anti-mass field."[6] He speculated ingeniously that the intense magnetic field required for this operation could be produced in a "large toroidal electromagnet with hollow tubular windings that are made from a heat-proof ceramic material," with the windings filled with molten metal. This explanation for the recovered specimens remains an untested hypothesis. It would require objects of very large size and would only be applied with difficulty to the cases where witnesses describe UFOs of moderate diameter. At this point, however, all we have is speculation, and we should welcome any attempt to make sense of the data.

Perhaps the major obstacle we find in this research is the preconceived notion that UFOs, if they are not imaginary, *must* necessarily represent advanced spacecraft from another planet. This notion represents the worst example of a jump to a conclusion in the face of insufficient data. *Although I am certain that UFOs are not imaginary, I will be disappointed if they turn out to be nothing more than advanced spacecraft.* As we will see in the balance of this book, they promise to be much more: a challenge to many of our concepts in physics, perhaps a clue to the existence of unknown dimensions beyond space-time.

This unfortunate polarization between the "nonsense" hypotheses and the extraterrestrial hypothesis has not come from discussions among informed scientists but from media hype and the heat of television debates, which, by definition, have to be designed as a contest between advocates and detractors of a statement arbitrarily taken as a target. If your goal in life is to discuss UFOs with Phil Donahue, Oprah Winfrey, or Johnny Carson, you have to be either pro or con the extraterrestrial hypothesis. This is like saying that the moon is either made of green cheese or it does not exist. In such polarized debates we are given no room for a third, a fourth, or a fifth hypothesis because the audience at home would soon be bored or lost in such a discussion. The founders of modern astronomy were indeed fortunate to live in a world in which television had not yet dominated public opinion!

In purely scientific terms, it is becoming clear that the UFO phenomenon is not all nonsense; yet the evidence *against* the extraterrestrial theory has been mounting steadily in the last decade. Fortunately, there is a wide spectrum of alternative theories that have not yet been explored seriously by the UFO research community. They need to be confronted with well-documented, carefully researched facts. To gather some facts we have to go back to the places where the phenomenon has been reported.

We must continue with our fieldwork.

This chapter has placed on record several cases in which physical samples have been obtained in connection with a UFO report. None of these cases constitute a proof or even a strong indication of the existence of intelligently controlled, nonhuman craft in our environment. However, they do illustrate the frequency with which a material residue has been found in connection with unexplained sightings. It is important to analyze such samples carefully, if only to refine our methodology for the time when a truly fantastic object may be discovered.

The private UFO groups are in the best position to conduct such a study. If they are serious about contributing to this research and putting their case before the scientific community, they should poll their members to collect as many of these samples as possible. There may be as many as thirty specimens in the United States alone.

The private organizations also should pool their resources to generate a catalogue of the most frequent components found in such samples, together with the dates and circumstances of the sightings. Even if the results were mundane, such a study would clear the underbrush. And it might show some unexpected correlations. It would throw new light on the total mystery.

Specific recommendations in the handling of such samples range from the obvious (the need to enclose them as soon as possible after discovery in an inert, sealed container) to the more sophisticated requirement to preserve a chain of evidence. The investigator should always ask himself or herself this question: if challenged by a court or a scientific committee, would I be able to prove that the sample that was analyzed was in fact the same one retrieved at the site?

There are precautions that go a long way toward establishing due diligence in the handling of the specimen. A simple way to establish an error-reduced chain is to keep the specimen in sealed containers bearing the signatures of the witnesses; to open these containers only in the presence of others; to take pictures of the specimen lying on the front page of a daily newspaper, clearly showing the date, whenever it is transferred from one group to another; and to have the recipients again sign the new containers. These may not be absolutely foolproof methods, but they will place the investigator beyond any accusation of negligence.

One of the first operations to be performed on such a sample is a test for radioactivity. As most people do not possess a Geiger counter, an alternate sensitive method for detecting radioactivity is simply to place the specimen, in complete darkness, over a photographic plate, to leave it there for a day or two, and to have the plate developed. The results will actually be more sensitive and, in the view of some investigators, more reliable than a Geiger counter reading.

The next step is to send the material for study to a reputable laboratory. Unless the sample is extraordinarily small, you should keep most of the material after carefully sawing off or breaking off small pieces to be given to the analysts—before and after photographs are mandatory, so that anyone auditing the operation at a later date will be able to see where each fragment came from.

Although many universities have facilities for such work, they usually lack the funds and the time to run these analyses. Whenever possible, it is far better to hire a professional industrial laboratory to perform the required tests.

3

Infinity Focus

reader of *Dimensions* wrote to me enthusiastically: "Thank you for not including blurry black and white pictures of alleged UFOs." I am afraid my happy correspondent may be disappointed in the next part of my fieldwork, because it has to do with some of the physical characteristics of UFOs that are best measured on photographs—many of which are black and white, and very blurry indeed.

Even when they are not blurry, as we will soon discover, they pose unusual challenges to the analyst. Sensible, rational, understandable UFO photographs generally turn out to be fakes.

It would seem that photographic evidence would be the simplest and most direct way to characterize the shape, the luminosity, and the structure of UFOs. Unfortunately, the data does not support this expectation. Very sharp UFO color photographs have indeed been produced (such as the celebrated Meier pictures alleged to have been taken by a Swiss farmer), but the circumstances of the observation were extremely suspect. In a few cases reliable observers have produced useful photographs, but the analysis of the film raises more questions than it answers.

To date, the most complete analysis of a UFO photograph in the literature is found in an article by Dr. Richard Haines published in 1987 in the *Journal of Scientific Exploration*.[1] The article reported an incident that took place on October 8, 1981, on Vancouver Island, British Columbia. The techniques described in it represent the current state of the art. They would be adequate to detect most hoaxes. However, as sophisticated as they are, they cannot "prove" anything about the identity of the object shown in the photograph.

The four cases reviewed below are further illustrations of this point.

I discovered the first case in Costa Rica, the second in Argentina. In my opinion both of them are genuine. In both instances the people involved intended to take a picture of an ordinary target; the photographer focused on infinity, triggered the exposure, saw nothing unusual, and yet he ended up with frustrating images that have puzzled every scientist who has examined them.

The date was September 4, 1971, the time 8:25 A.M. A mapping aircraft of the government of Costa Rica was flying at an altitude of 10,000 feet over the northern part of the country, three miles north of Arenal and some twenty-five miles south of the Nicaraguan border. A camera running automatically under the fuselage was taking a picture of the terrain every seventeen seconds. On board the airplane were Sergio L.V., a specialist in aerial photography, as well as a pilot, a geographer, and a topographer. As the plane flew over Lago de Cote it caught a peculiar disk-shaped object. Unfortunately, this object only appears on one frame and it was never observed visually by the pilot or his three crew members.[2]

It took several years for this photograph to find its way into the hands of Ricardo Vilchez, who, with his brother Carlos, runs a very well-organized civilian research group in San José. In 1980 Vilchez met in person with Sergio L.V. and discussed the circumstances surrounding the flight and the photograph. He then sent the Arenal picture to a UFO group in the United States, the Ground Saucer

Watch (GSW), whose leader, William Spaulding, examined it visually and through computer enhancement.

Four things are immediately remarkable about this photograph. First, it was taken by a high-quality professional camera; everything in the image, which covers a territory of seven miles by seven miles, is in sharp focus. It is possible to distinguish trees, roads, even farm animals. Second, the object is photographed while looking *down*, from a known, fixed altitude, so that a maximum distance can be established, hence a first approximation of the object's size. Third, the object is seen against the black background of the lake, which presents a uniform surface in sharp contrast with the unknown disk. Fourth, the dimension of the UFO on the negative is considerable (4.2 mm) with remarkable detail.

While most UFO photographs are taken hurriedly by inexperienced operators pointing up at the uneven background of the infinite sky, we have here an almost ideal set of conditions. The Costa Rican laboratory that first processed the photograph estimated the object's diameter at seventy-one meters (about 220 feet); Spaulding reached a figure of forty meters (about 120 feet). He noted that "the trailing edge of the UFO is slightly lacking sharp resolution." The analysis did not progress beyond this point.

In 1985 I visited Ricardo Vilchez in Costa Rica, and he was kind enough to supply me with a copy of this negative. Later, he also obtained for me copies of other photos (see plate 4).

My first attempt at analysis was through a photographic interpretation laboratory located in Washington and connected with the U.S. government. At the request of a personal friend, an executive with a California high-technology company, the analysts agreed to look at the frame because it presented "an interesting technical problem." However, they could not devote much time to the analysis; they were concerned that any serious work "could be construed as a violation of the standards of conduct provisions against misuse of government equipment and personnel."

This cursory examination of the photograph disclosed that the shadows on the ground did not match the apparent shadows on the suspected UFO: the light did not appear to come from the same source. Since the UFO does not cast a shadow on the ground, they suspected that the picture resulted from "a deliberate alteration of the original negative"—in other words, a hoax.

In December 1987 a fourth analysis was initiated, thanks to the expert assistance of Dr. Richard Haines, a scientist in the San Francisco Bay Area. Dr. Haines began the work from scratch, digitized the photograph, enlarged it under various conditions, and observed:

> The disk image appears to possess lightness/darkness shading that is typical of a three-dimensional object that is illuminated by collimated light such as the sun. It appears to be a shallow cone with an axis of symmetry and a darker point or area at the tip of the cone.[3]

Noting that one side is in sharp "knife-edge" focus while the other side is diffuse and amorphous, he felt that the darker region might not be a shadow at all. It was possible that the disk was a source of light, with one side being brighter than the other for some unknown reason.

Remarkably, while this investigation of the photograph is continuing, new UFO observations have been made from the ground in the same area.

On October 25, 1986, at about 9:00 A.M., in clear weather, Joaquin U.A., a forty-year-old farm manager, and Ronald-Alberto L.A., a twenty-three year-old farmer, saw an object above the surface of the lake. Interviewed two weeks later at the site by Ricardo and Carlos Vilchez, they drew pictures of what they had seen and gave a detailed description of the events. First they saw, about 1,800 feet away, a row of three or four postlike cylinders reaching about three feet above the surface of the lake, which was quiet and flat as a mirror. Then they again saw a series of objects sticking out about three feet above the water and three feet apart. By then they had driven their tractor much closer to the lake, and they could clearly observe the cylinders, which were of a dark hue, either gray or coffee colored. After five or ten minutes the objects disappeared, the emerged portions tilting together as if they were attached to a single submerged structure, and the whole thing disappeared with much turmoil and waves.

It is noteworthy that such observations of submerged objects, although rare, are not unknown in the UFO literature. For example, on September 27, 1978, at 6:40 P.M. two fishermen in Falcone (Piombino), Italy, saw a luminous, bell-shaped object come out of the sea with a metallic sound and fly to within 150 feet of their location.[4]

The second case of photographic data from my files concerns a series of pictures taken in Argentina.

On April 22, 1980, I traveled to the town of La Plata, in the company of Fabio Zerpa, a highly respected Latin American researcher. He introduced me to a man named José-Maria B., who lives in La Plata and who gave me several very unusual photographs of an unidentified object. Unfortunately, he had failed to note the exact date.

There was a partial eclipse of the moon that winter night, and Mr. B. wanted to photograph it. Installing his camera outside in the street, he aimed it at the moon and took four exposures in succession, each of them one minute in duration.

When the pictures were developed, a large object, which seemed much more luminous than the moon, was in evidence. Furthermore, it had remained fixed in the sky, while the moon and the stars moved, leaving short trails due to the earth's rotation during the one-minute exposures (plate 5).

"Did you see anything unusual at the time?" I asked Mr. B. as we stood in the town square, at the exact spot where he had taken his photographs.

"I did see a bright point," he replied, "but I thought it was a star. To the naked eye it certainly was not brighter than the moon."

"What type of film were you using?"

"An AGFA ambiciliate, a standard commercial film. It must be more sensitive than the human eye to ultraviolet or infrared light emitted by the object."

"And the diaphragm opening?"

"At the maximum, fully open."

In La Plata, as in Arenal, the witnesses were not aware that they were photographing an impossible object, an image that would not provide any new evidence for the existence of UFOs but indeed would add to the complexity of the challenge.

Two more cases of photographic data are shown in plates 6 and 7. They are part of a collection obtained by a military team in Brazil in 1977. The photographs were taken during an intense wave of UFO sightings that swept through the state of Pará and the vast region of the mouth of the Amazon.

In both of these photographs a brilliant, disk-shaped object is seen maneuvering at low altitude over the beach of Baia do Sol, on the island of Mosqueiro. I visited the site in 1988 as part of my own analysis of phenomena recorded in northeast Brazil (see Part Five), and I found local witnesses who confirmed the trajectories and the patterns described in these photographs, as well as witnesses who had seen the military teams in the process of filming the objects.

In the study of this phenomenon many apparent contradictions must be expected. As we move from a consideration of the purely physical parameters to the investigation of more complex sightings involving multiple witnesses, the investigation of UFOs is certain to cure any lingering tendency to scientific arrogance: it quickly becomes a lesson in humility.

The public, the military, and most scientists assume that if an alien craft happened to pose for the perfect photograph or simply dropped some metal residue on the White House lawn it would be a straightforward matter to take this evidence to a state-of-the-art laboratory, where it would be analyzed once and for all. My own experience with a number of such cases provides a radically different picture. While we know what to expect when we analyze a piece of a satellite or a meteorite, or when we reverse-engineer a technical device, we do not enjoy such luxury in the case of a suspected UFO sample.

Laboratory analysts literally do not know where to start. The choices of investigative technique branch out to infinity, and there is little to provide initial goals. We do not even know what is significant: is it the presence of a particular element, or its absence, or its combination with others? Even in the Bogotá case, in which a sum of over $2,500 was expended on the investigation, we are left with more questions than answers.

A conversation I had with Aimé Michel in 1962 comes to mind in this connection. I was working at the time on a scientific project in which we were programming one of the first computers to use printed circuit boards or "cards" instead of discrete tubes. When something went wrong with a circuit, the IBM repairman simply ran a test that identified the card, replaced it, and threw out the old one, without bothering to find out which particular component— transistor, condenser, or other—had failed. The concept, at the time, was revolutionary. So was the degree of miniaturization.

At work that afternoon I had picked up a discarded board from the trash, and I held it out in my palm to Aimé. "I want you to assume that I am a fifteenth-century farmer," I told him. "Pretend that I have just found a strange object while plowing my field. You are the learned abbot of the local monastery. You have read the extant literature in Greek, Latin, and Hebrew. You are familiar with all the scientific knowledge of the time. Now, dear Father, will you tell me what this is and what I should do with it?"

I placed before him the printed circuit board. Aimé picked it up, admired the slick colored devices on one side and the flat silvery connections on the other. Gingerly, he returned it to me and said, "Burn it, my son. It is the work of the Devil."

Indeed there was no way a fifteenth-century scholar could ever imagine the purpose of such a device. Even if he had been able to analyze the material of which the transistors were made, what are the chances that he would have measured the impurities they contained? And even if he had measured the amount of impurities, what are the chances that he would have grasped *this* incredible concept: the impurities were introduced on purpose, in carefully calibrated quantities, to make the device fulfill its function?

63

The only hypothesis that accounted for the phenomenon, given the culture of the time, was the one Aimé had proposed: it was the work of the Devil, fit only for burning.

We may face a similar situation today. The metal fragments we analyze, hoping to gain some insight into the physical nature of UFOs, may be to the craft itself what the contents of the ashtray are to a Lamborghini. Even if we found consistent results from our analyses, it would be very foolish indeed to generalize too quickly. But it would be even more foolish not to examine the data.

This chapter has illustrated the fact that reliable UFO photographs are most often obtained by chance rather than design. As a result, they do not provide all the information the researcher would hope to have. Calibration is lacking, focusing is rough, and contours are blurry.

There is a definite need to systematically collect and analyze the few reliable UFO photographs we possess. If this collection were established under the auspices of a major research facility, the owners of the photographs might be willing to part with their negatives, and a truly scientific analysis might be launched.

In the absence of such a collection I have tried to show how much could be done even with fragmentary data. In the drawers and in the albums of many families there are unusual pictures that have never been seriously analyzed. An effort should be made to collect them. If I had not gone to Costa Rica, to Argentina, and to Brazil myself, I never would have heard of the cases reviewed above. How many more such photographs are there? And who will go and get them?

A word to the reader who may have the opportunity, some day, to photograph such an object: it would be very helpful if he or she also took a picture of a known light source at night at a known distance—for example, a naked 100-watt bulb forty or fifty feet away. This should be done with the same film, the same camera, and the same exposure time used in the UFO picture. Such a photograph would provide at least some calibration that could facilitate subsequent analysis.

The ideal situation, naturally, would be one in which the witness could turn over the unopened camera, containing the undeveloped film, to the group of scientists who will perform the analysis. If it were my camera I would demand to be present in the darkroom so that the development process could be controlled from beginning to end.

Part Two

LESSONS IN HUMILITY

Along with the instrumentation in the back of his truck, anyone going into the field in an attempt to document a UFO report should be equipped with a good sense of humor, a fair dose of skepticism, and a solid background in humility. Once you face the witnesses, once you stand on a lonely road or in an empty field or on a mountaintop with the wind in your hair and the rain in your eyes, it is not so easy to fool yourself and others with simple conclusions. Gone is the comfortable certainty you experienced when you first read the story, reclining by the fireplace in your favorite chair.

Sometimes an event that you found explainable by purely natural phenomena opens up before your eyes into a dazzling series of strongly articulated facts that challenge all your preconceived ideas.

At other times, contradictions pop up to cast doubts on the genuine nature of the story. The charming, reliable witness who came smiling through the pages of the report turns out to be a crank with poor eyesight or a certifiable loony who sees aliens everywhere.

That does not mean, of course, that such witnesses do not tell the truth. Much of the progress of modern science has been accomplished by cranks and loons. But do they tell you the whole truth? Are they aware of all the things that might have happened to influence their impressions? Those are the questions you have to ask yourself, and you have to do it without antagonizing or criticizing the witnesses. After all, *they were there*; you weren't. But even if they report truthfully and reliably on what they experienced, how do you know you are getting the full picture?

There is a story from Europe I regularly tell to myself in order to keep things in perspective, to maintain that essential humility.

It happens aboard a train going through the Alps; in the compartment are four people: an army colonel, a young soldier, a pretty girl, and a little old lady. The train goes into a tunnel and the four protagonists are plunged into complete darkness for several minutes. Suddenly, an intriguing drama unfolds. One hears a passionate kiss, followed by a violent slap.

The train comes out of the tunnel and the four people stare at each other in silence.

The little old lady thinks: *Good for her! This daring soldier kissed her, but she put him in his place. It's good to see there are still some young people with fine manners.*

The pretty girl muses: *This young soldier is cute. Why did he kiss that old woman when he could have kissed me?*

The colonel steams: *That's unfair. He kisses the girl and I'm the one who gets slapped!*

And the young soldier chuckles. Only he knows the complete truth. *This really is a special day: I kiss the back of my hand, I slap my colonel, and I get away with the whole thing!*

The moral of the story is that one can never trust appearances, and it is relevant to the investigation of UFO cases, a few of which will be described in this section. Some had all the earmarks of sensational events until I found that the facts were wanting and the evidence flawed. Others sounded vague and inconsequential on paper, but field research uncovered real phenomena of remarkable scope. Still others led to no final conclusion; at the end of the investigation we had accumulated heaps of facts, hours of testimony from genuine, sincere witnesses, and we still did not know any more than we did at the beginning. Was a real UFO involved? You will have to decide.

Returning from these journeys, I felt considerable sympathy for judges and police detectives who must deal with the vagaries of witnesses and with elusive facts in their professional lives.

This is a book about the scientific challenge of the UFO phenomenon, not about the unreliability of human testimony. But it is useless to deny that the two subjects are linked together.

To keep some order in the massive amount of data that seems to have clustered around me over the years, I have given mnemonic code names to some of the most interesting files. These codes are not meant to serve any security or secrecy objective. They are simply designed to capture the aspects of each case that make it unique, and that can assist in recollecting other details without a lot of searching. Calling each case by the name of the witness or by its location does not accomplish this purpose. Throughout this section I have changed the names of all main witnesses to protect their privacy, even when they had allowed publication of their identity in the newspapers.

In the following pages then, the reader is invited to join me in researching Winery Frog, Smoke Alarm, and a few other cases that can teach us something about the limitations of our technology, about the fallibility of our interviewing tactics. More importantly, they can teach us to remain open-minded.

4

Winery Frog

It sounded like a fascinating report, one of the best-documented close encounter cases in northern California in several years. The account of the sighting in the local press provided many remarkable details: an entire family had seen "huge, bright-colored lights" over Healdsburg the previous evening.[1] The mother and her children went to investigate. They were confronted by a fifty-foot-long craft.

"We saw three round things in the sky," the woman said. "They landed, flashed and zoomed. One hovered above our car about the height of the telephone wires. It had windows."

Other witnesses in the area had seen it. Richard Drager, assistant air base manager at Travis Air Force Base, told the newspaper that he had no knowledge of any unusual airborne activity in the area.

Healdsburg, a small town on the Russian River, ninety minutes by car north of San Francisco, is a place I know well. It is a quiet community of wine and leisure, with little shops that sell Indian artifacts and paintings by local artists. Not only have I investigated several other cases in the vicinity, but I have often traveled there on weekends with my family to rent a canoe near the old bridge and take a leisurely trip down the river with my children. In late summer we would just drift along the banks where they were overgrown with bushes and weeds, and pick the blackberries overhanging the boat.

Interesting as the case was, however, I did not jump to investigate it. When a report makes the newspapers, as this one did, the witnesses are generally swamped by all the private research groups wanting more data and by a good number of individuals eager to get in on the general excitement. I figured the witnesses' telephones were going to ring off the hook for the next few weeks, even though they had been careful to keep their names out of the newspaper. In a small town like Healdsburg it would not be hard to track them down. So I waited, and I heard through my friends in the research community that initial excitement about the case had been premature: although Travis Air Force Base was aware of no "unusual airborne activity," it turned out that the Air National Guard had been conducting maneuvers that evening. It seemed likely that the excited family had been watching flares and had mistaken them for unusual objects.

My interest in the case was revived in late January 1978, about six months after the event, in the course of a discussion with Mark Uriarte, a friend and local investigator. He had taken the initiative to pursue the case, and he reported that the National Guard explanation simply did not hold water. True, there were maneuvers that night, but they were taking place over the ocean, well off the coast of Bodega Bay, forty miles from Healdsburg. You cannot see flares from a distance of forty miles.

We agreed that it was time to go back to Healdsburg and ask a few questions. We found that two groups of witnesses had seen some very unusual phenomena indeed that Tuesday evening in and around Healdsburg.

The principal testimony came from Mrs. Cray, an articulate, intelligent woman in her forties, and her son Bob, who was nineteen.

72

Three other children, eighteen-year-old Cathy, ten-year-old Jeff, and three-year-old Josette, were with them. The "lights" were also observed by an unnamed couple in a car, a woman living in Alexander Valley who made an independent report to the police, and a man named Melville who watched the object's departure with the Crays. There are nine witnesses in all, spread over a ten-mile area. It is hard to say that nothing happened, or that all these people decided to have the same hallucination at 8:30 P.M. that particular Tuesday, August 30th, 1977.

Mark and I made a couple of site visits to establish the bearings and to locate the actual places where the objects had been seen. Whenever possible I travel to the locations repeatedly to see them under different patterns of light and weather, and to get a feeling for any local conditions that may have played a role in the reports. On such trips I ask myself:

- Are there any private airports in the area?
- What about power lines, television towers, or communications microwave facilities?
- Could the geography of the region limit or enhance the observation of objects in the sky? What about clouds, haze, water horizons, natural features to be used as references?
- Are there social, religious, or linguistic peculiarities that could bias the report, either in form or content?
- What other unusual events happened in the area in the two or three days preceding the reported phenomenon?
- Are there other groups of witnesses (radar operators, meteorologists, military personnel, forest rangers) who should have seen the phenomenon if it were real?

In late March 1978, Mark and I met with the Cray family. We went to their house first and they took us, step by step, through the entire event.

Young Bob Cray had been playing in a football game. The football field is located near the top of Fitch Mountain, a 591-foot, cone-shaped hill just east of Healdsburg in a bend of the Russian River. It was while driving Bob and her other children home from the game that Mrs. Cray first saw the lights.

They were large, round lights and they came up in the sky over the coastal hills in the southwest. Pulsating and blinking, they rose one after the other and seemed to come close to the ground between the observers and the horizon. (Five days after the event, Bob drew a sketch of the lights' configuration. There was a large cream-colored object and six smaller ones around it—green, red, and blue.)

Stunned by what they were seeing, the Crays realized they were blocking traffic on the narrow, winding road, so they drove down the hill and up again to a location where they could park their station wagon and get out. The objects were still visible! They stopped another vehicle, occupied by a couple who confirmed the sighting. The woman, in fact, became quite excited, but her husband merely asked the Cray family, "Don't you think it's rather dangerous to be parked here?" The couple left without giving their names.

The Crays decided to get closer to the activity. They got back into the station wagon and, with Bob at the wheel, they drove down the hill to Highway 101. When they reached the intersection with Old Redwood Highway, one object apparently detached itself from the group and suddenly "zoomed" within forty feet of the road.

Mrs. Cray was sitting next to Bob in the front seat. In the back were the three younger children. They were now going south on Old Redwood Highway. And suddenly it happened: the road was flooded with light. Mrs. Cray had to close her eyes because it hurt so much. The light was "much brighter than the high beams of a car at the same distance," she told me. "It was like the light was in my head." Jeff told me the same thing, although in his case, seated on the left side, he was shielded by the roof of the car. He showed me how he had put his hands over his eyes. Josette was terrified.

We went over the sighting in great detail. Mrs. Cray drew the object as it appeared when it was closest to the car. She estimated its diameter at fifty feet. It had several windows and two beams of light. She had made the same drawing five days after the incident. There were small differences between the two drawings: four windows instead of three, and more emphasis on lights around the object in the original drawing.

The older daughter, Cathy, had also drawn the oval object with its bright glow. She added an important detail: a face looking back at them behind the windows, a silhouette like a frog head.

When I probed their impressions about the sighting, three strange recollections came to their minds. First, they wondered, "Why does it seem we could touch the object, when it is at least ten or twenty feet away?" Second, the direction of travel was wrong: "Why is it moving north, since it is following us, and we're going south?" Third, they were confused about time: "Why is time passing *so slowly*?" The experience was like a dream where one is running in slow motion with much difficulty. Their destination—Mr. Melville's house—seemed to be a great distance away.

They were affected by the light in other ways: Mrs. Cray, Cathy, and Jeff felt nauseated. In fact, Jeff vomited upon arrival at Mr. Melville's place. Cathy and her mother developed headaches and nausea later that night and were upset for two days. The symptoms were "slightly less severe than stomach flu," and they were unable to sleep normally for several days. Jeff felt fine the next day but did not eat normally until the day after. None of the witnesses had any problem with their eyes. The youngest, Josette, had no health reaction at all.

After interviewing the Crays we drove to the house of Mr. Melville, who told us his side of the story. It was about 9:00 P.M., he said, when Mrs. Cray and her children pulled into his driveway and ran excitedly into the house, urging him to "come and see the flying saucer." Going out with them, he did see a luminous object about half a mile away, above the local winery, flying out toward Alexander Valley. It was about 9:00 P.M. when a woman who lived in town called the police to report an unidentified object.

We also thought it would be useful to check with the winery. Grapes are serious business in northern California, a crop worth about $25,000 per acre, so we were sure that if any damage had taken place the vintner would be aware of it. He told us that this particular property covered three hundred acres and that the grapes would have been ripe for harvesting at the time of the sighting. No significant damage had been reported.

For the wine connoisseurs among my readers, I must point out that, in the interest of completeness in my research, I did purchase two bottles of that particular year. I gave one to Dr. Claude Poher and I tasted the other with a wine expert in San Francisco. The unanimous verdict was that the UFO vintage was undistinguished.

I returned to the site several times with my wife, Janine, after those interviews, and I took additional measurements. The coincidence of the sighting with the National Guard maneuvers bothered me.

The very first object sighted by Mrs. Cray would have been close to magnetic south, and the object she thought was flashing at ground level would have been in the vicinity of the winery. Her recollection matched closely with the angles and the bearings we could measure at the site. Her statements about the departure of the object also matched what the other witnesses had seen. I filed the report away as a confirmed close encounter. But I was still unhappy with it.

In May 1978 I obtained the weather records for Santa Rosa and Healdsburg. There was no precipitation that day. The high temperature was 100°F and the low 71°F. At the time of the sighting, visibility was thirty miles, temperature 87°F, dew point 49, wind direction 17 degrees at six knots.

From their position high on Fitch Mountain, could the Cray family have been watching the National Guard maneuvers, just visible over the coastal hills? I wrote to the local commander and a few weeks later I received a phone call from Col. Grant Pyle, who had served as the director of flight operations at the time and was quite knowledgeable about the training procedures over the area. He mentioned that one of his subordinates had written a paper on UFOs and knew of my previous work. There was no reluctance on his part to discuss the possibility that the objects seen over Healdsburg represented a genuine unknown phenomenon.

Colonel Pyle told me that the Air National Guard was routinely flying helicopters for training in rescue missions. These craft carry very powerful floodlights and drop bright parachute flares. The path of the helicopters takes them from Hayward over Richmond, south of Novato and south of Petaluma. Given this flight plan, they would not have come close to the Healdsburg area under any circumstances: all their exercises are ten to twenty-five miles offshore, from Point Reyes to as far north as Jenner or Fort Ross. When they refuel off Point Reyes, they do use floodlights to illuminate the tanker.

I asked Colonel Pyle what the intensity of the lights would be and how far away they would be visible. He said the lights developed three million candlepower. On a clear night, which this was, they would be visible one hundred miles away.

The mission on the night of the sighting lasted from 8:30 to 10:00 P.M., at which time the helicopters had to be back on the ground in Hayward. Since the flight time to Hayward is forty-five minutes, the craft were in their training area from 8:30 to 9:15 P.M.—a time interval that overlaps precisely with the UFO observations.

The helicopters fly at an altitude of 3,000 to 3,500 feet during these missions. Given the structure of the terrain between the coast and Healdsburg, this altitude would have made them visible just above the horizon for the Cray family when they were driving down Fitch Mountain.

Now we have a real problem. It would be irresponsible to suggest that the objects first observed by the witnesses on Fitch Mountain could not have been the National Guard helicopters: the compass bearings, the times, and the altitude all check precisely, within five degrees of arc and five minutes of time! In fact, it is extremely rare to get such good agreement between a group of observers and the trajectory of a known phenomenon, a fact that speaks highly for the reliability and the accuracy of the Cray family's sighting.

But what about the extraordinary encounter over the winery?

Was it just a coincidence that a UFO flashed on the ground shortly after the Crays' attention had been alerted by the lights just above the southern horizon?

Did one of the helicopters break formation to stray over Healdsburg and buzz the Cray family's station wagon? Wouldn't they have recognized a helicopter by its noise and by the characteristic wash of its rotor, which would have kicked up dust and debris all over the road?

Or did the witnesses hallucinate the close encounter after the unusual experience of the distant lights had excited them?

If they did, what is it that Mr. Melville saw over the winery? And what is it that the concerned woman in Alexander Valley observed independently over her town, at a time consistent with the other reports?

"Winery Frog" remains one of the most frustrating cases in my files. I have gone back and forth between the various hypotheses without reaching a firm conclusion. The sighting over the winery is a high-class, well-documented close encounter. Why did it have to be triggered by the observation of a series of lights that happen to be explicable by a routine training flight?

Colonel Pyle told me that he would be interested in learning of my conclusions. I wish I could give him more than speculation. I wish there were a science of things seen at night, and of froglike silhouettes hunting peaceful families on lonely country roads. I wish I could say that all the witnesses are simply unreliable. But if we accept that they saw the helicopters between 8:30 and 8:45 P.M., they are among the most precise observers I have ever had the pleasure of meeting. How could they have changed so drastically in the next fifteen minutes to make up a fantastic tale of a monster craft over their car? These people told the truth, and the implications disturb me today as much as their experience disturbed them ten years ago in Healdsburg.

5

Smoke Alarm

It read like a front-page story in a supermarket tabloid or a chapter in the more sensational books about UFO abductions: a woman driving along a city street in Redding, California, with her two daughters and another girl had been frightened by a sudden burst of smoke that enveloped her station wagon. All sound seemed to stop around them as they floated along inside this cloud. In alarm, they went to a friend's house and found that they were missing an interval of thirty minutes, during which they could not account for their activities. They suffered various physiological reactions over the following hours, and the next day strange puncturelike spots appeared on the skin of two of the girls, who dreamed of men holding various weapons that were pointed at their heads.

The event had taken place between 9:05 P.M. and 10:10 P.M. on Wednesday, May 7, 1980.

The witnesses reported the case to the police, who referred them to a private UFO organization; since I had been investigating other cases in the Redding area, I was asked to join in the work. Less than three days had elapsed since the sighting when I arrived at the site; I spent two days there with my son, and with Bill Murphy, a former Redding science teacher. We covered every mile of the road over which the witnesses had experienced the cloud burst and the subsequent loss of time.

We met Mrs. Anderson, a forceful, articulate woman, and her two daughters, Janet, fourteen, and Connie, fifteen.[1] The fourth witness was a thirteen-year-old named Linda, who was about to join the household as a foster child. Mrs. Anderson is divorced and very religious.

The family took us back to Airport Road, where the events had happened. Mrs. Anderson had just picked up Janet at her karate class. It was 9:05 P.M. They were driving south, approaching the bridge over the Sacramento River, when they saw a luminous cloud "explode" and engulf the car. All sound stopped. Mrs. Anderson said they seemed to be "floating along." When they emerged from the cloud, they looked back but could see no trace of it behind the car. They stopped to buy some soft drinks and drove to their friend's house. It is at that point they noticed it was 10:10 P.M., over half an hour later than it "should have been."

Bill and I went over the information again in greater detail. Mrs. Anderson recalled that she had been following a truck when the cloud suddenly burst. "I first thought it was an atomic explosion," she said.

The cloud appeared to settle on the road and move toward them. Mrs. Anderson, who had worked at a nuclear research facility, described the cloud to me as an energized blast with a beam of light traveling at the top of it. It was glowing. She felt as if the flashing light "went through" her head with a painful sensation. It seemed to her that "time had stopped," but the feeling was not negative. In fact, Linda commented, "It's as if God had sent this cloud to us."

Janet, who had been crying in the backseat of the car because her boyfriend had just broken up with her, told me that she looked up when her mother screamed, "There's an atom bomb over the road." She saw the cloud and when they emerged from it she

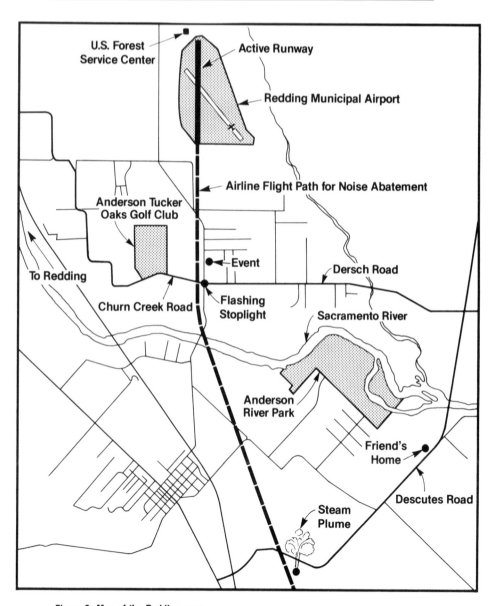

Figure 3. Map of the Redding case

thought it was strange that her tears were completely dry. Everyone in the car was extremely thirsty, so they decided to stop for soft drinks.

Connie, who was sitting in the front seat of the station wagon, remembers the events somewhat differently. She saw a pulsating light and the road became foggy. They found themselves inside a bright cloud. "Everything became silent, super-slow, and creepy," she told me.

All witnesses agreed that the weather was perfect, the stars were bright, with excellent visibility and no clouds.

The next day they all felt tired. Connie woke up with watery and sore eyes. (She did tell me she suffered from hay fever.) Janet slept in the same bed with her mother, who noticed several spots on the sheets in the morning. The spots matched marks on Janet's back on either side of her spine. These spots, about one inch above her belt, were still visible on the day of our visit. They did not look like puncture marks and had no depth, appearing as a superficial discoloration, about one-third centimeter in diameter. We also observed four spots on Janet's left arm and two on her right arm. They had no particular pattern. Connie had two similar marks on one arm. Linda complained of marks behind her ears and also reported that her eyes were red and painful that morning. I did find a small scar behind her left ear. All of the spots and marks could be explained as insect bites or ordinary scratches.

At my urging Mrs. Anderson had gone to a doctor, requesting a CBC blood test, including a differential for Janet and herself. She was very cooperative in all aspects of the investigation and authorized the release of the medical test results to me. All parameters came out in the normal range.

We visited Mrs. Anderson's house and spoke separately with Linda and Connie. Janet told us that she had had dreams of four men dressed in gray gloves and nylonlike armor carrying guns. There were two of them on either side of her and they pointed their guns at her head. Linda had become scared following the event. She had visions of a demon face with red eyes, and of two men pointing guns behind her ears and "clicking," while she received the thought that she "should not be afraid."

After these interviews, which gave a consistent picture of the events, with only small variations among the witnesses, we had to ask ourselves: What happened inside that cloud? Were the Andersons actually abducted by the pulsating light? Numerous UFO stories involve a pattern of loss of time, luminous objects, strange marks on the body, dreams of threatening beings. The Anderson story matched that pattern with a precision that was uncanny.

The sighting of a UFO is a complex event that cannot be analyzed purely on the basis of the story told by the witnesses. Their testimony, with its own terminology and structure, contradictions, and internal validation, is an important aspect of the case; but other dimensions, such as the physical layout of the site and the social framework around the witnesses, are equally important.

Bill and I went back to Airport Road. We drove south over the bridge that crosses the Sacramento River, and we studied the map of the area where the Anderson family had seen the cloud.

The road on which they were driving is precisely in line with and about two miles from the main runway at Redding airport. For reasons of noise abatement, aircraft make their approach slightly to the east for the last seven miles or so. This pattern takes them over Airport Road exactly at the site of the event. In fact, as we were standing at the place where the Andersons had seen the cloud, a Hughes Airlines plane flew over us at low altitude. We wondered if the witnesses could have been caught in some incident like the release of excess load by an aerial spraying plane. The pilots of these aircraft occasionally jettison what is left of the substance before landing. The practice is illegal, of course, and it will be denied by the pilot, but it does happen more frequently than it should. In the present case, however, we had to reject this idea: there are no scheduled landings at Redding airport after 8:30 P.M. and the tower closes at 10:00. One would have to assume that the pilot would have been late in his flight plan, that the Andersons would not have recognized the noise of the engine, and that they would have mistaken the spray for a cloud.

Other natural phenomena could have been mistaken in good faith by the four witnesses. The Roseburg Lumber Yard is located nearby, to the east of the runway line. The plant periodically releases a plume of smoke from its stack. But there were difficulties with that explanation, too.

A call to the FAA disclosed that the weather that night was clear, visibility eighty-five miles, wind from the north at eighteen knots. The wind would have pushed the plume in the same direction as the car rather than making it appear to travel toward them. And the flashing light would still be unexplained, unless we assumed that a train happened to come by at the same time, with its powerful oscillating white headlight. Wouldn't the Andersons, who live in the area, recognize the nature of the light if they saw a train?

There may be other natural explanations. In the middle of a city, a couple of miles from an airport in a busy area with residences and industry, a number of causes could have given rise to a sudden cloud and to a beam of white light. The Andersons did not see a flying object at any time, only a "luminous cloud," which dissipated without a trace. We find ourselves in a frustrating position in which we lack the information either to accept or to reject the sighting on the basis of the physical conditions at the site.

The most important component of this case may well be the social and psychological dimension.

I have mentioned that Mrs. Anderson, the main witness here, was "very religious." That first impression of mine turned out to be an understatement. The belief structure that surrounds the family is typical of a mystical obsession that borders on cultism. This obsession is widespread in the Redding area, where channeling, speaking in tongues, and other spiritual practices flourish under the combined impetus of fundamentalist Christian sects and occult beliefs that have grown since the Sixties. Although these two currents are superficially opposed to each other, in practice they blend to produce the peculiar philosophy of many small communities in northern California. Mount Shasta, which looms majestically less than an hour by car north of Redding, is a major center for this kind of belief. One finds communities there that worship Jesus as an "Ascended Master" (along with Count Saint Germain) and groups that await the day when the Lemurians will emerge from the depths of the earth to board their spaceships.

Against this spiritual background, the experience of the Anderson family takes on special meaning; every event in their life seems to assume providential proportion, evidenced by Linda's statement that it was "as if God had sent this cloud to us."

Two years before the cloudburst incident, in January 1978, Mrs. Anderson saw a dark brown object, with five black pipes protruding from it, in the sky. The moon reflected off its surface. The same month, on January 26, she saw a large white bird, with a wingspan of eight feet. Connie was with her as the bird flew into a tree and disappeared. Mrs. Anderson took this as a sign that she had found the right property to establish the religious community she was founding. It turns out that she is an ordained fundamentalist minister.

Since that incident she has experienced many phenomena of a religious nature. Conversations with the family are generally dominated by Mrs. Anderson, whose discourse is peppered with biblical quotations and references to other paranormal phenomena in her life. The other witnesses appear to be embarrassed by this behavior and frequently try to change the subject.

Two other incidents illustrate the type of exaggeration that surrounds this testimony. As we were driving in the area, Mrs. Anderson took us to a location where she thought "something must have landed" because the vegetation was darker. Three of us looked carefully at the field and could find no sign of abnormally dark grass and no depression or trace of any kind.

The second example of exaggeration had to do with the medical record, in which a nurse had noted: *Needs CBC and differential per suggestion Washington, D.C., official.* I later learned that Mrs. Anderson had told the nurse that "someone from the U.S. Air Force" had requested that her blood be tested. It took me a while to realize that this bit of hyperbole applied to me, although I had made it immediately clear that I was a private researcher living in San Francisco and that I had no governmental connection whatsoever. I saw this as evidence of a need for official validation and for ego gratification on the part of the witness, and as a signal that she was perhaps uncertain about the validity of her own experience.

I found this tendency toward lavish exaggeration in several other cases. For instance, reports of my trip to Niterói were published in the Rio papers with a reference to me as a "NASA scientist." In that case I had carefully explained to the reporter that I was strictly a private researcher. (I have occasionally worked as a consultant or as a supplier of computer services to NASA, but I have never been on the NASA payroll.) These distinctions were lost to the media. This personal experience has made me very careful when I now read books about government involvement in UFO matters. It has taught me to ask questions at a much more detailed and critical level than I would have assumed to be necessary.

This pattern of intense beliefs about the paranormal and of exaggerations in statements made about the case should naturally make us cautious about the event, but it does not mean that the Andersons have invented the whole sighting. I came back from Redding with the opinion that they were not lying, that they had seen something unusual, and that I would probably never know what it was. If I had to hazard a guess, I would say it was an ordinary phenomenon connected with the airport, but I could not prove this assertion. The loss of thirty minutes or so is not significant, since one clock could easily have been off by fifteen minutes, and the other clock by fifteen minutes in the other direction. Certainly the spots on the skin are not supportive of any UFO involvement.

A hardened skeptic of UFO phenomena would have come back from Redding with a whole repertoire of ready answers. The so-called sighting could be a hoax. Perhaps something like a bag of plaster simply fell from the truck that Mrs. Anderson was following, releasing a cloud of smoke or dust. She did not see the truck turn away or disappear, so it must have driven off while her car was engulfed in the so-called "fog."

A hardened UFO believer, on the other hand, would immediately have hypnotized the four witnesses, who were more than willing subjects. I have no doubt that it would have been easy to expand the testimony about scars, mysterious spots, and gunmen in gray into an elaborate drama featuring UFO occupants abducting attractive teenagers to subject them to medical examinations. The current UFO literature is filled with lurid stories retrieved under exactly such conditions from witnesses who are eager to cooperate in constructing cases of cosmic proportions. The UFO enthusiast would have rushed in to find out to which planet the girls had been abducted, without pausing for a moment to ask mundane questions about airports, train headlights, or industrial plumes. He would have gone home happy, with new validation of his preconceived belief. And the witnesses, too, would probably have been elated about the whole episode.

It is a strange impression, coming back empty-handed after all that work, and feeling that I had somehow let down the Anderson family. Not only was I not the Air Force official of their dream, but I was not even sure they had seen a UFO at all! Scientists are supposed to have answers. The public is disappointed and angry at an expert who dares say, "I don't know." Yet I really don't know what Mrs. Anderson and her daughters saw that evening in Redding. In all probability, I must accept the fact that I never will.

6

Beacon Probe

his is a report by a family who saw an extraordinary object at low altitude over a suburban development in Gilroy, California. Other witnesses confirmed the sighting, which was followed by the reported abduction of a forty-five-year-old woman. The incident happened within driving distance of my home, but the case was so badly mishandled by some of the local UFO investigators that I waited three years to conduct an independent assessment of the data. By then the resulting stresses and conflicts had been resolved.

For greatest clarity the case must be seen in the context of a series of unexplained sightings made on successive nights between Sunday, August 10 and Wednesday, August 13, 1975, over an area extending from Gilroy to the San Jose foothills. There were a total of twenty witnesses to these events, which involved bright red and white lights. Four months earlier, in the same area, a science teacher named Haley and three other people watched through binoculars a hovering object with a canopy, a white beacon, and an orange glow. The object remained in position for three minutes and vanished on the spot, "as if someone had turned off the light."

The main sighting started shortly after 11:00 P.M. on Sunday, August 10, when Mrs. Smith drove twelve-year-old Imelda Victor to her home. They saw a lighted object, initially "quite a distance up," according to Mrs. Smith. The object descended rapidly, close to their panel truck.

They pulled into the driveway and ran into the house. Imelda's mother, Frances Victor, was alerted by their cries. "I was in bed but not asleep when I heard them screaming," she said. "They were shaking. I had never seen such fright in my life. I ran outside in my nightgown thinking maybe there were hoodlums after them."

In her report made the next day to Officer H. Jones of the Gilroy Police Department, Mrs. Smith stated:

> The thing I saw was round, had four large landing gear-like arms coming out of it, evenly spaced all around. The round center section was larger than a car but smaller than a small house. Between the four arms were four small antennae-like protrusions from the center circle and each of these protrusions had a beacon mount on it, like a beacon on top of a police car except the lights were green and red and they rotated.

Mrs. Victor's recollection of the object was somewhat different:

> I ran to the street and saw this gigantic round flying machine with four large antenna-type landing gear coming out of it and all those white and red flashing lights. . . . It was gray metal looking and it was huge. It just sat there in the sky. . . . It was much higher than the trees.

Her husband, who had been sleeping, also went out into the front yard. He stated:

> It was big and I just saw it as it was going away. . . . I could see from the panel of all the lights to the top was triangularly shaped [sic]. The

89

vehicle was last seen north-northeast bound toward San Jose, traveling at a high rate of speed.

Officer Jones wrote in summary:

[I] can only conclude that [the witnesses] in fact saw something. All four witnesses were very upset and Mrs. Smith kept saying, "Why me? Why me?" All four witnesses were of good moral character and did not seem to be drinking.

Three days later Mrs. Victor commented:

I don't have to close my eyes to see it. It's in my mind like a picture. I can still see the beams from the headlight-like things. . . . It looked like a beautiful gem.

From my own observation of the area three years later (in 1978) and my reconstruction of the route followed by Mrs. Smith and Imelda Victor, the two women would have seen the object for about one mile over a series of shops and gas stations to their left, in the commercial center of the town.

After this first reconnaissance of the site, I wrote to Mrs. Victor and she replied that she would be delighted to discuss the case. We met in her house, with her daughter, her son, and two of his friends in attendance.

It is at that meeting that I learned not only the details of the sighting but the experiences of the family at the hands of UFO enthusiasts, reporters, and crackpots. My visit was timely, they told me, because it coincided with the reunion of the family after three years of deep crisis precipitated in part by so-called scientific investigators.

The son put it succinctly. After their sighting was published in newspapers, along with their names and address, he said, "Everything went wrong and all the bullshit came out." They were besieged by reporters; the Urantia cult held a prayer meeting on their lawn, and several card-carrying ufologists from the major civilian

90

groups pestered them. One man, from whom a strong and peculiar "stink" emanated, gave a false name and a false address. "He was slick," the family told me. He took the children out into the night "to see if it would come again." They eventually succeeded in getting rid of him.

Even more harmful was an effort by two Bay Area representatives of a nationwide UFO organization to extract from Mrs. Victor every possible bit of information about her experience. They had brought with them an amateur hypnotist, who got down to business and placed Mrs. Victor in a trance.

The hypnotic session quickly turned into a disaster. Mrs. Victor, a former nurse, reacted to some parts of the sighting and subsequent events with evidence of deep stress, and became very agitated; her body temperature dropped drastically, much to the alarm of the investigators who did not know how to bring her out of the trance. According to Mrs. Victor, she ran a serious risk of cardiac problems when the hypnotist finally woke her up. Hurriedly gathering their tape recorders, he and his entourage flew out the door, leaving her in a fit of anguish. She feels that this traumatic treatment contributed to a family crisis. Shortly after the experience, Mrs. Victor separated from her husband. One of her daughters ran away. "Even the cat and the dog left the house," she told me.

It was only two weeks before my visit that they had been reunited, a fact that reinforced my belief that when a sighting is highly publicized, the witnesses are best left alone for some time. Not only is it more ethical to proceed this way, but the quality of an investigation can improve once interest has died down.

Mrs. Victor and her children were visibly thrilled to be together again after all their trials. "Every morning we wake up more happy," one of them told me. It was as if the truth were finally emerging from a series of incidents that at first had seemed terribly evil.

We went over the sighting itself—and its aftermath—in complete detail, starting from the moment when Mrs. Smith and Imelda ran into the house. They were hysterical, said Imelda, because they thought the object "was going to take everyone away." They rushed from the car into the house, leaving the engine running and the doors open. (There was no interference with the car engine at any point.) The mother thought some young delinquents were after them until she saw the object up in the air across the road.

Mrs. Victor and Imelda stood with me on the front lawn. They pointed out where they were, where the object was at the time. "How large was it?" I asked. Mrs. Smith had reported an object "smaller than a small house" but larger than a car, while it had obviously impressed Mrs. Victor by its enormity. Three years later she was still confused about its dimensions. She pointed to the house across the street, to the round tree next to it. "It was about as big as the neighbor's house," she said. "Or as big as that tree, and yet it made everything else look smaller."

On September 15, 1975, more than one month after the sighting in Gilroy, Mrs. Victor was staying with a distant relative near Industrial City, California. She was sleeping in the front room after watching television when she suddenly woke up to find two beings standing near her. They were wearing silvery suits; they had slits for eyes, nose, mouth. The suit covered the entire body as if it were made of form-fitting painted latex. The surface was very smooth, free from wrinkles.

She felt very calm when she saw them. They communicated with her "telepathically," asking her to "go up with them." They were "seeking information."

"What about my friend?" she inquired, thinking of her relative who slept in another room.

"Don't worry about your friend," one of the beings replied as he and his companion lifted Mrs. Victor by her elbows. Together they went out the front door. Mrs. Victor felt that she was flying! She distinctly saw the flat top of the house, the garage. She saw the stars above her, and a hovering UFO. It was identical to the one she had seen in Gilroy.

They floated inside the object through its "core" and followed a ramp that ascended through at least three levels. One of the beings stayed with her, leading her to a circular room with an emerald-green floor, illuminated with a milky white light. The walls were soft silver, with large round instruments. She had a sensation of intense beauty.

To her left was a door. Something traumatic happened suddenly: she was blinded by a white light and she remembers nothing else, nor does she want to deal with the rest of the episode.

She woke up in her bed and saw that it was daylight. She went to speak to her friend and told her of the experience. They noted that the door of the house was unlocked and open. Oddly enough, her friend, who is an insomniac, had slept peacefully through the night, to her considerable surprise.

On May 15, 1978, another strange experience happened to Mrs. Victor, although it was not connected with a UFO sighting. She was in the house of one of her patients, an elderly woman, when she suddenly fell on the floor as if someone had thrown her down violently; over the next several minutes she was severely beaten by an invisible entity. The older lady reported that she saw Mrs. Victor turning and spinning on the floor, hitting obstacles in her path. She suffered multiple bruises, a sliver of wood punctured a vein, and she broke her leg. She had to spend six days in the hospital. At the time of my visit she showed me her bandaged foot, which had not completely healed.

I came away from my two trips to Gilroy with a feeling of anger and frustration. Witnesses like Mrs. Victor and her family should be helped, not thrown into further confusion by those who investigate the UFO mystery. In their eagerness to obtain definite answers, or simply to validate their own preconceptions about the extraterrestrial nature of the phenomenon, many investigators rush in, demanding answers, where they should first try to attend to the trauma and the stress surrounding the witnesses—even if that means postponing the inquiry itself by a few days or a few weeks. The most simple considerations of ethics demand this. Yet in the last few years, the number of untrained, unqualified hypnotists roaming the countryside in the name of UFO research has greatly multiplied.

In a case like the sighting by Mrs. Victor, hypnotic regression may be of considerable help. In the hands of a medical professional it could have relieved the mounting family crisis and provided useful details blocked by the witness because they were terrifying or challenged her sense of reality. Since future hypnotic sessions are generally conditioned by the very first regression, it is doubtful that the Victor case could be reopened. Although Mrs. Victor called me following my visit to say that she now felt ready to undergo hypnosis, my conclusion was that the shock of the first bungled attempt would bias any new results.

The sequence of the sighting, the abduction, and the beating is a very interesting one. Naturally, the latter incident fits into no theory of extraterrestrial visitation: if UFOs are spacecraft piloted by beings from another planet, why should the witnesses find themselves under unprovoked physical attacks by invisible entities? For this reason such incidents are generally withheld from publication by UFO enthusiasts. Yet they are consistent with another paranormal domain. The literature of religious miracles and the lives of mystics abounds with well-documented accounts of physical manifestations, including beatings, that are usually classified as possession phenomena or manifestations of so-called evil powers, although they generally do not cause permanent harm to the person. This body of literature should be diligently studied by those who are serious about investigating UFO sightings.

A case in point is found in the careful analysis of the life of Marie-Therese Noblet, a French nun and missionary who lived in the early part of this century. In the course of her mystical practices, which centered on a state of ecstasy induced by intensive prayer, she experienced a series of manifestations that physicians and other experts consulted by the Church were able to verify but not explain. These manifestations included not only classic stigmata but also beatings by invisible agents; some of these incidents were witnessed by her superiors in the Church.

A medical expert, Dr. Pierre Giscard (in the 1953 book *Mystique ou Hysterie?*), quotes his correspondence with a firsthand witness of the phenomena that affected Marie-Therese Noblet in Papua.[2] The witness, Father Desnoes, described the events taking place one evening as he prayed near Marie-Therese, who was gravely ill:

> After a while, as she seemed about to doze off, a violent blow like a punch from a fist to her back sent her to the side of the bed. She did not utter any complaint, not even a sigh. She resumed her position quietly. After a while the same thing took place again.

The priest heard a violent punch at the same time the nun's body was projected forward, with the back bent by the assault. Such phenomena occurred throughout the life of Marie-Therese, who frequently suffered visible bruises from such attacks. Similar effects abound in the lives of saints, mystics, and, of course, the subjects of exorcism.

Having met Mrs. Victor and her family, I reached the conclusion that an anomalous event did happen to them and that the sighting was authentic. The abduction experience, which took place one month later, could have been a source of extremely valuable insight if the data had been handled in a professional manner. Given the circumstances, however, this is another case in which the real truth may never be known.

OCCAM HAD A BEARD

The three chapters you have just read, which constitute Part Two of this book, can be summed up in one recommendation: *do not take anything for granted.* This is a field where every statement should be verified, every assumption challenged. How to maintain this critical attitude while keeping an open mind is very difficult. Human nature begs for certainty and clear answers. There are none in the three cases I have presented. I have offered my own tentative conclusions; they are highly vulnerable to a revision in the investigation, or to new data that may come to light.

I can unequivocally state three things about these cases: I was there; the witnesses exist; something happened.

This doesn't sound like much of an achievement, but it is more than can be said about the cases cited in many UFO books, which are based on hearsay or secondhand sources. Such books have their utility, of course. I have published a few myself, including the first catalogue of close encounters in which I was able to check only a few of the hundreds of cases quoted. But the main purpose of that catalogue was statistical. To get closer to the actual phenomenon we must first be able to answer yes to the three basic questions:

1. Do the witnesses exist?
2. Is the actual site known?
3. Did an abnormal event happen?

I realize this sounds trivial. But before you accuse me of wasting time, let me tell you about Mr. and Mrs. Vidal.

Every serious UFO amateur knows about the Vidal case; it is one of the most important UFO incidents in Latin America. The Vidals left Buenos Aires one evening to meet some people for dinner in Mar del Plata. They never arrived. Their car ended up in Mexico. They had found themselves engulfed in a thick cloud of fog and had lost all sense of time. They could not explain to the Mexican authorities how they had covered the distance without buying any gasoline or why they did not have passports with them. This event is described in detail in a dozen books.

When I visited Argentina it was one of the first cases I inquired about. My Argentine friends laughed. They had spent years looking for the Vidals. They kept finding people who knew people who knew the Vidals, even a few people who personally claimed they knew the Vidals. But they never found the Vidals.

There are no Vidals. The incident never happened.

There is a celebrated sighting in the French government archives that is equally educational in terms of investigative practice, although in a different sense. Witnesses had called the police because they had seen an extremely bright object flying low over their field, leaving a fiery trail. As it did so, it passed over a pond where all the fish subsequently died.

The police called the space research center, and investigators from GEPAN went to the site. They verified all the statements, ascertained the trajectory, and saw the dead fish. It seemed like a genuine UFO case with remarkable biological effects.

GEPAN went one step further and ordered an autopsy of the fish. The biologists reported that the fish had died of *poisoning*!

It was not a UFO event after all. An electrical phenomenon had traveled along a power line suspended above the pond, melting the insulating material that fell into the water and poisoned the fish.

The lessons are clear: one must not only pursue every possible lead but keep an open mind about the whole pattern.

For every case it is useful to follow the same systematic, step-by-step approach: obtaining maps at different scales; writing to the weather bureau to check the temperature, the cloud cover, the wind. If nothing else, this information enables an investigator to assess the validity and the accuracy of the recall by witnesses, and to ground the case in physical reality.

Perhaps the most important point to remember is to separate the physical parameters of the sighting from the testimony itself and the psychosociological characteristics of the witness and the environment. Each of these factors needs to be assessed independently of the others. Otherwise, the resulting synthesis is often invalid.

Another important lesson from this experience concerns the uselessness of Occam's razor. This expression is applied to a rule of thinking in science that states that one should never invoke a complex hypothesis when a simple one will fit. It all depends, of course, on what one means by "simple." The theory of a spherical earth spinning around the universe with over fourteen different motions is incredibly complex when compared to the elegant theory of a flat, motionless earth, with the sun and the celestial bodies simple lamps carried around by angels.

Occam must have had a beard.

In UFO research, as in other fields of science, one is frequently forced to set aside Occam's razor and to accept the frustrating complexity of the physical world—and the even more complex reality of the human beings within it.

Part Three

THE PRICE OF CONTACT

Until recently, every time I returned from yet another investigation, or simply from an interview with another witness, I would be more puzzled by the complexity and the subtlety of the phenomenon; I would find myself reduced to conjectures about the form of consciousness that stands behind it and about its motivation.

My own private conjecture, which deviates considerably from the accepted dogma among UFO believers, is that *we are dealing with a yet unrecognized level of consciousness, independent of man but closely linked to the earth.* For reasons that will become clear, I do not believe any more that UFOs are simply the spacecraft of some race of extraterrestrial visitors. This notion is too simplistic to explain their appearance, the frequency of their manifestations throughout recorded history, and the structure of the information exchange with them during contact. Instead, I have argued that an understanding of the UFO phenomenon would come only when we expanded our view of the physical universe beyond the classic four-dimensional model of spacetime. Like other paranormal phenomena, UFOs seem to be able to operate outside of known spacetime constraints. In this sense, they provide science with an extraordinary opportunity to enrich its physical models and perhaps to give us a new picture of our relationship to the universe, a new avenue of communication with forms of consciousness we have not yet recognized, perhaps including undiscovered levels of our own human consciousness.

While a full understanding of the structure of the UFO phenomenon is beyond our grasp, we do have not only physical but also biological data that can teach us something about the forms of energy it uses.

All biological systems are affected by close exposure to this phenomenon. The impact can range from simple transitory effects to permanent change or even death. In humans we are now able to categorize the types of symptoms that develop after close encounters.

In this part of the book I again will use firsthand cases to introduce some general observations about the effects of contact on biological systems, starting with plants (chapter 7) and moving on to human beings, where the impact can be either mild (chapter 8) or lethal (chapter 9).

7

Botanical Data

We begin with a simple case from northern California, which I investigated with Bill Murphy, who had brought it to my attention. The main witness, who will be called Jean Kirk, has never reported the case to the press or to UFO groups; this created ideal conditions for serious investigation.

PROJECT CITY

Mrs. Kirk's story was very straightforward. About 7:50 P.M. on April 23, 1976, Mrs. Kirk became unable to watch television because her set "blacked out," giving only static sounds and a series of random dots. She went outside, curious to find if there was some unusual cause for this perturbation; she observed a small but well-defined "cloud" three hundred feet away, coming toward her at ground level. All the dogs in the neighborhood were barking furiously. There was a brief episode of rain; trees bent wildly in the vicinity, although Mrs. Kirk could feel no wind. She later saw steady red and green lights flying through the sky, and that was the end of the sighting itself.

In the following months the weeds in the area where the cloud had been observed grew to a size double or triple that of identical plants in other areas. Furthermore, they continued to exhibit this pattern of exceptional growth for two years following the sighting, so that by 1978, when she reported the case to Bill Murphy, abnormal plants could still be observed.

We drove to the site—a small house with a large yard in Project City, north of Redding—and met with Mrs. Kirk and her husband to go over the details of the experience.

Jean Kirk confirmed that on April 23, 1976, she was quietly relaxing at home, watching *Name That Tune* on TV, when static drowned out the program. Her husband, Millard, went to bed with the intention of listening to a ball game on the radio, but the broadcast also suffered from static.

It was 8:15 or 8:30 P.M. when Mrs. Kirk went out to see what could be causing the disturbance. She noticed a cloud she described to us as "solid white with sharp edges" trailing along the ground in her yard. It hovered behind a nearby tree and was illuminated by a streetlight.

Mrs. Kirk is an active, dynamic person with a positive outlook on life and an open mind on unusual phenomena, and is free of any preconception regarding their possible nature. When she saw the cloud, which was moving toward her, her first impulse was to run inside the house. Then she thought that "a cloud could not hurt her," and her fear went away. What seemed odd was that the sky was cloudless with many stars.

The cloud moved directly over her while the neighborhood's dogs began barking. Mrs. Kirk could still see under and behind the cloud, but she observed no stars above it. She had a short spell of dizziness. Suddenly it started raining, and a forty-foot tree nearby bent as if whipped by some tremendous force, although the witness felt no wind. With that final display, the cloud disappeared.

Instead of a cloud there were now two big lights in the sky: a steady green light and a steady red light, slowly moving north without any sound. Soon she could see only the red light; it was large and hovered. "It was bright red," Mrs. Kirk said, "like the light of an ambulance, but bigger for that distance." It moved to the top of a hill, in the direction in which the cloud had first appeared; it was still hovering there when Mrs. Kirk, feeling cold, decided to go back inside.

The witness had felt nothing except the spurt of rain. She noted no unusual sound, smell, or taste. She did not feel or hear the wind.

In the following months she confirmed that the area of the yard where the cloud had hovered exhibited abnormally fast growth of the grass and weeds. At first Mrs. Kirk paid little attention, but in April 1977 she actually measured the weeds at eight feet, while typical weeds of this family reach only three and a half feet. The grass had grown densely to about five feet. Mrs. Kirk cut the weeds, but they grew high again and could still be observed in their abnormally high condition when photographed in May 1978.

My examination of the site did not reveal any natural factor that could explain accelerated growth of plants in that small area. There is a grassy patch some distance to the right where the washing machine empties, and there is a small vegetable garden to the left, but nothing special at the spot itself.

Conditions returned to normal after three years and a follow-up visit in August 1979 found no unusual plants. We were left with the possibility that the peculiar "cloud" seen by Mrs. Kirk had indeed stimulated the growth of the grass and weeds; but in view of the time that had elapsed since the event itself, it was difficult to document these changes with greater precision.

There are numerous reports of effects on vegetation in the UFO literature. An event that took place on August 2, 1978, in Vallenoncello, Italy, involved a bright oval object that descended while illuminating the ground. After the object's departure, the witness found an irregularly shaped burned area in the grass, about two meters in diameter. The grass had changed to a reddish color and was covered by a dark brown jellylike substance. The witness col-

103

lected some of that substance but eventually threw it away, not knowing what to do with it.

Vegetation only began growing two years later. The burned area was still visible in 1981, and it was covered with moss and small cactuslike plants that were not typical of the area. An analysis by the regional center of agricultural research found an abnormal level of calcium at the site, according to the June 1987 issue of the *Italian UFO Reporter.*[1]

Two cases that have taken place in France, which have become classics in the literature, have provided specific descriptions of botanical effects. In both cases there are some details of the investigation and the follow-up that have not been made public, and which I feel are important to document.

TRANS-EN-PROVENCE

I am indebted to Jean-Jacques Velasco, chief of GEPAN in Toulouse, and to Professor Michel Bounias of the National Institute of Agronomy Research in Avignon for the details of their investigation, which was published by GEPAN in summary form in March 1983.[2]

The sighting itself took place on Thursday, January 8, 1981, when Renato Nicolai saw a flying object that descended rapidly with a slight whistling sound and made a hard landing in his yard. Shortly afterward the object emitted another whistling sound, kicked off a little dust, rose to the height of the trees, and took off in a northeasterly direction. At that point, Mr. Nicolai, who was less than one hundred feet from the landing site, saw four openings about six inches in diameter on the underside of the object, from which neither smoke nor flames were emitted. The object had been on the ground for over ten seconds.

Once the object was gone, the witness noticed a circular imprint six feet in diameter, with some abrasion areas clearly in evidence at several points in the circle. The object itself had a diameter of eight feet and a height of six feet, was metallic gray in color, and had a thick band around it. It made a sound like a strong wind blowing, changing to the sound of a rock falling to the ground at the time of actual impact.

"When my wife came home that night, I told her what I had seen," Mr. Nicolai said. "She thought I was joking. The next day, when it was light, I showed her the circular traces and she called over our neighbor, Urbain, and he came with his wife. I told him about it, showed him the imprints, and he told us to call the police."

The gendarmerie in Draguignan came to the site the morning of Friday, January 9, took photographs, and collected soil samples. The French National Center for Space Research was alerted by telex on January 12. The soil samples were sent to GEPAN, while several vegetation samples were forwarded to a laboratory of the National Institute for Agronomical Research (INRA). Additional samples were later gathered at the request of INRA.

The physical imprint was in the shape of a ring, the inside diameter being seven feet and the outside diameter eight feet. At several locations the ring was noticeably striated, as if a metallic object had pressed the ground, leaving skid marks in the dirt. All traces of vegetation had disappeared in these striated areas.

In subsequent physical examinations, GEPAN found that the earth inside the ring had been compacted with a tough crust a quarter of an inch thick, predominantly composed of calcium, with very few traces of desiccated vegetation. Microscopic observation showed that this crust had been subjected to a rubbing effect somewhat similar to sandpapering. In microphotographs one can see a piece of flint that has been smashed and ground into the soil, with obvious fracture lines in the rock.

The samples were then divided among several French laboratories for double-blind study. A government laboratory, the Paul Sebatier University in Toulouse, the University of Metz, and the University of Pau were all provided with soil samples. The summary of these analyses confirmed that strong mechanical pressure had been applied to the soil by a heavy weight, causing erosion, striation, and heating (not exceeding 600° C), and detectable traces of oxidous iron or grains of calcium, with minute quantities of phosphate and

105

zinc. More detailed analysis of the "black spots" found in the striations disclosed that they were composed exclusively of iron and iron oxide, "literally plated over the rock," with a thickness of one micron or less.

In 1983, when I met in Paris with Nicolai, Velasco, and Bounias, I had the opportunity to review the case and to learn about the botanical analysis. The method followed in the taking of samples is naturally critical to the study. In this case, GEPAN had been able to provide law enforcement officers with detailed guidelines for the gathering of samples on the day following the sighting.

The affected plants consisted of wild luzerne (*Medicago minima*) at locations five feet from the center of the ring and sixty feet from that point; subsequently, a second series was taken at regular intervals from the center to thirty feet away.

Analyzing these samples, Professor Bounias found a weakening of pigmentary colors among the leaves collected inside the ring (five feet from the center). Specifically, levels of chlorophyll A and B were reduced by a third of their normal values. Beta carotene was reduced by half in the vicinity of the phenomenon, and 80% of violaxanthine was stripped out of the younger leaves.

These observations were consistent with advanced senescence; everything worked as if the aging of the plants had been accelerated by the proximity of the phenomenon. However, the resulting effects are not consistent with nuclear irradiation, and Professor Bounias refused to speculate on the nature of the non-ionizing irradiation that could have been responsible for this acceleration of the aging process. Here again, pulsed microwaves may have been the cause.

In November 1988, my wife and I traveled to Trans-en-Provence with Professor Bounias. We met with the Nicolais on their property and went over every detail of the sighting.

Thanks to a well-equipped Silicon Valley laboratory, we were able to reanalyze samples that had been collected on the ring itself, both on the surface and at a depth of about six inches. The laboratory found nothing unusual and no significant difference between the two samples, although the work performed included scanning electron microscopy and energy dispersive X-ray analysis. This new analysis allowed us to eliminate the possibility that chemicals, cement powder, or other surface contaminants could have affected the plants.

Mr. Nicolai himself did not report any adverse effects from the phenomenon. But we will complete this chapter with another classic case that combines traumatic botanical observations with a well-defined physiological impact on the witness himself.

VALENSOLE

The Valensole case is the best-authenticated close encounter incident in continental Europe. It involved hard traces, botanical data, physiological data, and detailed descriptions of beings associated with the object. It was investigated on the very day of the event by French government agencies, which concluded that the witness was not lying or hallucinating. It has been followed up by Aimé Michel, by prominent French astronomer Dr. Pierre Guerin, and by myself.[3]

In the early morning hours of July 1, 1965, a French farmer named Maurice Masse suddenly saw an oval object that had landed in his lavender field, about five rows away from the road. The site is located in the lower Alps, near the village of Valensole.

Mr. Masse, who was about two hundred feet away from the object, at first thought it was a helicopter, and he walked to within eighteen feet of it. As he was approaching he realized the object was egg-shaped and rested on six curved legs, with a central column directly beneath. Two beings wearing gray-blue-green suits but no breathing devices stood between him and the object itself. One of them pointed a small device in his direction, and he immediately felt unable to move. In this position the two beings had a brief dialogue and the object took off, leaving a deep hole and an area of moisture that hardened to the consistency of concrete.

It took twenty minutes for the witness to regain control of his muscles. His sleep patterns were drastically affected in the days

following the event, and he underwent a significant change of behavior. Although he has not reported his subsequent observations
to the press or to the authorities, it is known that he has seen the
object, or a similar one, on other occasions, and that he is in touch
with other witnesses of close encounters in the region. As for the
plants, they were affected by the proximity of the phenomenon, and
started to decay in direct proportion to the distance from the central
column. The calcium content of the soil at the landing site was
found to be much higher than in the soil taken from other places
in the field.

I visited Valensole with a friend on May 27, 1979. We had a drink
with Gilbert and Françoise, close friends of Mr. Masse, who joined
us later, as agreed, but told us that he was too busy to discuss the
case that afternoon. We negotiated a later time. The next day, while
sharing a drink of local Pastis with us, he confessed that in his
opinion the beings he saw were from somewhere else "but were
human." They had larger heads than humans, however. He declined to discuss the "paralysis" he had felt at the time. As for religious interpretations of what he had seen, he rejected them
completely.

Mr. Masse did confide to us that he had seen an object again,
at night, on his other property. He became enthusiastic and almost
lyrical when describing it. "It was beautiful," he said, "with many
colors, pretty colors, all whirling around." The colors changed so
quickly he could not see them clearly. "When you want to look at
the blue, it's already red."

He also told us that his testimony regarding the main object had
been reported in error: there were only four legs, he said, rather
than six.

My friend and I spent the afternoon on the Oraison Plateau,
where we visited the actual site of the landing; the next day we met
with Mr. Masse at his other field, which he was irrigating. Again
he became eloquent when describing the light he had seen there.
To observe something like this, he told us, was "the very best thing
I could wish to anyone." But he added that a witness should not

say anything, not even to his wife and children. "One always says too much," he concluded.

Throughout these discussions with Mr. Masse I had the feeling that I was in the presence of a very intelligent man, capable of deep emotions and rational thought. He is also quite humble; he has declined to appear on a television documentary with a nationally known journalist. He is helping a small commune of youngsters in the area, and he has taken a teenage delinquent under his protection. His friend Gilbert told us that it was as if Masse "saw everything from the outside."

It is also clear that Masse has never told the entire truth about his experience.

From the beginning he tried to minimize its impact. He told the gendarmes that the two beings were in reality "like kids," that they had hair, that only one of them was outside the craft. He had trouble confronting the strangeness of the encounter. It is only the next day, when the secret became too heavy, that he burst into tears and told the truth: there were two entities, they had large bald heads, they were unlike anything he had seen before.

Now he jokes about the letter of thanks sent by GEPAN to the gendarmerie, expressing the scientists' gratitude for his collaboration. "I told them almost nothing!" he says with a chuckle. In particular, he has never revealed to the official investigators that he had been able to communicate directly with the beings, without using language. And he has never shown to them what traces the "little men" left after they landed.

I had brought with me a photograph of similar traces left after another case. Mr. Masse looked at it with a mixture of amazement and relief that someone else was aware of these particular marks. He told us that he sometimes found them in his field: that's how he knows that "they" have come back. He always erases these traces immediately.

He also told us that he no longer irrigated his field at night, implying that he did not care to see the object again.

We also learned about other close encounters in the region, notably one involving Gilbert's cousin José. I was struck by the difference between this region, where the most remarkable sightings are kept as personal secrets by the witnesses who pride themselves on hiding significant parts of the experience from the police, the scientists, and the reporters, and the usual situation in the United States, where any reported sighting attracts hundreds of emulators, all clamoring for attention. The cases in Valensole were so private that we had to break the news to Gilbert that his cousin José had had an experience with the same phenomenon.

Gilbert agreed to drive us to his cousin's field, where we saw José in the distance working on his tractor. When we hailed him from the road, he drove over and told us what he had seen.

The first case had taken place in October 1969, four years after Masse's sighting. Two objects had landed in the field, close to an old stone structure. After they left, the leaves of two trees yellowed rapidly. Traces, shaped somewhat like a boat and thirty feet in length, were clearly visible in the wheat. José could see them for a long time, although he never reported them to anyone. When he came home, his wife commented that he was white as if the blood had drained from his face. He was unable to sleep that night.

In 1977 José had another, even more striking experience in broad daylight and fine weather. He was driving his tractor, a John Deere diesel in excellent condition, when the engine died suddenly. His transistor radio, powered by batteries, stopped working as well. He then became aware of a sort of whirlwind or atmospheric vortex to his right. Although he could not see any object, there was a definite phenomenon that moved away from him and ascended along the ridge, twisting the tops of the pine trees violently as it moved up, scattering leaves from other tall trees. The parallels with numerous incidents when flattened circles of vegetation have been formed in the fields is an interesting one.

When the phenomenon had passed, the tractor started normally. But when I asked about the batteries, José told me that one of them was found completely dry a few days after the sighting.

If the UFO phenomenon involves not only the devices with which we have been familiar for many years, but invisible objects as well, then all our ideas about potential "evidence" have to be revised.

Although he hints that he is now aware of some abilities he had never known before his sighting, Maurice Masse has not become mystical in his thinking. As he was walking along an old stone wall overgrown with plants with my friend, he told her, "Just look at these vines: they twist, they grow everywhere, they grab everything just like humans do. Then one day they die and there's nothing left, nothing at all."

8

Clinical Data

Beyond the effects of the phenomenon on soil and plants, the next level a scientist should consider is the impact on human witnesses. In some of the previous cases we have already touched on physiological reactions registered in close encounters. Maurice Masse, in particular, experienced a dramatic episode of temporary paralysis that continued well beyond the departure of the egg-shaped object itself. Here again, I do not pretend to draw an exhaustive picture of the biological effects that accompany UFOs, but only to rely on a few well-investigated cases with which I am familiar to build a base for future research.

The background of this particular topic is very rich indeed. As early as 1969 a special report, authored by Gordon Lore, Jr., classified ninety-five case studies into three categories: physiological effects, animal reactions, and physical evidence.[1]

Among the physiological effects, Lore quoted a witness named Deniler, whose skin peeled off his hands and feet after an encounter. Sunburns and other heat effects had been noted in a case investigated by the U.S. Air Force near Loch Raven Dam, Maryland, in 1958. Other cases of burns and paralysis abound. A classic 1965 case involved James Flynn of Fort Myers, Florida, who was almost knocked down by a blast of wind when he approached within a few yards of a UFO, which shot a light like a welder's torch. He was unconscious for a full day and woke up almost totally blind, with a dark spot on his forehead. His later symptoms included loss of hearing and numbness.

Another important case is that of Steven Michalak, who exhibited burns, severe nausea, and weight loss after a close encounter eighty miles east of Winnipeg on May 20, 1967.[2]

A professional mechanic who engaged in prospecting as a hobby, Michalak was looking for minerals near Falcon Lake when he saw two oval objects, scarlet red in color. One of the objects hovered, while the other landed. He approached within a few feet of the device and felt a scorching pain on his chest when it tilted toward him. He touched the surface of the craft; his rubber-coated glove melted and his shirt caught fire as the object flew off.

Michalak was treated at Misericordia Hospital for chest burns. In the following weeks, he suffered from constant nausea, vomiting, and diarrhea, and a drop in his white blood cell count. He lost twenty-two pounds. Five months after the incident, he reported new burning sensations and several large red spots where the chest burns had been. He also complained of dizziness and of swelling in his hands and chest.

The classic case of Dr. X, a French health professional who has been extensively interviewed and studied by competent researchers, is also relevant here.

HIGHLIGHTS OF THE DR. X CASE

This episode has been cited in so many books and magazines that most readers familiar with the UFO literature probably assume that every aspect of the case has been covered in complete detail, and that nothing new could be added at this late date. Yet the full story has never been placed on record.[3]

Dr. X was born in France in 1930; he pursued a successful education, became specialized in a health-related field, and also found the time to cultivate a remarkable musical talent. He lives with his wife and child in a large villa located on a hillside from which one can see a wide landscape.

His medical history includes one notable event: on May 18, 1958, he was wounded by a mine explosion in Algeria, where he was serving in the French army. He was left with a permanent disability on the right side of his body, which made it painful for him to remain standing for a long time or to support his weight on his right foot. He almost gave up playing the piano because of problems with his right hand. Three days before the sighting, Dr. X was cutting wood with an ax when he made a false move and wounded himself in the leg, cutting a vein. A hemorrhage followed and the area became inflamed. He was treated immediately, but was still in pain the night of November 2, 1968, when the UFO incident took place.

That night he was awakened after midnight by his fourteen-month-old son, who was crying. Without turning on the light he got up and went over to the child's room, noticing some flashes outside. His son was standing in his crib, pointing toward the window: behind the shutters a bright light was moving. He did not pay much attention to it but gave a bottle to the baby, who went back to sleep. Since the light effects were continuing, Dr. X went over to a window and opened the shutters to investigate. When he stepped out on the balcony he would have been visible to anyone observing the house from the outside. It was 4:00 A.M.

At that point, Dr. X clearly saw two large, identical disks, perfectly horizontal. The top of each disk was a silvery white, while the bottom resembled the color of the setting sun. On top of each object was a tall vertical antenna. On the side of each disk was a shorter, horizontal antenna. A white beam was directed toward the ground below. It illuminated familiar features such as bushes and trees, which enabled him to get a precise measurement of the distance of the phenomenon when he reconstructed the sighting in the following days. He computed the actual size of the disks: they had a diameter of two hundred feet and were about fifty feet thick. They were seven hundred feet away from the house.

The two objects moved slowly, got closer to one another, emitted small sparks between their horizontal antennas, and eventually merged into a single object that changed course and came toward him. It stopped suddenly, the vertical white beam underneath illuminating the roof of a neighbor's house. Dr. X noticed that the underside was divided into eleven sections, swept by a horizontal line that reminded him of the sweep of a television set. The witness was fascinated by the motion of the line within the red illumination of the object.

Finally, the disk made a movement that brought it to a vertical position, and the white beam caught the doctor squarely on the balcony where he was standing. He heard a bang and the object vanished, leaving only a whitish form like cotton candy, which drifted away with the wind. A "bright wire" flew off the center of the object as it dematerialized, rising up in the sky, where it changed into a point that exploded like fireworks. Everything was dark again. The doctor felt a nervous shock and went inside. The whole episode had lasted only ten minutes.

Dr. X woke up his wife to tell her about the observation, walking excitedly around the room apparently without any pain in his leg. Not only had the hematoma disappeared, but all traces of his war wound had vanished as well.

Going back to bed, he fell asleep quickly but started speaking in his sleep. He spoke until 7:00 A.M., and slept until 2:00 P.M. He reported the incident only to Aimé Michel, who visited him on November 8, finding him weak and having suffered some weight loss. The doctor experienced abdominal pain. On November 17 he noticed a curious striated discoloration around his navel. The next day the area was fully developed as a red triangle whose sides measured about six inches (plate 8). Aimé Michel suspected a psychosomatic effect because the witness had had a dream in which the object he had seen was associated with a triangular shape. But when the same shape appeared on the abdomen of the child, and when the same phenomena recurred in successive years, the psychosomatic explanation had to be discounted. It is noteworthy that Steven Michalak, too, had reported a V-shaped mark on his chest.

When I visited Dr. X and his family for the first time in May 1979, Aimé Michel and I spent the day reconstructing the events and the subsequent experiences reported by the witness, none of which have been published in the UFO literature.

Among these experiences are several claims of unexplained healing. Not only did the earlier condition disappear completely (although it had been tested and established without any doubt by military physicians), but Dr. X also had a subsequent spontaneous healing of an open fracture. In this case, he was so embarrassed by the rapid disappearance of the injury that he left town for a few days so that one of his medical colleagues (who had tended the fracture) would not ask questions as he saw him walking normally. Dr. X also told me that a dermatology specialist had been consulted about the triangular skin patch. He stated that the desquamation (dry skin) consisted of dead cells, but that he could not speculate on their probable origin.

When I asked him about any unusual people he might have encountered since his observation, the doctor revealed an entire sequence of events that are so fantastic as to stretch credulity, yet they appear to be verifiable by other family members.

The first contact took place as Dr. X was vacationing in the south of France, about a year after the sighting. He suddenly heard a whistling noise "inside his head," he told us, and "had the impulse" to go back to his hotel room. When he returned, the manager told him that someone was on the phone waiting to speak to him. The voice was that of a man who assured him vociferously that they would soon "meet in [the town where Dr. X lived] to discuss what you have seen."

Some time later, when he was back in his house, Dr. X experienced a similar whistling sound. He drove away and somehow felt

THE PRICE OF CONTACT

"guided" to a spot where a stranger was waiting next to a Citroen CX, at the time the latest and most expensive French car. He was tall, had striking blue eyes, brown hair, but was wearing ordinary business clothes.

The man astonished Dr. X when he began the conversation by apologizing for the strange happenings around his home; in fact, since the sighting, Dr. X and his wife had reportedly been plagued by poltergeist activity and by unexplained disturbances in the electrical circuits. In subsequent meetings the man instructed Dr. X in various paranormal matters, causing him to experience teleportation and time travel, including a distressing episode with alternative landscapes on a road that "does not exist," according to Dr. X, who has no explanation for these episodes.

The stranger (who never gave his name, but to whom Dr. X assigned the mnemonic Mr. Bied) often appears at a bend in a little dusty path that leads north of the house to a cluster of beehives.

On one occasion, Mr. Bied came into the house accompanied by a three-foot-tall humanoid with mummified skin, who remained motionless while his eyes quickly darted around the room. Such episodes, which bear considerable similarity with those in the life of some American witnesses like Whitley Strieber, caused some stress within the family. Dr. X's wife told me that she had gone through a very difficult time when he "sensed the presence of aliens around the house." She had to take care of their young son in spite of the fears and tensions generated by these events.

Although neither Aimé Michel nor I was in a position to verify the reality of these aliens, we did receive the proof of Dr. X's unusual musical talent when he sat at the piano and gave an astounding rendition of the "Dies Irae" by Liszt.

The following month Dr. X visited the United States with his wife and his son, who was now twelve years old. They came to our house in California, and Janine and I had a long, quiet conversation with them, during which the doctor related additional details of his experiences. The most striking was an episode that took place in 1971, when he and his wife were expecting friends for lunch. He told her that he was going to move the car out of the sun—and then didn't come back.

Once in the car he had felt the "impulse" to drive into town, where he again met the mysterious Mr. Bied. The stranger told him that they "had to go somewhere." Then Dr. X found himself lying on a bed in an unknown city. When he went to the window he saw that he was in Paris, near the Ministry of the Interior. He saw Mr. Bied's car coming down the street and entering the courtyard, the guards saluting. He found a telephone in the room and called his wife: twenty minutes had elapsed and their guests had arrived. After another twenty minutes Mr. Bied's car drove out and Dr. X found himself in his hometown again—returned safely to his family, completely baffled by what had happened.

Such episodes of fugues in otherwise normal, intelligent people are not rare: I know of such an episode in a leading computer scientist who disappeared completely (and innocently) for a week, much to the dismay of the major company that employed him and of the government agencies with which he held high-level security clearances. But there is no indication that Dr. X is prone to such fugues. His wife confirms the phone call from Paris. The best indication that a genuine, unexplained phenomenon has affected Dr. X comes from the medical evidence itself. The spontaneous, permanent remission of the war injury and the hematoma are well attested, and the recurrence of the triangular discoloration on his abdomen has been verified in successive years.

As recently as November 1984 my friend Jean-Yves Casgha, a radio reporter for France-Inter, observed and filmed the gradual appearance of the triangle (plate 8). He went further, and arranged for thermographic examinations to be made during the episode (on November 2) and when the skin had returned to normal (on November 16). Photographs were taken with and without cooling on both occasions (plate 10).

The observations made by the physician in charge on November 2 included the following:

Clinical examination: Intense cutaneous erythema, of triangular shape, centered over the umbilicus; absence of visible superficial vessel.

Thermography: Numerous curvilinear hyperthermic areas, spread over the umbilical and bilateral iliac region, corresponding to deep vessels, whose topography can be superimposed to that of the cutaneous erythema, and which are resistant to cooling.

On November 11, the same physician made a follow-up observation:

Clinical examination: Cutaneous area has normal aspect, a little more "sunburned" at the level of the visible erythema of November 2.

Thermography: Diffuse subumbilical hyperthermia, in a patch, corresponding to the usual thermographic appearance of the cutaneous plane.[4]

The disappearance of the injuries suffered in Algeria was documented again in 1985. While a 1958 decision of Veterans Administration doctors witnessed a "motor deficiency of the upper right and lower right members with Babinski syndrome and paresthesia with prickling and numbing," a medical report signed on January 8, 1985, concluded:

The neurological examination is normal; one does not find any sign of Babinski syndrome or any deficiencies in the sense of balance.

The other phenomena are puzzling but not unique. On December 9, 1968 (five weeks after Dr. X's sighting), a customs officer in Lima, Peru, reported that he had seen a UFO from the terrace of his house and that a purple beam had "hit" him in the face. He was astonished to discover that he no longer needed his eyeglasses, which corrected for myopia, and that his rheumatism was gone. An engineer named Emmano Manurio, who investigated the case for APRO, computed the distance of the object at approximately 1½ miles. The witness, he said, experienced a "paralyzing fear" that placed him in a state close to ecstasy for two to three minutes.

Neither is the observation of "alternative landscapes" a unique experience of Dr. X. Whitley Strieber has vividly described his own astonishment upon discovering fields of yellow flowers where no such field should have existed.[5] In October 1982 an Englishman who had read my book *Messengers of Deception,* and who lived just a few miles from Wethersfield U.S. Air Force Base, wrote to me that he knew

> a young man who told me that during his pilot training he had been allowed eyes-only access to a UFO file extending back to the nineteen forties. He did not claim any personal UFO experience. Most of what he told me was in the UFO literature with which I was already familiar, though his emphasis was different: they shoot back if fired on; they depart "straight upwards"; they "keep on changing shape." He also, however, talked about certain psychological effects.
>
> There were cases, it seems, when pilots attempting to intercept found themselves flying in illusory landscapes. In one case a pilot had to be talked in after he reported he was returning to base, navigating by familiar landmarks; in fact he was headed straight out to sea.
>
> A much-edited document concerned the scrambling of a number of fighters to intercept a UFO; the fliers returned to base almost at once, as a result, it was implied, of some sort of collective amnesia. In many cases pilots involved in close encounters suffered psychic damage of some obscure form and were transferred to other units. After reading your book, I find that last detail of particular interest.

The peculiar geometrical skin discoloration is also not unique. A U.S. Air Force medical expert has reported to me the details of one case he investigated in Tyler, Texas, in 1979. A young college student, identified as Greg, had an encounter with a bright green light and saw "two ships with a violet red light going back and forth." The doctor examined him and found a five-inch diamond-shaped red mark on his chest and small puncture wounds in his legs. The mark on the chest did not fade for months (see plate 9). The holes were approximately the size of those made by a hypodermic needle, but such needle marks would have disappeared more quickly.

In recent years medical doctors and government scientists in France have conducted a special study of the biological phenomena surrounding UFO observations. In particular, they have investigated the type of paralysis frequently reported by obviously reliable witnesses like Mr. Masse. The label *paralysis* really does not apply to this effect, which is more properly akinesia: the difficulty or the impossibility of making certain movements.[6]

One medical specialist, Dr. Daniel Mavrakis, has noted that in such UFO episodes "the posture tonus is not affected, the subject keeps his balance and does not fall. The heart is not affected." He concluded that the akinesia triggered by the UFO experience acted on the central nervous system.[7]

Some experiments conducted with magnetic fields are also relevant here. Work by Hodgkin has shown that cells produce and absorb different ions when they release energy.[8] A report authored by a French researcher of the "biological impact of electromagnetic installations" has explored the possibility for intense magnetic fields to influence the trajectories of these ions. A series of experiments conducted on mice by Guiot with fields ranging from 12,000 to 23,000 oersteds gave effects that included the inhibition of defensive reflexes, the inducement of sleep, the creation of a convulsive state, or even death.[9]

Other, more sophisticated models involving the direct action of pulsed electromagnetic radiation on muscle cells have been developed recently by French researchers, but I am not at liberty to publish the details of the work.

It is noteworthy that microwave effects impacting the central nervous system could cause the witnesses to experience hallucinations, a fact that may be important in the interpretation of many close encounter cases or abductions with absurd factors. The same phenomenon could also induce long-term belief system changes, contributing to an explanation of the seemingly miraculous happenings that the contactees often report in good faith. Yet such a physical interpretation fails to account for the full range of the observations that are recorded in the literature.

In a careful review of the effects of UFOs upon people, James McCampbell has noted that the often-reported phenomenon of sunburns could not be due to ultraviolet radiation alone (since it often appears in areas of skin covered with clothing, which would stop ultraviolet waves) but is best explained by microwaves. At one-centimeter wavelength, people can feel definite warmth at less than one-tenth the energy flux from the sun. As noted by McCampbell, "Burns would naturally be caused by much higher intensities."[10]

On January 23, 1976, seventeen-year-old Shelley McLenaghan saw a "weird" red and green light in the sky near Bolton, in the north of England. (It was 5:15 P.M. and she had just gotten off the bus.) The object was the size of a small house, flat on top, with sloping sides and three legs. She felt "a terrible pressure on my head and shoulders, an off taste in my mouth. My teeth seemed to vibrate. When I tried to run it was like being in a nightmare. My arms and legs moved, but in slow motion. I tried to scream; nothing came out."

That weekend, Shelley became ill: a purple rash covered her neck, chest, shoulders, and upper back. Her eyes and joints ached. In her mouth her top fillings had come out, and the bottom ones had crumbled.[11]

An Army officer who served during the Korean war has described an even more remarkable incident in which an orange luminous object came over a village that was being shelled by a whole artillery unit in the Iron Triangle area. It hovered at low altitude, apparently unharmed by the powerful explosions. When it moved up the hill over the gun emplacements, permission was sought to fire at it with a precision rifle; the object was visibly displaced by the impact of the bullet. It then proceeded to sweep the hill with what the officer described as a strange beam: "You could not see the light unless you were right in it," he said. The next day the entire artillery unit was violently ill and had to be removed from duty, but no formal report was ever submitted to identify the source of the strange illness.[12]

122

The clinical data that have been collected by serious investigators of the UFO phenomenon thus form an impressive body of empirical facts. Various explanations have been proposed, from magnetic fields to pulsed microwaves. They account for some of the effects, although no single explanation accounts for all the phenomena.

Given the complexity of the reported observations, I propose to postpone the analysis of these effects, and to consider carefully the evidence from the most extreme cases: those that involve lasting injury or death.

9

Lethal Impact

On my return from my first trip to Brazil, I decided to place a high priority on cases where encounters with the phenomenon had resulted in fatalities similar to the Niterói tragedy. My purpose in gathering this kind of information was twofold: I felt it was high time to bring these cases to the attention of forensic experts, and I wanted to carefully prepare a return trip to Brazil to continue fieldwork. I found that the list of such fatalities was more significant than the general UFO literature indicated. Furthermore, it was getting longer.

The year was 1946 and two men, Joao Prestes Filho and his friend Salvador dos Santos, were returning from a fishing trip near the Brazilian village of Aracriguama. As they reached the village where they lived, they bade one another farewell and went their separate ways. The time was 7:00 P.M.

An hour later Prestes showed up at his sister's home with a strange story. A beam of light had hit him as he was reaching his front door. It stunned and blinded him. He fell to the ground, without losing consciousness. He managed to get up and make his way to her house.

That same evening Prestes's condition deteriorated rapidly. Witnesses said that his flesh literally detached itself from his bones. It was as if it had been boiled in hot water for a long time, so that his skin and the underlying tissue fell off. Prestes was not in pain but was understandably in an increasing state of terror. Soon he was unable to speak. The villagers placed him in a cart, intending to take him to the hospital, but he died en route, about six hours after having been hit by the beam of light. He remained conscious until the end.

When his body was brought back, the flesh had fallen off to the point where the corpse looked "decomposed." Some local people, none of whom had any medical background, signed a certificate according to which the death of Prestes was due to "generalized burns," and he was buried. A police inquest brought no new information. Nothing unusual was found near his house.

Could Prestes have been hit by lightning? According to a Brazilian researcher, Dr. Felipe Machado Carrion (who first published the case in December 1971 after interviewing Salvador dos Santos, who was still alive), the weather at the time was clear and not conducive to thunderstorms. We have not been able to locate the village and the witnesses, and given the fact that the case occurred over forty years ago it is unlikely that we will be able to confirm it.

On August 19, 1962, in the small town of Duas Pontes, Brazil, Rivalino do Aleuia Mafra and his three sons were awakened by the sound of heavy footsteps; they saw shadows in human shape floating through the house, and they heard voices that threatened them.

Two days earlier, in the evening, Rivalino was said to have observed two small beings "digging a hole" near his house. They had run away as he came close, and moments later an object had taken off from behind some bushes. It was "shaped like a hat and surrounded with a red glow."

125

On August 20, the eldest son, twelve-year-old Raimundo, went outside to get his father's horse. As he later testified to the police,

> I saw two balls floating in midair side by side, about a foot apart, and three feet off the ground . . . they were big . . . one of them was black, with a kind of irregular antenna-like extension and a small tail. The other was black and white, with the same outline. . . . Both emitted a humming sound. . . .
>
> I called my father out of the house. . . . He walked toward the objects and stopped about two yards away. At that moment, the two big spheres merged into each other. There was only one now, bigger in size, raising dust from the ground, and giving off smoke that darkened the sky. With strange sounds, that large ball crept slowly toward my father.
>
> I saw him surrounded by the yellow smoke; he disappeared inside it. I ran after him into the yellow cloud, which had an acrid smell. I saw nothing, only that yellow mist around me. I yelled for my father, but there was no answer. Everything was silent again. Then the yellow smoke dissolved. The spheres were gone. My father was gone. . . . I want my father back.

According to a private researcher, Harry Helms, Jr., Raimundo was interrogated by the local police chief, Lt. Wilson Lisboa, and by a priest, Father José Avila Garcia, who found no contradictions in the story and no indication of foul play.[1] A psychiatrist, Dr. Joan Antumes de Oliveira, examined the boy and stated he was normal and "telling what he thinks is the truth."

The investigators heard corroborating testimony from a local physician, Dr. Giovani Pereira, who had seen a disk-shaped object in the vicinity on the day of Rivalino's disappearance.

If accidents are included in the study, along with cases in which victims are directly exposed to a hostile light, the list of deaths related to UFO cases becomes significantly longer.

As early as 1873, a team of horses was frightened by a large silvery object that flew low over the countryside near Bonham, Texas. The wagon they were pulling overturned and the driver was killed. On October 6, 1961, a large luminous object flew over Lake Maracaibo in Venezuela, frightening many fishermen, who jumped into the water. One of them, Bartolome Romero, was drowned.

On November 23, 1953, a military jet was scrambled from Kinross Air Force Base in Michigan to chase an unidentified object. The aircraft was tracked on radar as it merged with the target over Lake Superior. Both objects disappeared. An intensive search was conducted but nothing was ever found.

In the spring of 1959, according to Navy physicist Dr. Bruce Maccabee, a U.S. Air Force jet was ordered to intercept a stationary object that had been picked up on radar off the northeastern coast of Japan. The pilot saw the object visually and was authorized to fire on it. The rockets had no effect on the unknown craft, which started chasing the jet while radar followed the whole event. The two spots merged; the resulting single object remained stationary for a while, then disappeared. Searches conducted over several days failed to find any trace of the jet. Dr. Maccabee received this information from a firsthand witness.

Other reported accidents have involved aircraft hitting unknown aerial objects. One of the most carefully investigated cases, which took place on October 21, 1978, over the Tasmanian Sea, has never been solved. A well-documented book by Dr. Richard Haines, entitled *Melbourne Episode*, details the analysis of the last moments of the plane as its pilot, Frederick Valentich, described an object that seemed about to collide with the aircraft.[2] Valentich's body was never found.

In December 1982, the Associated Press reported that forty-eight-year-old Laverne Landis had been found dead near Grand Marais, Minnesota, after a four-week wilderness vigil. She had claimed to receive messages from "a higher power" instructing her to await the arrival of a flying saucer.[3]

Landis was found in the front seat of a car, which had run out of gas a few hundred feet off the road. The autopsy showed that she had died of hypothermia, dehydration, and starvation.

Her companion, thirty-eight-year-old Gerald Flach, an electrician from West St. Paul, was found semiconscious on Gunflint Trail, forty-one miles northwest of Grand Marais. He was treated for hypothermia. According to neighbors and friends, Flach had become obsessed with the subject of UFOs; he was an intelligent, gentle man who "just changed his whole personality, his whole life in the past six to eight months." He became convinced that he was receiving messages from a higher power through the channel of Landis. The most recent message had allegedly directed them to go to the end of Gunflint Trail and await further contact.

Since no UFO was reported, I do not include this case in the tabulation of lethal effects, treating it purely as an accident. Cook County Deputy Sheriff Frank Redfield stated there was no evidence of foul play. No criminal charges were filed.

In March 1986, in a situation strangely reminiscent of the Morro do Vintem tragedy, two young men were found dead on the beach at Grumari, just outside Rio de Janeiro. They were Olavo Mena Barreta, a computer technician from a prominent family, and Wellington Barros Wanderley, an office worker and former engineering student with an interest in Rosicrucian traditions. Olavo was the organizer of a small UFO group to which Wellington belonged.

Near the bodies were two empty bottles of Guarana, smelling of something else, similar to ammonia. The police noted no signs of violence; the two men had not been robbed. They died with their arms outstretched.

Were the two experimenting with drugs to induce an out-of-body experience to contact UFO beings on what occultists call the astral plane? Had they simply died from an overdose of the strange-smelling substance found in the bottles? Could a similar scenario explain the deaths of Manuel and Miguel in Niterói? But what about the sighting of the large luminous object above the mountain that day?

Since no UFO was described in connection with the Grumari case, the incident does not seem directly relevant to the question of the lethal impact of UFOs, but it does provide an important indication of the social context of the phenomenon in Brazil, where

UFO cases cannot always be separated from occult practices and beliefs.

Accidental death of occultists attempting to contact "higher-level entities" is not rare. The English magician Dion Fortune, for instance, had a friend named Netta Fornario who died in 1930 under bizarre circumstances. According to the biographer Alan Richardson, Miss Fornario was an artist who had written many articles on the occult under the name Mac Tyler. On a trip to Iona

> she was found . . . nude on a bleak hillside, her body covered in scratches. Round her neck was a cross secured by a silver chain, and near at hand lay a large knife which had been used to cut a large cross in the turf. *There were rumors on the island about blue lights having been seen in the vicinity where her body had been found* (author's emphasis).[4]

Dion Fortune herself commented in her book *Psychic Self-Defense*:

> She was half-Italian and half-English, of unusual intellectual calibre, and was especially interested in the Green Ray elemental contacts; too much interested in them for my peace of mind, and I became nervous and refused to cooperate with her. . . . She was not a good subject for such experiments, for she suffered some defect of the pituitary body. Whether she was the victim of psychic attack, whether she merely stopped out on the astral too long and her body, of poor vitality in any case, became chilled lying thus exposed in mid-winter, or whether she slipped into one of the elemental kingdoms that she loved . . . who shall say?[5]

Stories of UFO-related deaths have also come from the African continent. In June 1954, eleven-year-old Laili Thindu told authorities in Nairobi that he had seen strange lights coming from the direction of Mount Kenya and flying near his village of Kirimukuyu. The lights hovered over a neighboring village where drums could be heard, celebrating a marriage ceremony. The objects sent down rays of light, and the drums became silent.

The next morning the boy was told that the entire population of

129

that village and the livestock had been "burned to death" by the light rays.

On July 5, 1969, near the small town of Anolaima, Colombia, about forty miles northwest of Bogotá, at 8:30 P.M. two children saw a luminous object three hundred yards away. They grabbed a flashlight and sent out signals. The object came closer—about sixty yards from them. The children called the rest of the family, and all thirteen people who lived in the farmhouse watched the light as it flew off and disappeared behind a hill, the glow remaining visible. The father, fifty-four-year-old Arcesio Bermudez, took the flashlight and went to investigate.

When Arcesio came back he was scared. From a distance of less than twenty feet he had seen a small person inside the top part of the object, which was transparent, while the rest of the craft was dark. He saw the being when he turned on his flashlight. The object became bright and took off.

Over the next few days his health started to deteriorate. Forty-eight hours after the sighting Arcesio felt very sick. He was cold. His temperature dropped. He was unable to eat and he had dark blue spots on his skin. There was blood in his stools. On the seventh day after the incident his family took him to Bogotá, which is two hours away. He was seen by two physicians who diagnosed acute gastroenteritis. They were not told of the UFO incident. Arcesio died shortly before midnight.

Since gastroenteritis is the third leading cause of death in Colombia, the diagnosis was accepted and Arcesio was buried. One of the doctors commented later, "If I had known of his experience, I would have performed more tests."

I have in my files a copy of a letter from Dr. Luis E. Borda to John Simhon of the APRO research group, in which he states:

I was called by the family at 9:00 A.M. on July 12. I arrived at 11:00 A.M. and found Arcesio Bermudez suffering from vomiting and diarrhea; the pulse was almost unnoticeable, his face was pale. I gave him 2 centigrams of "emetina" because the liver was inflamed, and

I also gave him a tonic for the heart (drops of a preparation containing a digitalis tincture).

I returned to the house at 6:00 P.M. and found him worse; I could not find any pulse and the temperature was below normal. I suspected a state of food gastroenteritis and I asked him what he had eaten last. He answered with difficulty: "sardines." Later I understood that the whole family had eaten sardines and sausages.

Antecedents: About a year ago he suffered from a kidney problem, with blood in the urine, and was cured. Otherwise, Arcesio Bermudez was a healthy man.

I also have a copy of a statement by Dr. Cesar Esmeral Barros of Bogotá reporting on two clinical observations, the first one by Dr. Borda at 10:00 A.M., the second one by himself at 7:30 P.M., both made on July 12. Dr. Esmeral gave the following details:

The victim's temperature had dropped to 35° C. The cardiopulmonary system exhibited pericarditis, asphyxia, cough, painful thoracic oppression, slow pulse. The digestive system was affected by bloody diarrhea, black vomit, dry mouth, painful abdomen, especially on the right side. Mental faculties and nervous system: normal. The skin was dry, pale, cold, dehydrated.

Arcesio received emergency treatment (antidiarrheal drugs, analeptics, antihemetics) and died at 11:45 P.M. on July 12, 1969. The physician noted at the bottom of his report: "Two days after the death there was news that this gentleman had been a witness to extra-natural phenomena."

The weather at the time of the sighting had been very clear, with the stars visible, normal humidity (65%), and a temperature of 17° C (about 62° F). The farmhouse is located in hilly country, with abundant vegetation. It is a primitive area and there is no electrical power on the farm. It is noteworthy that most incidents have taken place in such remote locations, away from modern medical facilities and cut off from communication with the rest of the world.

In recent years the most remarkable cases of UFO-related injuries and deaths have taken place in the northeast of Brazil, in a vast region that extends from the mouth of the Amazon (Belém and the island of Marajo, which is located on the equator about 300 miles from French Guiana) to São Luís and the town of Teresina, 200 miles up the river from the coast.

This is a vast area, the size of California, with many rivers, scattered hills, and poor villages. The cases around Teresina were first reported in December 1981 by journalists Gary Richman and Thomas Muldoon, who did not go to the site. Given the remote nature of this region there was no follow-up by private researchers, except for a U.S. tabloid that sent a reporter to speak with some of the witnesses. He spent only a few hours in Teresina. In 1983, fortunately, an American architect who frequently works on construction projects in Brazil, and who speaks fluent Portuguese, took the time to investigate the cases, bringing back numerous photographs, maps, reports, and taped interviews. We studied these documents together.

On the basis of the information gathered so far, there seem to be three major clusters of cases: around the small town of Parnarama, around São Luís, and around Belém.

At least five people are said to have died near Parnarama following close encounters with what were described as boxlike UFOs equipped with powerful light beams. These objects, which have been called *chupas* by the local population, fly over the wooded areas and the river valleys at night.

All of the victims in Parnarama were deer hunters who had climbed into trees during the night, as is frequently the case in that part of Brazil. People hunt and fish, not for sport or entertainment but to supplement their family's food supply, and they do it at night because it is cooler and because they have a greater chance of finding game in the woods.

In most cases the witnesses reported rectangular objects (sometimes compared to ice boxes) flying over the treetops and shining a beam toward the earth. The chupas are said to make a humming sound like a refrigerator or a transformer, and this sound does not change when the object accelerates. The object does not seem large

132

enough to contain a human pilot. It has a light on the bottom and a light at one end, giving a sealed beam like a car headlight.

The victims were Abel Boro, who died on October 17, 1981, while hunting with Ribamar Ferreira; Raimundo Souza, who died on October 19, 1981, while hunting with Anastacio Barbosa; José Vitorio and Dionizio General, who died on an undetermined date, the latter three days after the UFO encounter; and a man named Ramon, who lived in Parnarama.

Muldoon and Richman quoted the mayor of Parnarama as confirming the cases, and the chief of police, Geraldo dos Santos Magela, as stating that he had examined two of the bodies, finding that the blood had been "sucked from them."

Ribamar Ferreira described a light coming over him and his friend Abel Boro: it was so bright that it turned night into day, he said. Abel screamed as the object—looking in this case like a giant spinning truck tire with lights on it—surrounded his body with a glittering glow. Ferreira ran to Abel's house and returned with his family: they found Abel Boro dead, his body white "as if drained of blood." (It is normal for corpses to develop a whitish-gray color because the hemoglobin breaks down after death. This does not mean that the body has been drained of blood, as witnesses often assume.)

In another case, Dionizio General was atop a hill when an object hovered above him and shot a beam in his direction; it was described as "a big ray of fire." The witness, José dos Santos, testified that Dionizio seemed to receive a shock and came rolling down the hill. For the following three days he was insane with terror; then he died.

The article by Muldoon and Richman also mentioned José Virginio dos Santos, a TV station worker, who fired five rifle shots at an object near his home. The object started to chase him, sending what appeared to be bursts of flames that lit up the area.

The interviews with witnesses conducted at the site by my architect friend confirmed only some of these reports, which until then had been based on public rumor; understandably, these interviews also enabled him to fill in many details and to correct some mistakes. Since Brazilian authorities waited two months after the deaths were reported to visit the site, official information is sketchy and unreliable. The mayor and the police chief have changed. Officials now decline to discuss the subject.

The area around Parnarama is forested and very primitive. Most dwellings have no electricity, except in the town itself (population 3,000). Six power lines of 238,000 volts do run through the region, but there is no local transformer. The sightings were not in the immediate vicinity of these power lines. There is much hunger in the area. The local people are skilled hunters and excellent observers. Crime is practically unknown. There are no modern means of communications, and only logging trucks can negotiate the dirt roads. The major religious denomination is Catholic.

The hunting technique used in the region is unique: the hunters climb ten to fifteen feet into the trees, then spend the night in a hammock waiting for deer or other game. They take a flashlight with them to spot the animals.

A theory among local people is that the chupas are attracted by the flashlights, come over the hammocks, and strike the victims with their concentrated beam. However, I found little consistency in the descriptions of the beam itself. One witness compared it to an electric arc. On an interview tape another witness said he remembered a "bad smell" like an electrical odor (ozone?) and saw a blinding light, with pulsating colors inside, a description consistent with many I have heard in France and in the United States. He felt heat at the same time.

Several people reported being exposed to the chupas in late 1982 as they were lying in their tree hammocks. At the time of the interviews a year later, they still complained of headaches and general weakness. They had lost their previous vitality. A forty-three year-old man who "used to be afraid of nothing" now lives in constant fear. He is "scared of things that are not part of my experience."

Another victim who had shot a deer early in the night and had gone to sleep in his hammock, intending to retrieve the animal at dawn, was awakened by a chupa but felt nothing unusual at the

134

time. Later he became ill; at first his legs could not carry him. He was very thirsty, seemed to become "hysterical," jumped around and tore at bushes. He developed blotches on his skin.

Why have these people never been examined by a competent doctor? The closest physician is a long way from the site, in the town of Parnarama itself. There was no way to go and get him. No autopsies were performed. Because of the heat, the bodies were buried quickly.

It seems that the UFO activity in this region began in 1981. It reached a peak in April and May 1982.

My friend returned to Brazil in the fall of 1984 and gathered more anecdotal information. He heard that two physicians, a Dr. Enrique and Dr. Nicolao Waquin Neto, had investigated the deaths, indicating a rising level of official interest, but he was not able to contact them. He also learned that new incidents were now taking place near Chaval, on the northern coast of Brazil. And he was told of another cluster of cases near Sobral, in the area of Santana do Acarau.

The Santana events had taken place ten years before those in Parnarama, between 1972 and 1975. Objects were said to hover near the Acarau River, emitting peculiar flickering light beams with which a sensation of cold was associated. Here again, the objects were described as boxlike, similar to a VW bus. One of the firsthand witnesses stated that he had escaped the beam of light of a chupa by hiding under a tree overhanging the river.[6]

A local rumor claims that the chupas are "American prototypes" that take the blood of the victims to send it to the United States! But when I tried to find out how the so-called bloodless character of the corpses had been documented, it was clear that the assertion was not supported by careful observation.

There are descriptions of "small beings" in connection with the chupas, and also of a larger, disk-shaped object, the size of a house. No reports of harmful effects are associated with this circular craft.

In recent years Bob Pratt, an American researcher, has gone to Brazil several times to investigate a series of events that took place in 1977 on Crab Island, near São Luís. In that case one man died and two were badly burned. Pratt reported in 1987 that similar incidents had taken place at the same location in 1986, with one man dead, another injured, and two others unconscious for 15 hours.[7] He stated, however, that the link to UFO activity was "tenuous" at best in both reports.

One of the cases investigated by Bob Pratt concerns Luís Fernandes Barros, a wealthy businessman and rancher in Quixada, who was found dazed at 7:00 A.M. on April 23, 1976. Barros, who was fifty-two at the time, gradually recovered; he reported that two hours before daybreak he had seen a large luminous object that projected a beam in his direction. Here again, the victim's health soon deteriorated: he suffered from nausea, diarrhea, and headaches. He was seen by his physician, Dr. Moreira Megalhes, in Quixada. The medicine he was given did not help. Other specialists were consulted. They diagnosed a brain lesion and sent him home.

In the following months Barros's health continued to worsen. He no longer told his story, because no one believed him other than Dr. Megalhes and his wife. Dr. Megalhes himself was ridiculed by his colleagues for taking the report seriously.

In three months the victim's speech deteriorated, and his hair turned white; six months later he had regressed to the level of a one- or two-year-old child. Pratt, who met with Barros in 1986, found him staring ahead, apparently seeing nothing. However, Dr. Megalhes showed him that Barros had control of his arms and legs and had not suffered a stroke.

A dedicated researcher, Daniel Rebisso Giese, has compiled a well-documented report on another cluster of lethal events in the Belém area.[8] In that report he mentions a doctor in charge of the health unit on the island of Colares who stated that UFO incidents had begun there in September 1977. A number of patients started coming to her with complaints related to the chupas. At first she discounted these reports as a popular myth, perhaps related to local sorcery. When every day started bringing a new patient she realized that the complaints were serious; she conducted a more thorough study of the lesions exhibited by the victims, notably burns that resembled radiation injuries.

These lesions, according to the physician, Dr. Wellaide Cecim Carvalho de Oliveira, began with intense reddening of the skin in the affected area. Later the hair would fall out and the skin would turn black. There was no pain, only a slight warmth. One also noticed small puncture marks in the skin. The victims were men and women of varying ages, without any pattern.

One day Dr. Carvalho found a woman waiting for her when she arrived at the dispensary at 7:30 A.M. The woman was very agitated, and she said that she had been hit by a chupa. Opening her blouse, she revealed extreme reddening of the skin on her left breast; again, there were two puncture marks.

"I tried to calm her down," related Dr. Carvalho when she was interviewed in 1985. "I told her it was nothing serious, that she should not let it impress her. I gave her five milligrams of Diazepam; she could barely raise a glass of water to her lips. She complained that she had trouble breathing. She suffered from dizziness and felt weak. I later found that these were characteristic symptoms, along with headaches and a decrease in the number of red blood cells. . . . Three hours later I was urgently called to her house. I found her in a state of deep coma, the body totally rigid, gasping for breath. She had no fever and she did not vomit. I tried to take her to Belém in my car, but I did not have enough fuel, so she was driven there in the car of the Prefecture. I waited for news. Hours later I received a medical statement and a death certificate from the Renato Chaves Medico-Legal Institute giving heart failure as the cause of death."

This official diagnosis totally ignored the data that Dr. Carvalho had forwarded along with the patient. The physician became suspicious, and since the authorities remained silent about the whole situation, she stopped sending statements about such cases. In fear and frustration she even destroyed a thirty-page document she had compiled about her clinical observations, which included blood test results and biochemical analyses.

It is noteworthy that a team from the Brazilian Air Force had arrived on the island early in October, a few weeks after the events had started. They came in two vehicles, two officers and a dozen men, engineers, geologists, and a biologist. They were between thirty and forty years of age and came from the south. They erected two shelters and asked the witnesses to keep quiet about what they had seen. At night they set up telescopes and cameras to photograph the chupas.

By the time the wave of sightings subsided in November 1977, Dr. Carvalho had seen no fewer than thirty-five patients claiming injuries related to the chupas. All of them had suffered lesions to the face or the thoracic area.

Like most of the private investigators of this phenomenon, I would like to be able to conclude that any injuries sustained by human witnesses in connection with UFOs are accidental—perhaps the result of careless approach to a source of energy that has proven unpredictable in its manifestations. Unfortunately, the reported facts do not support this idea. On the contrary, they seem to betray intelligent behavior on the part of the objects.

The Brazilian military, which has been engaged for many years in one of the most serious investigations of the phenomenon conducted anywhere around the world, took the 1977 events around Belém very seriously indeed. Starting in 1974, the Belém headquarters of the 1st Regional Air Command (COMAR), covering an area four times as large as France, maintained a UFO field investigation team. Until it was disbanded in 1982, this team operated under the following mission statement:

1. The UFO phenomenon deserves serious objective study.
2. All possible information and witness reports about the phenomenon must be gathered.
3. Public statements about the events must be avoided.

When the events of 1977 started in the area around Belém, the Air Force, as noted above, sent a field task force to the region, notably to the island of Colares. Its mission lasted ninety days. The task force came back with three hundred night photographs and several motion picture reels. A five hundred-page report was compiled, accompanied by a catalogue of the sightings, maps, and interview transcripts. Copies were sent to Armed Forces Headquarters in Brasília, and the originals went to Barreira do Inferno (the Gate of Hell) in the state of Rio Grande do Norte. Some researchers believe it is an appropriate destination for such a report about the elusive chupas and the unfortunate human victims caught in their impossible light.

The theme of this chapter—death of human subjects as a result of direct exposure to UFOs—highlights a turning point in this research. Here again, the temptation has been strong among the UFO community to speculate on the basis of little data. Some writers have immediately concluded that "flying saucers are hostile," while others insisted that the incidents were due either to the carelessness of the victims or to accidents that were not deliberately designed by the "ufonauts."

Both theories, naturally, make the unstated assumption that the UFOs are spacecraft piloted by aliens with perfectly anthropomorphic motivations. If this were the case, and if the aliens were simply "hostile" in the first-order sense of the word, they could have taken over our planet a long time ago.

Forensic pathologists who have reviewed the above data at my request offered only tentative recommendations. What UFO witnesses describe as "light" may, in fact, be a complex combination of ionizing and non-ionizing radiation. Many of the injuries described in Brazil, however, are consistent with the effects of high-power pulsed microwaves. Preliminary as they were, their recommendations to explore specifically nervous system impacts enabled me to return to Brazil in 1988 better equipped to ask victims and witnesses the kinds of questions that would clarify the nature of UFO-related injuries. The results of this subsequent investigation will be given in Part Five. Before we study those results, a discussion of the "active" involvement of scientists in search of UFO data is necessary. Such a discussion is our topic in Part Four.

Part Four

STALKING THE INTRUDERS

For the past forty years the UFO phenomenon has been analyzed and passionately discussed, leading to the accumulation of massive amounts of data of the kind we have reviewed in the first three parts of this book. A key challenge now is to shift our research from this passive mode into an active phase, in which we may be able to interact with the facts. Only such interaction can allow us to determine which of the leading theories of the phenomenon is correct, or even if the theories should be superseded by more innovative concepts.

It is not necessarily true that the progress of science demands such active experimentation. In astronomy, for instance, researchers are reduced to observation and analysis with no opportunity to interact directly with stellar or galactic phenomena. But in a field that potentially involves an unknown form of consciousness, it is critical to determine if interaction is possible and to initiate it.

Over the years some crude attempts have been made to implement such interaction, usually from the basis of the extraterrestrial model. Under this model, the UFOs were assumed to be spacecraft carrying exploration crews. It was suggested that adequate actions on the part of humans would be to signal to them with various forms of luminous effects, to build landing facilities of the kind displayed in the movie *Close Encounters of the Third Kind*, or to lure them to a specific location by relying on the relationship they may have established with special subjects such as abductees.

As an illustration of the latter scenario, Janine and I recall spending two days in the summer of 1964 with Betty and Barney Hill, Dr. Benjamin Simon, John Fuller, and several other ufologists in a large meadow in New Hampshire, where it was thought a UFO might land. I set up a Questar telescope on a folding table next to a vast chalk circle in the grass, and we entertained ourselves all night while spraying each other with mosquito repellent. The major discovery I made on that occasion was that John Fuller had a wonderful repertoire of very funny stories, many of them involving his numerous trips to France. We did see a large number of anomalous lights in the surrounding woods that turned out to be fireflies, to the disappointment of the people who had set up the experiment in the expectation that Betty Hill would serve as a "transceiver with extraterrestrials." My strong recommendation to anyone wishing to repeat our experiment in New Hampshire in summer would be to set up strong bug-killing lights at the corners of the perimeter, if only as a courtesy to the expected Visitors.

A more realistic approach involves the development of permanent magnetic or gravitational anomaly detectors that are triggered by the proximity of a UFO. It is then hoped that an alert can be given, allowing trained teams to be dispatched to the site in an effort to initiate contact. Many such instruments have been designed and built. Under the impetus of the group *Lumières dans la Nuit*, a

French network of magnetic detectors was set up in the 1960s, which led to some interesting sightings. Similar results are occasionally reported in the United States.

Perhaps the most publicized project of this type was designed by UFO researcher Ray Stanford in Texas. It used a sophisticated set of electronic sensors, including radar, to trigger computer-controlled reaction sequences, with an instrumented van as the key component of the expected contact.

My major concern with the project is that it used a fixed location, while UFO waves are known to vary widely in their geographical patterns. The approach used by Brazilian Intelligence in 1977, packing teams of experts into trucks and dispatching them to the center of the sighting cluster, seems more promising to me.

We are naturally hampered in this effort by the lack of an adequate model of the phenomenon. It is time to acknowledge that the extraterrestrial theory (which assumes that UFOs are spacecraft piloted by beings from another planet who conduct a survey of the earth), a hypothesis that seemed the best avenue of research in the years following World War II, contradicts at least five major facts:

1. The total number of close encounters far exceeds the requirements for a sophisticated survey of our planet.
2. The appearance of the UFO operators is overwhelmingly humanoid; they breathe our air and display recognizable emotions. Not only does this make an extraterrestrial origin very dubious, but it implies that the operators are not making use of genetic engineering to optimize a space mission, as interstellar travelers presumably would under the extraterrestrial hypothesis model.
3. The reports regarding abductions display behavioral patterns on the part of the operators that contradict the idea of scientific, medical, or genetic experiments. Simpler, more effective methods are already available in earth-based science to accomplish all the alleged objectives of these Aliens.
4. The patterns of close encounters, contacts, and abductions

are not specific to our century, contrary to what most American ufologists have assumed. In fact, it is difficult to find a culture that does *not* have a tradition of little people that fly through the sky and abduct humans. Often they take their victims into spherical settings that are evenly illuminated, and they subject them to various ordeals that include operations on internal organs and astral trips to unknown landscapes. Sexual or genetic interaction is a common theme in this body of folklore.

5. Both the UFOs and their operators are able to materialize and dematerialize on the spot and to penetrate physical obstacles. The objects are able to merge together and to change shape dynamically.

As an alternative to the extraterrestrial hypothesis, I propose to regard the UFO phenomenon as a physical manifestation of a form of consciousness that is alien to humans but is able to coexist with us on the earth.

When the object we call a UFO is visible to us in the reality of everyday life, I think it constitutes both a physical entity with mass, inertia, volume, and energy, and a window toward another mode of reality. In this alternative reality the witnesses describe psychic manifestations reminiscent of our own dreams. We can consider these reports as a source of important symbolic meaning, or we can ignore them. But like our dreams, they may also shape our lives in ways that we do not fully understand.

Purists will point out that this form of consciousness might very well be extraterrestrial. Indeed, if reality is no longer restricted to three axes of space and one axis of time, the Visitors could be from anywhere and any time. The fact remains that a strong symbolic relationship seems to have existed since the dawn of history between these Aliens and humans on the earth itself.

It is against this backdrop that the next three chapters should be read. They represent an attempt to take UFO research out of a passive mode and a few steps closer to the phenomenon it tries to study.

Chapter 10 reviews the characteristics of the beings seen in connection with UFO cases. Again, I have used only firsthand reports I have personally investigated at the site. The purpose of this chapter is to extract the essential characteristics that might make interaction possible.

Chapter 11 summarizes a remarkable cluster of cases in Happy Camp, California, where abductions had taken place and where a team of investigators tried to see the phenomenon.

Finally, chapter 12 is an account of another complex case, called Copper Medic, where we developed new instrumentation and attempted to catch the phenomenon in the act. From these efforts can be drawn some useful lessons for any future project involving an active response to the UFO mystery.

1. On a hilltop in Rio.

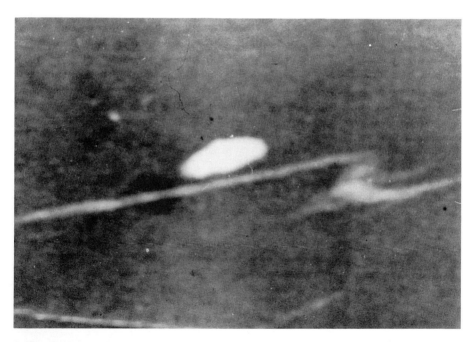

6. Mosquiero photo #1.

7. Mosquiero photo #2.

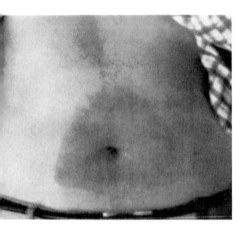

8. Skin discoloration, Dr. X case.

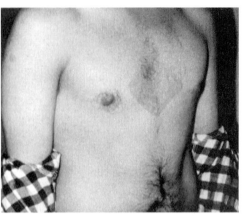

9. Skin discoloration, Texas case.

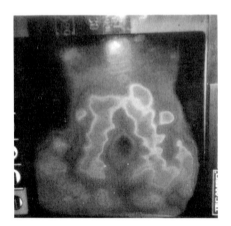

A. November 2, 1984.

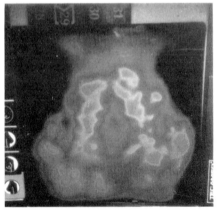

B. Same date, after cooling.

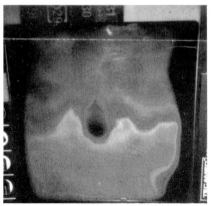

C. November 16, 1984.

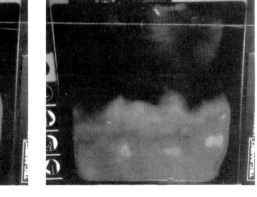

D. Same date, after cooling.

10. THERMOGRAPHY TESTS, DR. X CASE.

11. Happy Camp: the first being, based on witness reports (reconstruction by the author).

12. Happy Camp: the abduction site and the object, based on witness reports (reconstruction by the author).

13. Cosmo the fisherman.

14. Santana do Acurau.

15. The beach at Baia do Sol.

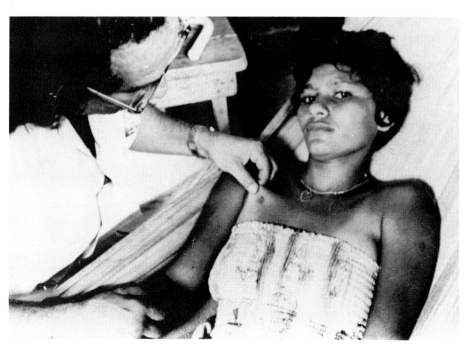

16. Typical wound from a beam.

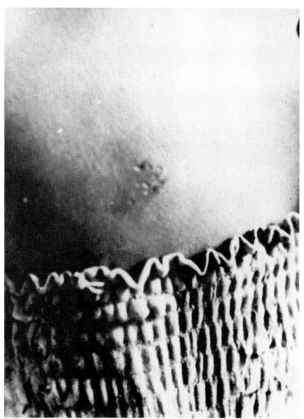

17. Close-up of the wound.

10

Visitor Profiles

It was a fine afternoon in late April or early May. A seventeen-year-old boy was driving along an unpaved country road about ten miles west of Yakima, Washington. The time was about 4:00 P.M.

As he reached the top of a slight rise, the teenager, Floyd Dillon, saw an object coming into view in the sky. It was about seventy-five feet off the ground and moved slowly. The object appeared to be a metallic hexagon with a domed top, olive drab in color, about twenty-two feet wide and seven feet high. Dillon could see rivets along a vertical section, and also a two-by-three-foot window set in a metallic frame. In that window he observed the head and upper torso of a man dressed in a dark blue uniform, who "would pass for an Italian in this world."

The object moved slowly but did not stop. The occupant looked intently in the direction of the car; then the object rotated, flew across the road, and abruptly went off at a "terrific speed."

I classify this report as a typical sighting in the MA3 category—

a maneuvering object with a being on board. (See the appendix for a description of the classification system I now use in this research.) There was no effect on the car, no sound or smell, no unusual taste. There was no physical evidence, no change of color in the object, no static electricity, no lights of any sort.

The really remarkable thing about this case is the date: the event took place in 1928. The car was a Model T Ford.

In his letter to me dated April 6, 1978, the witness insisted that he "was not on booze or dope"; he did not even smoke cigarettes. He added that he "wasn't a bit afraid of the ship." And he stated his personal beliefs as follows:

> I've always been interested in astronomy ever since I was a small boy of nine or ten. I believe that there are many planets in the universe that support life. . . .
>
> I didn't mention [the sighting] to anybody until about twenty years ago. . . . People just don't believe anything that they don't understand.
>
> It happened fifty years ago just about this time of year. I'm sixty-seven now. I don't expect you or anyone to believe this story. But it is the absolute truth.

A month later I made the four-hour drive to Redding, where Mr. Dillon lived in a mobile home that we found exceptionally clean and well kept. He told us his story again, stating that he had not seen anything like that object since. He was able to pinpoint the location on the U.S. Geological Survey map of the area I had brought with me, easily recognizing the terrain and the road. It is the same road, although it is now surfaced.

In response to my questions, Mr. Dillon stated that at the time of the sighting he was finishing high school. He also picked fruit and made boxes to earn additional income. On that particular day he was driving from a school in Yakima to his home in Weibel, where his father was manager of a plant.

From 1922 to 1941 the witness lived in the state of Washington, working in canneries and warehouses. He also did construction work for the highway department. He enlisted when World War II

148

started, serving in the 9th Armored Division in England, France, and Czechoslovakia; he was at the Battle of the Bulge. After 1945 he was employed by McDonnell Douglas for twenty-two years as a machine tool operator in Los Angeles. He eventually retired to Redding.

Mr. Dillon, who was very calm throughout our discussion, displayed an active, curious intelligence and a willingness to consider various theories about what he had seen, although he has accepted the idea that the "man" he saw came from another planet. He believes that the occupant stared at him while inspecting the landscape. The craft was swinging silently as it followed the terrain, passing over the road and to the right of Dillon. There was nothing remarkable about the underside of the object; it was rounded and smooth. The witness is adamant that he saw a number of rivets at the edge of each side of the craft. He is not surprised at this rather "crude" technology, although at the time, naturally, the machine appeared ultramodern to him.

At my request, Mr. Dillon drew the object and also the being he saw, a perfectly human character with normal hair parted in the center. The man seen by Dillon, who "could have passed for an Italian," does not match the extraterrestrial stereotype, the bald-headed, bug-eyed dwarf popularized in recent American books and movies.

Neither does another remarkable case I investigated in northern California with researcher Mark Uriarte, who had learned of it through a telephone conversation with the Colusa (California) sheriff's department. The officers stressed the reputations of reliability of the witnesses. We visited the site within three weeks of the sighting, while the details were still fresh in the minds of all concerned.

The close encounter had taken place in an area initially developed by ranchers and farmers who hoped to grow various crops. Unfortunately, it proved worthless for cultivation, so that the local properties were gradually abandoned. It is in such an old ranch that the two main witnesses live. They are brothers, descendants of an almost extinct tribe of local Indians, the Cortina tribe, whose language is derived from that of the Digger Indians. I was told that only seven Cortina Indians still survive. The elder brother, Amos, was in his early sixties.

We found the old ranch well kept, with a main cabin that had no water or electricity but was clean. It was heated by a wood stove. The two brothers made a living by hiring themselves out as ranch hands to neighboring farmers. They had two horses and raised some chickens of their own.

The case became known when Amos confided in broken English to a local farmer that every summer for the last few years he had seen a strange "airplane" land on the ranch. Furthermore, a small human-looking occupant would come out of this airplane and enter the cabin. "They probably would be back tonight," Amos stated. Curious, the farmer watched the sky and he did see a luminous object come from the east, stop in midair, turn to the north, and disappear. Amos later reported that he had seen the "stranger" about 3:00 A.M., after his neighbor had gone home.

We asked Amos to draw the object for us, and we compared the sketch with one he had produced for Mark some days earlier. The differences were minor. Amos also drew the creature and told us more about him: The "little stranger" is always alone. He measures three and one-half to four feet and wears a one-piece brown suit. He gives off a bad smell. The drawing by Amos shows a humanoid with long hair and a large nose, no mask or respiratory device. A most remarkable feature of this being is his ability to go through the walls of the cabin and to hover above the floor without touching it. When seen outside, he is capable of darting away suddenly without actually walking.

Amos does not like the little stranger who visits him during the summer months. In fact, he would like to get rid of him. When he is around the horses go wild and it is hard to hunt the next day, he says, because all the animals go into hiding.

We observed no unusual burns or indentations at the site where the object was said to land. We found only bundles of fibers a number of donut-shaped circular patterns, unlike those an animal would produce, and some definite areas of twisted grass.

On October 18, 1977, shortly after 1:30 A.M., an investigator friend of mine was returning from a visit to Amos with the neighbor to whom the case had been reported. They saw a bright light approaching from the south. They stopped their truck but could hear no sound, even when the engine was turned off. The object flew to the right and my friend prepared his camera, but he experienced a peculiar thought that to film it would just be a waste of time. Instead, he looked at it through binoculars: he saw four square lights on what appeared to be a fuselage, without wings or tail. The light was bluish-green. To this day, my friend regrets having obeyed the bizarre impulse to put down his camera.

The lesson we must draw from such cases is a straightforward one: the UFO entities do not follow a simple pattern, as many ufologists would like us to believe. They are not always gray beings with bald heads and large eyes, or robot-like monsters. Instead, we are facing a complex phenomenon, and we do not understand its relationship to the witnesses and to human society at large. We do not know how much of the event is generated by an external phenomenon and how much is supplied by the human mind. We should acknowledge this complexity.

In 1980 William Sambrot, a science fiction author, wrote to me after reading *Messengers of Deception*. In May 1962 he had published in *Playboy* a short story entitled "Control Somnambule." It was pure fiction:

> about an astronaut on our first sub-lunar flight whose signals unaccountably disappear from all monitors. Hours later they just as mysteriously resume. When he returns to earth he is puzzled to learn that there had been such a hiatus . . . he is put under deep hypnosis and discloses that he'd been kidnapped by aliens, taken aboard a flying saucer, given a complete physiological exam inside and out and then returned to his capsule, after having first been given a command to forget the entire incident.

151

Since the story had been written over a year before, it clearly antedated the abduction of Betty and Barney Hill and their subsequent hypnosis. In their later correspondence, Sambrot and the editors of *Look* magazine, who had published the Hill case, expressed their mutual puzzlement. Remarkably, Sambrot's astronaut had been given a series of geometric tattoos during his abduction by the UFO operators; the story anticipated both the Hill case and the experiences of Dr. X (see chapter 8).

It would be nice to be able to follow the skeptics who, like aerospace writer Philip Klass, have already jumped to the conclusion that all close encounters are imaginary. After reading the testimony of Sambrot, one is tempted to ascribe great power to the creativity of the human mind. Yet that theory does not fully explain the facts, either. It does not account for the traces, the injuries, the photographs.

Ten years before Whitley Strieber's blockbuster books became national nonfiction best-sellers, a Cortina Indian in California had described in poor English a small being who glided along the ground and came into his home by going through the walls. Yet the entity did not look like the wise, benign being on the cover of *Communion*. Instead, he had a prominent nose and long hair.

I believe these observations by clearly sincere witnesses cannot be understood in the everyday reality that both the ufologists and the skeptics have taken as their standard. It is time to accept the fact that the UFO phenomenon is able to act upon the minds of human beings, to induce thoughts and images that are similar to those described by people who have had near-death or out-of-body experiences and even to medieval witnesses of demons and elves. While the UFO research community has embraced literal interpretations of the close encounter and abduction cases, and has run into a massive brick wall in the process, the vast amount of information that exists on psychic realities experienced at death or during certain altered states has rarely been examined in this context. Yet these psychic realities are just as real as the reality of the everyday investigator who is looking for a flying saucer in hopes of "kicking the tires," as a San Francisco ufologist of the nuts-and-bolts persuasion once described to me as his lifelong ambition.

The next two cases may help to illustrate this point for most of my readers, although I have given up explaining to the UFO enthusiasts that there was such a thing as psychic reality and that it did not contradict the physical world. But then, there are still many people who have never accepted the fact that light has both the nature of a wave and the nature of a particle.

It is one of the wonders of human existence that a person can live a long and happy life without once becoming aware of the reality of consciousness and its ability to transcend the immediate physical level. At the instant of death, will time suspend its rule long enough for such people to realize what they have missed?

Any active measure directed at interaction with the UFO phenomenon will have to take into consideration its ability to take control of the witnesses' perceptions and to alter their psychic reality.

Within a three-week period in September 1978 there were four dramatic UFO cases in Venado Tuerto, a small town three hours south of Rosario, Argentina. In the first case, a young carpenter named Alberto saw seven objects and two beings on the ground. In the second case, a twelve-year-old boy named Oscar saw three objects and went inside one of them, interacting with a very tall man and a small robot. In the third case, a sixteen-year-old baker named Francisco felt intense heat from a luminous object during a blackout of the local transformer. And in the fourth incident, a fifty-three-year-old man who was driving at night was "teleported" over four miles and had to be admitted to a local clinic for chest pains.

When I went to Venado Tuerto in April 1980, I found a rural area of very flat land with some modern estancias, many swamps, and lagoons. We met with several members of CIC, an Argentine investigation group, who, with Fabio Zerpa and his wife, took us to the actual site of the boy's sighting. The following is a summary of their excellent report.

On September 6, 1978, Oscar was sent to gather a herd of horses as he usually did in the morning. Riding his gentle horse Cometa through the fog, he felt something fly overhead and saw an object arrive from the south, another from the west, a third from the east. They started dancing, emitting powerful lights of changing color.

The boy lost control of Cometa; his horse bolted and galloped madly toward the wire fence, where Oscar barely managed to stop it. His father, Don Felipe, scolded him for not bringing back the other horses. "Father," he said, "in the field I found a big, round thing."

The father did not want excuses, and he sent the boy back into the fog. There Oscar found one of the objects on the ground. Cometa became nervous again; the herd ran madly in all directions. The object was about thirty feet in diameter, fifteen feet high, ending in a half-sphere dome with several round windows. A door opened and a ladder unfolded to the ground. A being appeared in the opening. He was over seven feet tall and was wearing long gloves and a cylindrical helmet.

This being, who seemed to be tethered to a breathing apparatus linking it to the object, invited Oscar to come inside. Bravely, the boy tied the reins of his horse to the ladder, climbed up, and stood next to the "giant." From this position he was able to describe the ship's interior, with a panel of buttons, tables, and a small "robot" occupied with cutting into pieces the large bones of some animals, similar to horses or cattle.

Impressed and a little scared by what he saw, he jumped back down from the object to the field. The tall being joined him, and Oscar asked him for one of his gloves as proof of the experience. When the giant complied, the boy observed that his hand was green, with the middle finger shorter than the others, the nails like conical dark blue metallic claws. With one of these claws the being pricked the boy's right arm near the shoulder; it felt like a mosquito bite.

But when Oscar, carrying the huge, heavy glove, rode toward the estancia, two flying craft caught up with him and emitted a small slab and a sphere that joined together in the air, brushing against the horse and pulling off the glove like a magnet.

Oscar's family showed very little interest in his breathless story, although Don Felipe admitted to having heard a "strange humming sound, like the flame of a torch moving rapidly through the air." The parents also reported that during the following days the boy had no appetite and frequently woke up at night screaming. According to Oscar, "I dreamed I was inside the saucer and they took me and did things to me."

At the spot on Oscar's arm where the giant had pricked him a small line developed, two inches long. It started itching that night, and he washed it with water and soap. Two or three days later the ends healed, and he was left with a small depression in his skin. In addition to this mark he experienced a series of spots resembling psoriasis, which were thought to be "of nervous origin."

Six days prior to the sighting, Oscar's father had found a dead cow on the property; the hindquarter and the ribs were missing. This was very puzzling to him. He told the investigators from CIC, "If it had been thieves, they also would have taken the hide."

When we met Oscar he struck us immediately as a quiet, serious child; he was very reserved at first but warmed up to us and told his story soberly. We were impressed by the feeling of profound dignity that came from both the son and the father, one of the last men in the area to dress in the traditional garb of the proud gauchos, with a wide leather belt encrusted with gold coins. The family is descended from a race of white Indians who go back to the Incas, and Oscar's face shows remarkable Inca features.

We inquired about the horse. After the incident, Cometa had become very shortsighted and eventually died. During the event the horse had tried to kick the ladder of the craft, suffering an injury on the back left leg.

Oscar repeated before us that he had seen three objects, with lights that changed rapidly: green, red, yellow. "My eyes started getting cloudy."

The time of the sighting is estimated at 6:45 A.M., but this is only an approximation for the simple reason that nobody on the estancia wears a watch, as we were able to verify.

After these initial interviews we went over to the site itself, an immense flat plain rolling to infinity. The entire area has a kind of quiet, tragic beauty and an uncertain future; every year the lakes and the lagoons are gaining on the land. Nobody seems to know where the water is coming from. Entire villages have already been submerged, and in places the road to Rosario is a mere levee with wide lakes on both sides. Here and there one can see the top floors of old houses and formerly proud hotels emerging from the gray waters.

The family lives on a forty-hectare farm that was given to them by the previous owner of the estancia in his will. They grow corn, wheat, and soya. The family members are very close and obviously happy together. They did not have a television set at the time of the sighting.

Walking quietly across the field, Oscar reconstructed for us in a simple, direct way the dimensions of the object, the position of his horse, the gestures of the beings.

After we left the site we reviewed reports written by Oscar's schoolteacher and by a clinical psychologist who had examined the boy, administering a Rorschach test to him. The teacher described Oscar as a normal child who paid little attention in school but behaved well. "He likes to talk of life outside the school, when he is out in the field; he likes horse riding; he loves nature. He talks about the real, the everyday, what happens in his home, but no fantasies. In class he never showed any imagination. . . . He is very honest and tells the truth. . . . He is not an imaginative child."

The clinical psychologist noted that the Rorschach responses often related to "saucer" and "rocket," a fact he interpreted as an echo of the boy's experiences. He added, "Oscar's intelligence was observed to be of the logical-concrete type with great difficulties to pass on to the logical-formal period, possibly due to the limited stimulus he has had . . . in a restricted rural environment." It is noteworthy that hypnosis was not used in this case and that all recall by the witness comes from conscious memory.

A remarkable series of events happened in Venado Tuerto. In

addition to Oscar's experience, three other independent close encounters took place, one of them involving an abnormal power failure that was verified by utility personnel.

A flying hexagon piloted by an Italian-looking man near Yakima in 1928, a hairy dwarf with a big nose who flies through walls in California, and an extraordinary encounter in a remote region of Argentina with a giant and a small robot: all firsthand cases for which I have no explanation. The witnesses are sober, sincere individuals who are not seeking publicity or financial gain from their experiences. Nothing in their lives indicates a pattern of unusual incidents or even an interest in the paranormal. None of these cases have been reported to the media.

A skeptic is entitled to the opinion that all of these people were lying or hallucinating, but I do not believe this explanation. Neither do I believe the literal interpretation of the UFO enthusiasts, according to which the various beings seen by the witnesses should be automatically regarded as interplanetary visitors.

At close range, the UFO phenomenon acts as a *reality transformer* (or, in Bertrand Meheust's words, a *reality exchanger*), triggering for the witness a series of symbolic displays that are indistinguishable from reality. These displays, which frequently begin with a bewildering series of blinking colored lights of extraordinary intensity, induce a state of intense confusion for the subjects who are vulnerable to the insertion of new thoughts and new visual experiences.

The response of the ufologists to the confusion of the abductees has been disastrous. By taking the symbolic displays at face value, and by hypnotizing the witnesses in an effort to dispel their confusion, many well-meaning researchers have actually reinforced the alternative reality induced by the UFO sighting, thus exacerbating what may be a spurious side effect and losing sight of the main experience. Hypnosis, which could be a very useful exploratory technique, unfortunately has become a fanatical obsession with American UFO researchers today. In the process, investigators untrained in clinical hypnosis have undoubtedly created false memories in their subjects in response to leading questions and subtle cues. These false memories may satisfy the ufologists' craving for a simple, factual explanation of the reality of UFOs as interplanetary spacecraft, but they are only spurious results. The process may be harmful to the witnesses, who are artificially forcing the UFO experience into an impossible integration with conscious memory, wedging the round peg of extraterrestrial visitation into the square hole of their confusion. As one disgusted UFO witness wrote to me:

> You're right to warn people about the dangers of manipulation. . . . Abduction victims are extremely vulnerable to one-on-one manipulation that can amount to almost total control of the individual. Humans are picking up on the control of individuals where the aliens left off.

I know of several witnesses who have been hypnotized again and again, sometimes in front of other "abductees." They become unable to distinguish between reality and dream, and get carried away into a realm where their own fantasies and private terrors are actually encouraged to overlay the confusing, traumatic UFO encounter. The precarious state of well-being that is created in this fashion is dangerous and deceptive.

The belief pattern that has been created around the UFO abductions is reminiscent of medieval theories of abduction by demons, pacts with Satan, and flights to the Sabbat, complete with the Mark of the Devil on the body of the witch. As French sociologist Pierre Lagrange has pointed out to me, the only missing element is the familiar—the black cat or the owl that used to accompany the witches!

Hypnotic regression of abductees is not the sort of active measure we need. Instead, we should recognize the UFO as a reality transformer, and we should carefully scrutinize the symbolic process it induces in the subject's consciousness. When it is used carefully by a professional trained in its use, hypnosis can provide some valuable insights into the experience, but it does not explain it.

In 1978 I had the opportunity to meet another witness whose

ordeal sheds some light on the whole issue of abductions and of the nature of the beings associated with them. It also sheds light on the blatantly unethical and unprofessional behavior of some of the scientists who have been charged with an assessment of the phenomenon.

On December 3, 1967, Sgt. Herbert Schirmer was on patrol near Ashland, Nebraska, at 2:30 A.M.—a clear, moonless night—when he saw some red lights that he thought were on a truck. When he checked the location, however, he noticed that the lights came from the windows of a saucer-shaped object hovering above the highway. His next conscious recall is of the craft glowing brilliantly and rising with a sirenlike sound while emitting a flame-colored material from its underside. He had a feeling of paralysis at the time and was nervous, weak, and sick when he returned to his office.

Dr. Leo Sprinkle of the University of Wyoming was one of the first professional psychologists to take an interest in UFO abductions and to use hypnosis as an investigative tool. When he met with members of the Condon committee, who had been funded by the U.S. Air Force at the University of Colorado in 1968, he reviewed with them a number of cases that could be used for demonstration. The committee selected the Schirmer case because of the loss of time experienced by the witness.

When Sergeant Schirmer arrived in Boulder for a series of psychological tests, he asked to see Professor Condon; he had been induced to make the trip because of its potential scientific significance. He had been assured that serious interest existed in his sighting and that Professor Edward Condon, the well-known physicist, would attend the session in person.

Unfortunately, Dr. Condon was not on campus at the time, and the scientific committee realized that the trick they had used to get the officer to come and to be tested threatened to be exposed. So, Sergeant Schirmer told me, they introduced someone else to him as Professor Condon.

Schirmer was no fool. During the ensuing conversation somebody came into the room and addressed "Professor Condon" by a

159

first name which had no resemblance to Ed or Edward. Schirmer confronted the scientist. "You're not Condon!" he cried, and a very embarrassing scene followed.

From that point on, the credibility of the University of Colorado project was very close to nil in the eyes of the witness. When he was shown inkblots and was asked to say what he saw there, he stated the obvious: he saw inkblots.

"Well, can't you imagine that they are something else?" asked one of the psychologists.

"Doctor, I'm a law enforcement officer," Schirmer replied. "I'm not supposed to imagine things. I am trained to report on things that are real."

Schirmer told me he was afraid that if he started seeing butterflies or copulating elephants in inkblots, the scientists would quickly conclude that here was a nut case who could just as easily see flying saucers where there was only a cluster of clouds.

During our meeting I asked Sergeant Schirmer directly about any health effects he might have suffered as a result of the UFO encounter.

At the time of the experience the witness felt a "tingling" in his body for a few seconds and local pain behind the base of the ear (he showed me the precise location), as if a needle had been inserted there. A red welt with tiny holes developed at that spot. For three years after the sighting he experienced throbbing headaches that lasted two hours and were not alleviated by aspirin. For the first three weeks following the sighting these headaches would actually wake him up.

I also inquired about his dreams, and I learned that they included a vision of a landscape with three mountain ranges, strange domes, and UFOs.

Dr. Sprinkle noted that after the sighting the witness drank two cups of hot, steaming coffee "like it was water"; he often experienced a "ringing, numbness and buzzing in his ears before going to sleep, and other violent disturbances during his sleep."[1]

Sergeant Schirmer presented me with a detailed pencil drawing of one of the "operators" of the craft as he remembered him under hypnosis. It shows a stern-looking man with a piece of dark clothing covering the head. The opening for the face has an ogival shape that gives it a very Gothic appearance. The forehead is wrinkled. The eyes, nose, mouth, and eyebrows are of normal size, although the pupils are enlarged and elongated, giving the eyes a penetrating, fascinated look. Over the left ear there is a small round device with a short antenna, less than two inches long. And over the right shoulder is a patch insignia representing a winged serpent.

Schirmer recalled being taken out of the patrol car, unable to use his radio or his gun. He was given a tour of the saucer. The operator asked him, "Are you the watchman over this place?" And when they reached the top of the craft the man told Schirmer, "Watchman, some day you will see the Universe!"

At the time of our meeting, many years after the event, his dialogue with the operator stood out as the most significant event in Schirmer's life.

UFO encounters are complete frameworks into which the personality of the witness becomes projected. Like a movie that terrifies you, makes you cry, laugh, or perspire in anguish, the experience becomes part of the witness's reality. The ufologists behave like social researchers who, trying to understand the phenomenon of the cinema, would randomly interview people coming out of theatres and take their testimony at face value; like the UFO witnesses, these people are not lying. Some of them have seen Godzilla, others have seen Bambi. The experience, in every case, was real to them.

But the reality we should inquire about, the reality UFO researchers are often ignoring, is the movie projector high up in a small, dark, locked room near the ceiling. In that room is the technology that will give you both Bambi *and* Godzilla, *Star Wars* and, yes, even *Close Encounters.*

Like the technology of the cinema, the UFO technology is a metasystem. It generates whatever phenomena are appropriate at our level, at a given epoch, in a given state of the "market."

As Bertrand Meheust has brilliantly proven, the symbolic display seen by the abductees is identical to the type of initiation ritual or astral voyage that is embedded in the traditions of every culture.[2] In that sense, the UFO experience is a very real trigger that releases powerful imagery we are all carrying in our "collective unconscious" (in Jungian terms). It is useless to ask why some witnesses see giants and others see dwarfs, why some abductions are benign and some are harmful, why some encounter victims are shown sophisticated technology, while others report rapes and other indignities.

While our fellow ufologists are clustering on the sidewalk interviewing moviegoers, I think the real questions are elsewhere. My own research takes me up the back stairs where nobody goes. My goal is to pick the lock of the projectionist's secret little booth, to discover at last what makes the reels turn and the machine tick.

11

Happy Camp

Rarely does one find a single, genuine episode in which all the facets of the UFO phenomenon are concentrated. I have decided to devote a whole chapter to the Happy Camp case because it constitutes a veritable laboratory of the problems we face, and it provided me with a direct, although very brief, experience of the phenomenon. It also presents an interesting case of multiple abduction.

Happy Camp is a small lumber town at the northern border of California, about forty miles from Oregon. A single road, running east to west, goes through the town, seventy miles from the main expressway that connects the two states. The town has one bar and one cafe. It is nestled in a magnificent site of mountain streams, pine and redwood forests, and steep canyons.[1] Lumber mills provide the primary source of employment. Most of the UFO witnesses work for the mills, directly or indirectly. There are many Indians in the area. It is also useful to know that the major form of transportation is the four-wheel-drive pickup truck. Local people communicate with CB radios and generally carry rifles in their vehicles.[2]

I first heard of the case in late 1975 through four separate sources, including a local representative of the Mutual UFO Network (MUFON) who had visited the site. Subsequently, interest rose to the point where several reasonably factual articles appeared about the case in the San Francisco papers. However, the investigators continued to suspect that some of the witnesses had never revealed the whole story. In mid-1978, when general interest in the events had died down and Happy Camp had returned to a routine existence, I packed my gear into my Cheyenne and made the all-day trip to the region. Three experienced investigators—Paul Cerny, Tom Gates, and Mark Uriarte—made the journey with me. We reviewed the known facts of the case.

On October 25, 1975, two lumber mill electricians, Stan Gayer (then nineteen) and Steve Harris (twenty-six), were in their truck in the area of Shivar Saddle and were testing their CB radios when they saw two starlike objects of unusual brightness. One of the objects suddenly moved over the ridge and oscillated in a surging motion "as if fighting the wind." It came down toward them "like the lit end of a cigar," glowing red. They drove away and later saw a large, red, glowing object on the ground on the side of Cade Mountain.

Two days later they returned to the site with a third man, a twenty-nine-year-old master mechanic who describes himself as an "interested skeptic." They were equipped with a metal detector and a spotlight. Being practical mountain men, they had explored the area and found a pile of strange micalike material at the site of the first landing and they expected to discover additional traces. The mica, when analyzed, turned out to be common isinglass of the type used in old woodstoves.

What they did not expect was a set of glowing silvery eyes in the bushes and a sirenlike sound. Turning the spotlight on the area they could see nothing at all, only darkness where trees and bushes should have been. At that point, they felt it was prudent to get back

164

into their pickup and return to town, where they told their story to a seventeen-year-old student and to Helen White, who became a central protagonist in the subsequent events.

At the time of the sightings, Helen White was sixty-two. She had lived in Happy Camp since 1949 and had worked at the mill for nineteen years. One reporter described her adequately as having "specs, kindly eyes, and a bundle of gray hair that makes her the perfect picture of the grandma she happens to be."

It was this group of five widely different individuals who drove back up into the mountains. Reaching the site where they had seen the eyes, Steve Harris became somewhat agitated. Whether in frustration or to impress the others, he started firing at random into the underbrush, a somewhat unconventional way to investigate unknown phenomena. While I would not approve of this method, I must admit it could have been effective in flushing out any hoaxers or joking outsiders lurking among the madrone and manzanita.

Instead of jokers or hoaxers, the five witnesses saw two silhouettes wearing helmets like a welder and surrounded by a peculiar light. The sirenlike sound was heard again. Helen White, who had brought her camera, was unable to take a picture.

The eerie luminescent creatures approached within fifty feet of the group. They felt a strange warmth in the air. Steve recalls choking as if the air were too heavy to breathe, "like in a sauna or steam bath where the air is heated up, only much worse." Helen White compared it to having pressure on the chest. Steve thought they had been gassed. The group retreated in panic, chased down the mountain by a glowing red object.

The main event took place five days later, on November 2, 1975, when the same principals (Steve, Stan, and Helen) and two other people drove down a dirt trail into the canyon at the base of Cade Mountain. They were still trying to find an explanation for what they had seen earlier, and they explored the area in more or less systematic fashion.

In the canyon, however, they found an area of heavy fog that forced them to turn back, and they became very confused about subsequent events. They remember heavy boulders falling off the cliffs and bouncing around the truck. They remember the door locks being opened and a strange being telling Steve "you won't need that" when he reached for his gun. They believe they saw a hovering object. Helen recalls being lifted inside a room, but she is confused about the time sequence. One occupant had a dialogue with her, in the course of which he described a transparent object as being made of gold. Helen answered that she knew what gold was like, and it surely was not transparent. The being answered simply, "There is such a thing as gold that you can look through. It's in your Bible."[3] Steve thinks he was in a craft with a transparent window on top and bottom, through which he was able to see China Mountain.

Their next conscious memory is of driving down the mountain, singing a chorus of an old church song. I find it interesting that the hymn they were singing was "There Is Power in the Blood of the Lamb."

After this major incident, sightings were made throughout the area by various witnesses, up to the time of our site visit. These incidents include other episodes of strange fog with a humanoid shape inside, high-pitched sounds so piercing that they hurt the witnesses, and various kinds of spherical or oblong objects flying over the town, sometimes with an Air Force jet in hot pursuit.

On February 8, 1976, two of my investigator friends were in Happy Camp taking testimony from witnesses when they heard someone on the CB reporting an orange light over Slater Butte. They observed the light over the ridge, going up and down twice. The object was a brilliant, deep orange and its glow reminded them of "a forest fire behind a hill."

In the fall of 1977 two people on Benjamin Creek Road saw a Douglas fir being snapped in two while an unknown force dragged their pickup in reverse around a bend for fifty feet. The top eighty feet of the large fir tree was thrown about sixty feet away, while a glowing white sphere moved over the area. One of the witnesses, deeply upset by the incident, refuses to return to the spot.

166

My friends and I arrived in Happy Camp on Friday, June 2ふ 1978, and took our quarters at the appropriately named Rustic Inn. Although I am familiar with the back roads of California, from the Mojave Desert to Yolla Bolly and the Mendocino Coast, I have to say that the beauty of the Klamath River region, which combines rugged precipices with soft, gentle brush and majestic forests, just takes one's breath away.

We had dinner at the town's only eating establishment, Lois's Cafe. Several of the local witnesses came to our table and introduced themselves. We met Lorraine, who in the company of her daughter had seen a disk-shaped craft on September 6, 1977. "It was lit all the way around," Lorraine said.

We were joined by Pat, a cheerful woman in her forties who was puzzled by a series of poltergeist events at the time of the sightings. One night she heard heavy footsteps on the roof. Another night she observed a huge bird flying low in the glow of a streetlight. On July 17, 1977, she saw a sphere of light near her bed and in the morning she discovered that all the doors in the house were open.

Over the next two days we inspected the entire area, including the Douglas fir on Benjamin Creek Road. Loggers had lost no time in cutting down the good part of the tree at ground level. The top section, however, was still resting in a ravine across the road. The night of the incident had been quiet, with no thunderstorm or violent weather.

We also visited the abduction site itself, taking the dirt road that leads into the canyon. There is indeed a sharp cliff on the west side, from which boulders can fall on the road and the area below. At the site Mark discovered silvery strands of very strong hairlike material, similar to the fibers we had found in Colusa (see chapter 10). Identical fibers were also present at a third close encounter site in Happy Camp. Although our hopes were high that we had hit on a common element in cases involving entities, subsequent microscopic inspection, which I entrusted to a forensic laboratory, revealed that the material was not unusual.[4]

The disk-shaped object seen by Helen, Stan, and Steve had hovered over bushes near a sharp turn in the road. At this site, as in many other locations we visited, there was in evidence a strong element of violence that clashed with the almost pristine beauty of the forest. There were spent shells in the grass, and many road signs had been shot so full of holes that they were unreadable. We were left to wonder about the frustrations and the need for power over nature that made such violence necessary. Perhaps it was due to the very scale of the landscape, the cliffs, the narrow gorges, the immense sky; man can easily feel boxed in, insignificant. If this interpretation is correct, then it is relevant to the terror and the fascination induced by the UFO sightings and by the confrontations with tall beings that did not seem to fear Steve's large-caliber rifle. It is also relevant that the surrounding mountains have been a source of numerous reports of a large apelike creature similar to the Canadian Sasquatch. There are also local legends about the Puduwan, strange beings with paranormal powers.

The witnesses we interviewed at length confessed to us that there were many unreported incidents. The very first sighting in the area had been made by a law enforcement officer named Dick McIntyre, who later retracted his report and denied everything. Most witnesses decided to shut up, we were told, after the publication of a full-page article about Happy Camp by the *San Francisco Chronicle*. Several highway patrolmen have been followed by strange lights in the area but have made no official report.

Among other previously undisclosed cases was a sighting by Lorraine's son of a large glowing object, steel blue in color, with a red light on it. Smaller objects were "darting" all around it, in a manner reminiscent of the "cloud cigar" sightings documented by Aimé Michel.

We met with Helen White and had the opportunity to talk with her at leisure while watching a Little League baseball game in which her grandson was playing. She filled in the details of the incidents in which she participated, confirming or qualifying many of the reported observations. She did stress that, at the time of the abduction, "everything seemed to happen in slow motion."

Other aspects of the episode bothered her because they did not seem to make sense. During the abduction she spoke to a man wearing a long, floating coat. An avalanche of rocks was falling. "Watch out for those boulders!" she cautioned the man. "Don't worry, they won't hurt me," was the answer. She felt herself bathed in light as she rose into the object. She wanted to take something away as proof and was given permission; yet later the beings forbade her to keep anything, and she wailed at them in frustration, "You lied to me."

The most puzzling fact in the experience was the size of the object. As in the case of Mrs. Victor (described in chapter 6), the craft into which Helen White was abducted was much larger inside than outside.

Although aeronautical engineers will scoff at this bizarre remark, the topologists among my readers may be as intrigued as I was by the possible interpretations it opened. If there are more than four dimensions, as many theoretical physicists now suspect, it may be interesting to speculate: a hypercraft capable of topological inversion into our spacetime continuum could indeed be larger on the inside than on the outside.

That evening we transferred into our truck the equipment brought up from San Francisco by Tom Gates and Paul Cerny, and drove up to the site itself, stopping first at the Saddle, then up to the highest point at the end of the trail before returning.

It was 11:15 P.M. when we saw it. It was just a very bright light, white with a tinge of red, and it lasted no more than ten seconds. The light was straight ahead, several miles away across the valley, on the slope of China Peak, at a site where no vehicle would likely be. But the sighting was too brief for us to stop and set up Tom's telescope. The light remained a puzzling footnote to our investigation.

The Happy Camp events encompass abductions, suffocating fog, large birds, small beings with welder helmets, chases by jets, poltergeists, gravity anomalies, and broken trees. Coming from an isolated town that does not even have a movie house, this concentration of cases is remarkable. But it would not be complete without its own Man in Black episode.

Thus I was almost relieved to learn how, early in 1976, a stranger who had never been seen in town happened to stroll into Lois's Cafe. Helen and Pat were there, quietly having dinner at different tables.

All conversation stopped when the man came in. He ordered a steak dinner but proved unable to use a knife and fork, and eventually left without paying, a sure way to be remembered by the local people. Pat told me that he had pale skin and "oriental" eyes. He wore a bizarre sort of shirt and no coat, although it was the middle of winter. He smiled constantly at people in a strange, forced grimace. Among the peculiar things he did during his extraordinary dinner was a brave attempt to drink Jell-O out of his glass.

THE ABDUCTION QUAGMIRE

Helen White's account is an illustration of the abduction reports that have come to dominate the study of UFOs in recent years. Starting with the Hill case of 1961, researchers have frequently noticed that UFO witnesses failed to remember some key features about their sighting and even experienced amnesia between the moment when they had their close encounter and their return to normal reality. The missing period was measured in hours or even days.

To many investigators, hypnosis appeared as an ideal tool for the recovery of missing memories. Indeed, whenever it was applied to the UFO abduction cases it opened the floodgates to a veritable torrent of new material. Not only did witnesses suddenly describe in great detail the inside of the UFOs, but they gave precise data about the occupants, their behavior, their actions, and the dialogue with them. In some celebrated cases this interaction seemed to continue beyond the sighting itself.

When Dr. Andrija Puharich hypnotized Uri Geller, he claimed to recover not only information about an extraterrestrial civilization called Hoova but an entire plan that involved Geller, Puharich, and many others in a grandiose psychic plan for the conditioning of the earth.[5]

More mundane, but more reliable, is the data retrieved from their subjects by two assiduous researchers: Wyoming psychologist Leo Sprinkle and New York City artist Budd Hopkins, who has published two books on the subject. Both are strongly convinced that the phenomenon is due to the intervention of extraterrestrial visitors.

Sprinkle and Hopkins, who separately have performed hypnotic regressions on several hundred abductees, find somewhat different patterns in their data. The aliens reported by Sprinkle's patients tend to be helpful and benevolent. Those reported by Hopkins, on the contrary, are sinister and even sadistic, performing outrageous operations on the bodies of their victims, especially women. Fetuses are removed, needles are inserted in helpless bodies, devices are implanted for future tracking. Both Sprinkle and Hopkins are convinced that such operations, bizarre as they may seem, are necessary for the aliens to pursue their systematic program of scientific analysis of our planet.

In recent years Sprinkle and Hopkins have been joined by other researchers who have used hypnosis specifically to perform regressions of abductees. Among them is Dr. David Jacobs, a history professor at Temple University. Another prominent researcher who has been using similar techniques since the Sixties is Dr. James Harder, an engineering professor at the University of California at Berkeley.

The growing body of information retrieved from the minds of abductees has been tabulated statistically by Thomas Bullard under a grant from the Fund for UFO Research.[6] It has been found to be exceptionally consistent and robust, a fact cited by most UFO researchers today as evidence that we are indeed visited by aliens from outer space. Only a few exceptional cases do not seem to fit. For example, the experiences of Whitley Strieber, as described in his best-selling books *Communion* and *Transformation*, do not follow the standard template.[7] Neither do numerous cases of interaction with entities that do not entail medical examination or space travel.

Such discrepancies have created a new cleavage among ufologists. The majority follow Sprinkle, Hopkins, and Jacobs, although they do not necessarily buy all their conclusions, while a minority questions the validity of the hypnosis technique and the preconceptions that seem to propel the whole research into the extraterrestrial framework. Given the high level of expectation that is created by numerous books and television programs in the minds of witnesses who suspect they have been abducted, perhaps it is not surprising that a majority of them do "recall" highly structured situations and similar beings.

Lurking in the background are two other relevant thoughts. First, a very creative series of experiments conducted by Alvin Lawson and several hypnotists in Los Angeles has shown (under admittedly contrived conditions) that imaginary abductees, who had never seen UFOs but were asked to imagine that they did, came up with stories practically indistinguishable from those of true abductees.[8] Second, UFO skeptic Philip Klass has raised the important question of "pseudo-memories" that can so easily be planted in a subject's mind under hypnosis. In a 1979 paper entitled "The Use and Misuse of Hypnosis in Court," Dr. Martin T. Orne cited experiments showing the possibility for fabrication and elaboration of evidence even under deep trance, and reminded the reader that the patient's fantasies and the unconscious pressure exerted by the hypnotist commonly introduced false memories.[9] As usual, Mr. Klass uses such well-observed critical material as a springboard to deny the existence of the entire UFO problem.[10]

In the course of my own investigations I have not invited abduction cases, but many have naturally come my way. I have in my files statements and tape transcripts going back to the mid-1960s that include continuing abductions monitored before, during, and after the event. In several cases I referred the witnesses to experts in hypnosis, and I studied the results with them. I have also investigated several firsthand events, like the cases of Mrs. Victor in

172

Gilroy, of Oscar in Argentina, and of Helen White in Happy Camp. All three involved abductions I felt to be actual events.

I have emerged from these experiences with a healthy respect for the complexity of the human mind and a great deal of skepticism regarding the methods used by some ufologists. One psychiatrist whose help I tried to enlist in a particular case declined to be involved because he did not feel that he had enough recent clinical experience with hypnosis. Furthermore, he said he knew too much about the subject of UFOs to be unbiased. In another case, a team of two doctors (an M.D. who uses hypnosis in his work and an expert hypnotherapist) agreed to conduct a regression of a witness I brought before them, but only under the guidelines for the acceptability of hypnotic evidence before a California court. A video recording was made of the entire session, including the induction phase; a pulse monitor and a galvanic skin response monitor gave continuous data throughout the session. At the end of the evening we agreed that we could not ethically continue the process without a therapy contract with the witness and funding to take future sessions as far as they needed to be taken.

The experts I consulted, when I showed them the current UFO literature, were amazed and upset at the superficial conditions under which UFO investigators used hypnosis. Unanimously, they considered it unethical for anyone who had already reached a strong personal conclusion about UFOs to interrogate a witness under hypnosis. Yet one is forced to admit that of the leading abduction researchers I have mentioned, none has a medical degree, none has professional knowledge of psychopathology, and all have extremely strong personal conclusions regarding the UFO phenomenon and its cultural or religious meaning. In other words, in every case there is much more than scientific curiosity involved: although working with the best intentions, the hypnotist is already committed to a particular conclusion and is trying to verify it. This sense of commitment is especially strong in Dr. Sprinkle, who stated in 1988 that he had been abducted by aliens as a child and regarded himself as having a "mission" on their behalf.[11]

An interesting book published in 1964 by Helix Press in New York under the auspices of Garrett Publications has some fascinating observations to contribute on this subject. In *Hidden Communion*, the author, Dr. Joost Meerloo, an associate professor at the New York School of Psychiatry, draws on his clinical experience in hypnosis and telepathy to illustrate the strong evidence for "unobtrusive and unconscious communication." He points out:

> Exploration of the psycho-therapeutic process has brought to light the existence of unconscious pre-verbal communication as well as unobtrusive subliminal communication, both making use of infinitesimal verbal and gestural clues, and also extrasensory perception.[12]

What Dr. Meerloo calls "mental induction" is a communication phenomenon that is enhanced by hypnosis. Yet enthusiastic UFO researchers who hypnotize their witnesses in an effort to validate their established theories are ignoring this fact. Even when they are careful to avoid leading questions and blatant contagion, their belief system is already obvious to their subjects and it can only be strengthened by the hypnotic process—not to mention possible telepathic contamination.

These observations do tend to discredit much of the hard work that has gone into hundreds of case investigations over the last decade. Yet I cannot agree with Philip Klass's conclusion that the witness is making up the whole episode. The abduction experience is real, even if the "missing time" is filled in after the fact with fictitious material.

I have a problem with the very concept of "missing time" for the simple reason that the time in question has never been shown to be missing in the first place *in the time line of the abductee*. Given an interval of one hour, as measured by the watch of an outside (reference) observer while a close encounter witness is "abducted," it is not necessarily true that time is passing at the same rate within the region of space occupied by the phenomenon. Some theories of UFOs, whose authors I respect, would, in fact, demand relativistic effects under which the abductee might spend only a few minutes or a few seconds inside the phenomenon during the full hour of "reference time." The mind of the witness, to retain its sanity, might later fill itself with an imaginary overlay drawn from collective unconscious material or personal fantasies to account for the discrepancy.

Even if time inside the object flows at the same rate as reference time, an altered state of perception might be created that would also demand such an imaginary overlay. When the experience is over, subsequent hypnosis would retrieve and amplify the overlay rather than "what really happened."

Abduction researchers raise a valid objection against the idea that many recollections are fantasies. Not only do hypnosis subjects remember certain patterns, but witnesses who recall the whole episode consciously (like Oscar in Venado Tuerto) describe similar patterns. Yet current research on memory, and especially research on the recollections of crimes by witnesses in court, should make us very cautious on this point. An article in the October 14, 1983, issue of *Science* magazine tested the validity of the forensic use of hypnosis. Subjects tried for a week to recall sixty previously presented pictures. "They were then either hypnotized or not and encouraged to recall even more pictures. *Most of the newly recalled material was incorrect, especially for highly hypnotizable subjects in the hypnosis condition*"[13] (my emphasis).

As for lie detector tests, which are routinely used by ufologists and the media to "prove" that UFO abductees are "telling the truth," their effectiveness is practically nil, as a long list of scientific references would show. Most recently, the University of California's *Wellness Letter* pointed out that such devices are "a good example of pseudo-science in action."[14] The Congressional Office of Technology Assessment has concluded that the tests were highly flawed, and a recent Harvard Medical School study has shown that truthful people flunked polygraph tests more often than actual liars. A possible explanation is that innocent people react to the stress of the test, while the guilty do everything in their power to remain calm.

175

In the midst of these conflicting indications, can help be provided to the traumatized witness who has experienced a close encounter and possibly an abduction? Absolutely. He or she should be directed to a qualified, professional hypnotherapist who is open-minded on the question of UFO reality and who has reached no personal conclusion regarding the nature and origin of the phenomenon. And the ufologist should only be in the room at the request of, and under the control of, the therapist. Any other procedure, in my opinion, is unethical and unprofessional. Besides, it runs the risk of polluting the delicate, complex abduction database with fantastic and spurious material. It can drive UFO research over a very dangerous cliff.

Even if we disagree with skeptics like Mr. Klass, we must acknowledge the fact that after recording more than a thousand abduction reports, we may have accumulated countless pages of very fascinating material but not be any closer to an understanding of the precise nature of UFOs. None of the abductees have provided verifiable information on their origin and purpose. On the contrary, every theory logically deduced from the data leads to absurd conclusions. Budd Hopkins's conclusion, for instance, that the ufonauts' purpose is genetic experimentation and hybridization as part of a scientific mission, is contradicted by several obvious facts; even in our current primitive knowledge of medicine the operations performed on the abductees by the aliens would be cruel, unnecessary, and unreliable. Simpler procedures could yield more accurate results without leaving scars. Memory could be erased in the subject beyond any chance that a hypnotist, amateur or otherwise, could retrieve any information at all about the event.

We are compelled to conclude that many abductions are either complete fantasies drawn from the collective unconscious (perhaps under the stimulus of an actual UFO encounter acting as a trigger) or that actual beings are staging simulated operations, very much in the manner of a theatrical play or movie, in order to release into our culture certain images that will influence us toward a goal we are incapable of perceiving. Neither theory is completely satisfactory.

If the second scenario is correct, the more we engage in the kind of abduction research advocated by Hopkins, Jacobs, Sprinkle, and others, in search of a first-order explanation for the overt behavior of the ufonauts, the more we do, in fact, play *their* game and reinforce the artificially projected imagery. Perhaps we have no choice.

One of the most powerful images in our society is that of the extraterrestrial alien. Over the past twenty years he has assumed a powerful persona, so much so that expectations are now high that he actually exists among us, looking like a tall, blond Aryan or a stocky humanoid with large, dark eyes.

There is another very important aspect to the entire abduction problem that has never been considered seriously by American ufology, obsessed as it is with immediate facts and first-order explanations. By ignoring this other aspect, we reduce considerably our chances of understanding the entire question. What I am referring to is the simple fact that abduction stories are not specific to the UFO phenomenon and certainly did not begin with Betty and Barney Hill in 1961. I pointed out in *Invisible College* that the structure of abduction stories was identical to that of occult initiation rituals. Several years before, I had shown in *Passport to Magonia* that contact with ufonauts was only a modern extension of the age-old tradition of contact with nonhuman consciousness in the form of angels, demons, elves, and sylphs. Such contact includes abduction, ordeal (including surgical operations), and sexual intercourse with the aliens. It often leaves marks and scars on the body and the mind, as do UFO abductions.

Reaction to the publication of these facts was curious. In the United States, many ufologists simply denied or ignored them. As late as 1988 Budd Hopkins summarily rejected the *Magonia* data as "folklore of obviously uncertain authenticity."

After all, if one has a strong personal commitment to the view that UFOs are extraterrestrial aliens on a scientific mission to earth, it is difficult to accept that they have interacted with us for centuries.

177

Yet the material studied by ufology is only valuable to the extent that it fits into the much wider tapestry of worldwide beliefs about contact with aliens throughout history.

Even the excellent and scholarly analysis of UFO abductions compiled by Thomas Bullard under the aegis of the Fund for UFO Research falls into the same trap with its very first sentence:

> Perhaps the least controversial generalization about abductions is to say that they are a recent phenomenon. Most UFO events have a prehistory reaching back through ghost rockets, ghost fliers (etc.). Among those few novel exceptions are abductions. Since they went public with the . . . revelation of the Barney and Betty Hill case, abductions have built up a substantial literature of their own as the most spectacular aspect of the UFO phenomenon.

Such a statement ignores not only the repeated invitations by 1897 airship occupants to take human witnesses on aerial trips, but the persistent stories of abductions by dwarfish creatures throughout the folklore of every culture. Archbishop Agobard of Lyons, France, in the ninth century, has left a very clear description of the four individuals who were about to be stoned to death as sorcerers because they came out of a "cloudship" from Magonia. The abduction stories began with Ezekiel on the shores of the river Chebar in 593 B.C. and never stopped.

In Europe, to my amazement, *Passport to Magonia* had the opposite result. Some researchers embraced the idea that ufology was modern folklore and carried it to an extreme: everything was folklore and there was no physical reality behind the sightings at all. This gave rise to a series of psychological exercises tending to explain UFOs by various psychic mechanisms where the actual material facts of the case were now completely ignored.

It is time to restate the argument in its simplest terms: the UFO beings of today belong to the same class of manifestation as the entities that were described in centuries past, abducting humans and flying through the sky.

If my research into this aspect of the UFO enigma was perceived as heretical, later research by experts like Bertrand Meheust was even less welcome. Yet Meheust has thrown an extraordinary new light (along with buckets of cold water) on the entire question of abduction cases and his analysis should not be ignored.

In his diligent, painstaking research, Meheust has found new material that had been missed by all of us. Typical of his case material is the following abduction report, involving Mr. Belans, a Belgian who suffered missing time and amnesia following an encounter with a flying craft. The incident occurred at dusk, as he was walking in an isolated area of Brabant where suspicious traces—notably crushed vegetation—had been noticed by farmers in their wheat fields. At the site he saw a man dressed in black waiting for something under a tree. Intrigued, Belans stopped and watched. Soon a strange feeling of tiredness came over him, as if another entity had taken control of his actions. He heard a buzzing sound, soon followed by a very bright light, as an elongated craft landed near him. A door opened over a faintly luminous rectangle, and the man in black climbed into the object. A force impelled Belans to follow. He found himself in a room that was evenly lit but without any observable source of light. A faint vibration was felt and the craft took off. An opening then became visible in the wall of the room and a very tall man entered. He seemed to "guess" Belans's every thought and was able to answer him in French. He revealed that he came from a faraway star.

"Why don't you establish open contact?" asked Belans.

"Because we do not wish to force the rapid evolution of elements that are foreign to our own civilization," the tall ufonaut responded.

Belans was eventually returned to earth, with a significant period of missing time.

The most interesting fact about the Belans abduction case is that it is a science fiction story written in 1930 by Ege Tilms. Entitled "Hodomur, Man of Infinity," it was first published four years later.

Meheust has accumulated an enormous textual and pictorial database covering such science fiction material published before World War II, and in many cases before World War I. This material contains stories of UFO beings chasing trains and automobiles, stalling cars, hitting people with strange beams, and abducting them into spherical structures.

Abduction by alien beings constitutes a central theme of the science fiction literature of the early twentieth century. Meheust has found it in hundreds of stories, especially in French and English, published between 1880 and 1940. When this research is extended to earlier folklore texts, it becomes obvious that the accumulated material about alien abductions (real or imagined) published before 1940 literally dwarfs the database studied by modern ufologists.

It is predictable that many researchers will go on ignoring this fact and hypnotizing traumatized witnesses in a futile, desperate effort to regain control over a phenomenon whose elusiveness is a key feature. To me, the abduction of Helen White, like that of Mrs. Victor and of Oscar, is interesting precisely because it matches a much wider pattern that extends through the centuries. These cases are new examples of a motif that repeats endlessly in the tapestry of alien contact. I feel privileged to have touched them, but I do not know what they mean yet.

12

Copper Medic

very professional has a favorite case, a special place in his heart for a particular event that marked his work. For an attorney it may be a special trial, a colorful client, a dramatic moment in court; for a detective, a remarkable crime; for a surgeon, an operation from which he drew new knowledge.

For me, Copper Medic fulfilled all of these emotions. Perhaps it was the site itself, the rugged landscape of the hills around Redding, the backroads of French Gulch. Perhaps it was the lingering aura of the Gold Rush, the vision that is still alive in the old claims where dreamers return again and again whenever gold mining rises above its economic threshold. Perhaps it was the long drives up and down Highway 5 and the quiet talks with my son, who did all the electronics for the project. Perhaps it was the personality of the two witnesses, Clint Chapin and his gutsy wife, Jane, who was still packing a Colt revolver when I met her. She was seventy-five then, a tough, bossy woman with horn-rimmed glasses and a big jaw.

Clint, a strong man with a bald forehead, white hair, and easygoing ways, was her lifelong companion.

When I look at pictures I took of their home ten years ago I see a clean, shiny trailer with a big picture window, a folding table and a chair set near the door, a gas bottle and a small aluminum storage shack to the left. The site is clean, everything is in its place. No broken appliances, no old tires mar this place.

What attracted the interest of local ufologists to the case wasn't so much the repeated sighting of a small, egg-shaped UFO on the Chapins' property as the strange material they claimed to have recovered at the site. This material consisted in a curious pile of sand containing pale yellow-green glass fragments and a block of silver-gray metal that looked like a copper alloy of some sort.

The Chapins invited me into their trailer and we spoke for four hours, seated at the breakfast table. Jane did most of the talking, with occasional interruptions by Clint. There was no animosity between them. Their life had revolved around their claim, an open pit gold mine with five veins, which also produced some iron. They worked it for forty-six years, living in a cabin built on the property, "and never one cent of welfare, either." I found them to be pleasant, dynamic people who worked hard and who liked to have fun. They made frequent trips to Nevada to have the ore assayed and to sell their product. Their life had been active until the UFO came. Now they were somewhat discouraged, they told me. Clint had been gaining weight and, although intellectually alert, rarely moved from his armchair. Jane suffered dizzy spells and was primarily preoccupied with warning everybody that UFOs existed and that they were hostile to humans.

So, exactly what did they see, back at the old Mary Hazel Mine, I asked? In the flood of information that followed, mixed with recriminations about neighbors, oil companies that wanted the land, and colorful stories of the area that dated back to the Gold Rush of 1849, I gathered that there had been three separate UFO incidents.

FIRST INCIDENT: OCTOBER 30, 1969, 10:30 A.M.

On a bright, sunny morning the Chapins, who were then in their mid-sixties, killed a rattlesnake. According to custom, they cut off the snake's head, buried it, and put a stone on it "so nobody will step over it." Jane was going to take a picture of the body when she suddenly saw something behind the tall grass, among the trees. She thought it was a trailer, then realized it was oval, about the size of a VW Beetle. It appeared cream-colored to her. Clint, who saw it from a different perspective, thought it was gray. Both saw how the object lifted up, paused for a brief moment, then disappeared at an amazing speed.

An oval depression, smaller than the object itself, was found in the ground, as if a large weight had rested there. It is when they inspected this area that they discovered the strange pile of sand and the metal. There were no physiological effects reported in connection with this episode. They stored the metal in the shed next to their trailer.

SECOND INCIDENT: DECEMBER 27, 1976, 11:00 A.M.

The Chapins were driving up the road carrying a dead parakeet to a spot where they bury animals. There was ice on the pavement, so Clint stopped the truck and walked ahead. Suddenly he yelled, "Jane! Bring the gun!"

She jumped out and started running, but she seemed to hit a wall, an invisible barrier, and she fell on the ground while Clint was thrown back against the side of the road, one arm pinned behind him. Both lost consciousness for about fifteen minutes. When they came to they found that they had urinated. Clint remembered seeing an object shaped like a half-egg standing up, which took off rapidly. They drove back home immediately, feeling very sick and cold.

Clint suffered a dislocated shoulder in this incident, and afterward he walked with his left arm noticeably out of place. When I met him, I saw that he frequently held it with his right hand.

THIRD INCIDENT: OCTOBER 13, 1977

Clint and Jane were at the mine again when they suddenly felt something like a heat wave. Both became ill, vomiting violently. The sky was overcast. They felt no strange odor, saw no strange object, heard no sound. Again, they drove home as soon as they were able to do so.

My check of the weather records shows that on October 30, 1969, both Redding and Red Bluff reported temperatures around 70°F at the time of the sighting, with no clouds, excellent visibility. On December 27, 1976, the skies were clear, visibility unrestricted, temperature 64°F. On October 13, 1977, there were thin, broken cirrus clouds at high altitude, visibility unrestricted, temperature 82°F. The latter observation seems to contradict the Chapins' statement about overcast skies. However, these official readings are for Red Bluff, which is a significant distance from the canyon where the mine is located.

THE INVESTIGATION

After the second incident Jane complained of a "buzzing in her head," of deteriorating vision, and of pains in her arms and legs. A local physician dismissed the symptoms as "old age nervousness." She and Cliff went to other doctors, insisting that the cause of their illness was probably the presence of the "strange rock" next to their trailer. (I had a sample of it in my home for several months, handled it often, and never suffered any ill effects.)

When I became involved in this case, I was just beginning to realize the potential significance of the medical injuries. Like most researchers in this field, I was placing a higher priority on physical evidence then on the details of the close encounters themselves. Thus I concentrated first on the allegedly peculiar material gathered at the site.

Two scientists conducted an analysis of the sand material. First, Dr. Edward Zeller, director of the radiation physics laboratory at the University of Kansas Space Technology Center, examined the components of the sand. He found that it included very pale green glass, nearly white sintered silicate, feldspar, quartz fragments with minute traces of gold, pyrite, and other sulfide ore minerals, magnetic dark minerals (magnetite), and various organic fragments. He concluded that the glass and sintered silicate were not natural products.

Second, Dr. Richard Haines submitted the glass to a NASA scientist who went one step further by subjecting four samples to element identification using an instrument called an X-ray EDAX (energy dispersive analyzer). He found the material to be made up primarily of silicon with traces of potassium, chlorine, titanium, and iron.

Another sample was submitted to the mineralogy/crystallography laboratory at Paris University. The technicians there found sodium, silicium, potassium, and titanium. No iron and no chlorine. Their conclusion: "Nothing extraordinary."

My next step involved geologists, who are more likely than space scientists to know what can be found around an old mine. Bulletin #193 of the California Department of Mines contains a section on French Gulch. "It is the most important lode-gold district in the Klamath mountains," writes the reporter, who notes that the area was originally prospected in 1849 by French miners. From 1900 to 1914 the output from the district averaged $300,000 to $500,000 worth of gold per year.

> The ore contains coarse, free gold usually associated with considerable pyrite and smaller amounts of galena, sphalerite, arsenopyrite, chalcopyrite and occasionally sheelite ... the district is underlain predominantly by slate, shale and siltstone of the Bragdon formation.[1]

This description did not account for the sand.

During one of my trips to the mine itself, I gathered rocks, dirt, and sand at the site and took it to the same geologists who had agreed to look at Jane Chapin's samples. The results were not particularly exciting.

185

At the U.S. Geological Survey in Menlo Park, a field geologist with considerable experience offered me a cup of coffee and told me frankly, "The problem with your sand is that it's not sand."

"What do you mean, it's not sand?" I exclaimed. "It looks like sand to me."

"Perhaps it looks like sand to you, but it's not alluvial sand or stream sand or beach sand or mine-tailing sand or any kind of naturally formed sand."

He had poured my "sand" on a piece of paper. Using a fine point and a magnifying glass, he had separated the components into little piles.

"Here is some siltstone," he began. "Here is volcanic material; here, sulfide-bearing rock; green crystals; feldspar or porcelain; pyrite cubes. No quartz and no mica. All the fragments are very angular. All the components are common, but they don't belong together. This is a composite of rock fragments and manufactured materials.

"It's as of somebody had taken minerals from very different areas and had ground them together until it looked like sand. As for the glass, it does seem that it was produced by a sudden burst of heat, but that could occur in a variety of natural ways."

The "organic material" that was duly noted by NASA might very well have come from Jane's trailer. When I visited her, she overturned the bottle of mystery sand on her kitchen table and gathered up some of the stuff for me—hardly the sterile conditions required by precision work. I suspect the sample that had reached NASA had been obtained under similar circumstances. I would not be surprised if they found bread crumbs and chocolate chips in it.

As for the metal sample, which fitted in the palm of one's hand, it was very heavy and unusually contoured. It seemed to have been poured and solidified into a mass of indefinite shape. The outside was a dull, silver-gray, the inside a shiny gold color. Shavings taken from it turned out to be copper, with traces of chromium and tin. (The Mary Hazel mine produces gold and iron, but no copper.) In other words, the sample was a fairly ordinary alloy that could have come into existence in a variety of natural ways.

The physical evidence was proving to be very elusive, but the Chapins, I was convinced, were not lying. If they had invented the whole story, I do not doubt that Jane would have come up with something more imaginative and more colorful than an oval-shaped object with pockmarked skin. Some of the details, she told me privately, bothered her considerably, to the point of keeping her awake at night.

An investigator for one of the civilian research groups, who had done an extensive analysis of the case, reported in print that the object "rose up off the ground a few feet, then took off like a shot up the canyon, swaying but not striking small trees as it went." Jane gave me a different story: the object had flown off *into the trees*, passing through them as if they did not exist.

"Why didn't you tell that to the UFO investigators?" I asked her.

"I could see they wouldn't believe me if I told them the truth. They were such nice people. I didn't want to shock them."

On my second visit to the Chapins' trailer Jane told me her life story. She had been born in France in 1903. Her family was from Marseilles and later moved to Nice and to America. Her brothers had gone back for visits to France, but she never returned. She moved to Redding with Clint in 1933.

"So what do you think UFOs are?" I asked them. Jane said they were probably enemy devices from Russia or China. Clint disagreed with this; he thought they came from inside the earth, a theory he had picked up from a recent television show about the "holes at the pole" allegedly found by Admiral Byrd, a spurious story still rampant in the dense mythology of UFO lore.

"Have the two of you experienced anything strange since the sightings?" I asked. Jane made me promise not to tell other investigators. On January 14, 1978, she had seen an entity appear near her bed. She did not see any feet. She drew a silhouette for me. The head was flat, with large eyes and a big nose, an extended arm.

187

She was very concerned that this deviation might discredit her as a UFO witness.

Although I was slowly gaining the old couple's confidence, I still had the feeling that some details were withheld from me, as they were from other investigators. The Chapins were ill, they were scared; they wanted people to believe their story, to the point of amplifying some details and of trying to use the strange samples as corroborating evidence. Yet they did not especially seek or enjoy attention.

Early in February 1978 the case became public knowledge through what I thought was rather irresponsible action on the part of local ufologists, who gave the story to the newspapers and sent reporters to the site. The results were predictable: a sketchy, inaccurate report was printed and the Chapins became quite upset. However, they did not associate me with the leaking of their story. They continued to correspond with me and to welcome my visits, which centered increasingly on the medical parameters of the case. At my request, Jane gave me a list of the doctors she had seen and allowed me to write down the medications she was taking. I obtained an independent assessment of her condition through medical specialists who took a private interest in the case. I offered expert attention to her and to Clint, at no expense to them. But Jane, always suspicious, misunderstood my questions. She thought that if I probed into the nature of their symptoms it was because I doubted their story.

Yet I saw it as my job to document every element, every detail, from weather reports to records of their mining claim.[2]

In late February Jane Chapin wrote to me that they would accept no further visits, allegedly because an investigator from the Center for UFO Studies (CUFOS) had visited their neighbors, asking questions about them.

In March 1978 she wrote again to complain about the "UFO amateurs" who were harassing them. She pointed out various inaccuracies in a report they had published. She sent me a sketch of the area showing her exact location during the second encounter.

I replied with several specific questions about Clint's injury, again offering specialized medical help if they wished it.

On March 15 Jane replied in a rambling, uncooperative mood, without answering my questions, again complaining bitterly about the UFO groups. But a week later she returned a map I had sent her, on which she had marked exact locations for the various sightings. She also indicated that Clint was going to the hospital for tests and X rays: "Clint sweats when sitting on a chair, and at night he turns real red in the face."

On May 9, in response to one of my letters, she again seemed to misunderstand the objective of my questions: "I have proof from doctors that four years before this happened I did not have this, or Clint did not have heart trouble. So, I will not sit and answer any more questions."

About August 1, 1978, the twelve-year-old son of a local doctor saw an unusual humanoid creature near Lewistown, not far from the Chapin mine. The boy was deeply upset by the encounter.

In early September Jane wrote to me in a more friendly mood, indicating that she and Clint were feeling better and wished to have "all their valuable material returned," although she allowed me to keep some of the glass, which in my view, was the only substance with possible relevance to the phenomenon.

In October Jane sent another friendly letter with a picture of her and her husband at the mine. She added: "When it cools off, we will take you to the UFO favorite place."

She did not mention that, according to local rumors, she had placed dynamite under a pile of gravel where the UFO had hovered before, hoping that it would come back again. When I questioned her about it, there was no hesitation in her mind: if it did return she would blow it to smithereens once and for all, and then we scientists would really have something to analyze!

We corresponded throughout 1979, but I was still unable to get precise data out of Jane, who regarded any specific probing as an indication that I doubted her veracity or her beliefs. I continued to talk with geologists in the United States, with physicists in France, and with medical experts who, for obvious professional reasons, could not step in without being invited by the patients or their attending physicians.

I became increasingly frustrated with the case, now christened Copper Medic, which had grown into a three-inch file. Here was a site where, if we believed the witnesses (I did believe them, and still do) extraordinary phenomena had recurred time and time again at the same location.

SLEEPING BEAUTY

When the Chapin case developed into a full-scale puzzle, my son and I had been working for some time on the design of a system for long-term photographic surveillance of UFO sites, an idea that began with the Happy Camp sightings but which was never implemented there. In July 1978 I had even obtained clearance from the state of California to install equipment on top of a mountain that overlooked the whole area, but we were not ready with our equipment. Two other reasons discouraged us from using Happy Camp as our first test site: we did not have anyone locally whom we could trust to monitor the equipment and it took an entire day for us just to drive up to the location.

The situation at Copper Medic was very different. Our friend, Bill Murphy, who lived in Redding at the time, was enthusiastic about the project and shared our frustration with the case. And the four-and-a-half-hour drive from San Francisco made it possible to accomplish a round trip in a single day, leaving time for work at the site.

Between August 1978 and August 1980 we developed the capability to take photographs of remote sites in the field using an automatic camera camouflaged as an ordinary rock. The device drew power from a separate buried battery unit. Our camera took sixty exposures during a six-hour period each day, then went to sleep for eighteen hours, starting again at the same time the next day. It produced 16mm color exposures using ordinary Kodak film.

The images could conveniently be enlarged to give clear three-by-five-inch prints. Our battery pack was capable of powering the camera for a whole month.

I will explain below how we came to design this configuration and what technical choices we had to make in the process, since other investigators may want to adapt our technique to their needs.

The first step was the purchase of three Bell & Howell pulse cameras using 16mm film in fifty-foot rolls. If timed to take one picture every six minutes (ten pulses per hour) for six hours each day, it produced 1,800 exposures in one month, filing up a whole roll of film. The power source was a set of two Eagle-Picher batteries mounted to give a twelve-volt direct current source.

Such was the theory. In actual practice the implementation took a bit longer than we expected.

Although the cameras I bought were of a standard type used in military reconnaissance projects, they were designed to take film at twenty-four frames per second, giving an exposure time of one-fiftieth of a second. We began by replacing the lens with a 25mm Berthiot lens that could be set from f1.9 to f16, and we decided to use the slowest possible daylight film.

The decision to take pictures in daylight was guided by the fact that the sightings by the Chapins had occurred between 10:00 A.M. and 11:00 A.M. We could just as easily have taken nighttime pictures in the form of six-minute time exposures. In retrospect, we really should have done both.

The next hurdle was the design of a reliable intervalometer timing circuit to send pulses to the camera. It had to draw a minimum amount of power from the battery pack, since we did not expect to return to the site more than once a month. On such a project it helps to have an energetic teenage son who majors in physics. After some breadboarding, his final circuit, which used a wire-wrap technique, proved extremely reliable.

It is one thing for such a device to work in the lab (it took pictures of our street through the living room window for a whole month without failing) and it is another to package it so that it will function when it is buried in the hillside, where it runs the risk of being found by picnickers or hunters, dislodged by a frightened deer, obscured by spiders and wasps who find the lens convenient, or bitten by a field mouse.

After some trial and error we designed a concrete shell for the camera. It was very hard, shaped like a rock, with encrusted bits of wood and leaves so that it would blend in naturally with the hillside. The shell was split in two so that the top could be removed, exposing the camera itself. It was filled with wax to insure a very tight fit, leaving no room for insects and creating a water seal around the device.

We had located a site, high up on public land on a local hill, from which one could gain a plunging view of the canyon, including the area of the Chapin claim. After a period of adjustments both to the equipment and to the location where it was buried, we set the device, which we called Sleeping Beauty, to take pictures every day from 6:00 A.M. to noon.

Unfortunately, no UFO turned up, and we eventually had to discontinue the experiment, but we drew interesting lessons from it. Today much progress in electronics and camera technology would make such a surveillance project easier to accomplish, and I wonder why such technology is not used on a routine basis whenever there is recurrence of UFO phenomena over a given area.

By the time we stopped our tests on July 24, 1979, the round-trip to Redding had become routine. Our only problem was to locate our camera each time because it was so well camouflaged that it really did blend into the landscape.

Late in 1979 I gave up on Copper Medic, only occasionally staying in touch with the Chapins. I offered to return to Jane the rest of the samples. Then, on the last day of July 1980, a letter came from her: "I found you too late," she wrote. "Clinton died June 10th. . . . He went into a coma at 8 o'clock, at 10:20 he died in my arms. You can keep the UFO material."

She added that on April 4, 1980, before Clinton's heart attack, they had had another encounter:

We were looking at a road that had been cut through our property and we turned to go down the road, west, and there was a skinny thing in the road, and his egg [author's note: "his egg" is Jane's reference to the oval UFO] was not 25 feet from us. . . . and he took four steps toward us and my hand fell on my gun and he turned around and walked back. He was in a gray suit, and he left no print or prints of the egg. Clint could not move either . . . the thing vanished, then the egg went up in the air and turned west, and we both looked at the back of the egg and it opened like a horse trailer door.

He was four-foot tall and skinny, maybe ninety pounds. I don't know what he wants . . . well, maybe he will take me to where Clint is.

Part Five

THE HEART OF THE MATTER

I t will be recalled that Part Three of this book left open the question of claims of UFO-related injuries. Were these injuries real and if so, should they be interpreted as hostile behavior on the part of the phenomenon? What was the nature of the injuries and by what means were they produced? These key questions have never been adequately researched. Equipped with the data we have reviewed in the last few chapters, we can now return to this problem.

Over the past decade I have gradually withdrawn from the study of run-of-the-mill U.S. cases to give the highest priority to those incidents in which reliable physical and biological data could be obtained. In 1988 I returned to Brazil with Janine to assess and analyze the numerous medical claims that seem to have concentrated in that part of the world.

More than twenty years ago, in our book *Challenge to Science: The UFO Enigma*[1] we uncovered the basic patterns in close encounter cases. One of these patterns is the "law of the times," which states that the peak in probability for a close encounter is reached between 1:00 A.M. and 3:00 A.M. The second law states that close encounters are likely to happen in areas of very low population density, isolated regions with poor communication with civilization, in sites located away from dwellings.

Our return trip to Brazil validated these two laws with great accuracy, and it also illustrated one of the fallacies of UFO research. Most ufologists live in big cities and work from newspaper clippings mailed to them or from interview reports by local volunteers. They may verify this information over the telephone, but they rarely travel in person to the site of the events they write about. Those who review their books, and the skeptics who criticize them, are concentrated in offices in New York and Washington, or on academic campuses where they earn their living. Thus most of the arguments about some of the key cases in this field are conducted on a purely intellectual level, unpolluted by contact with reality, and without anyone having actually spoken to the witnesses at the remote site where the event took place. No wonder the public and the scientific community are getting a confused, distorted, often sensationalized picture of the situation. No wonder they find it easy to ignore it.

From San Francisco it took two full days of air travel to reach our base of operations—Fortaleza, one of the major cities in northeastern Brazil. Fortaleza, with a population of 1.2 million, is a thriving business and academic center where several active Brazilian researchers of the UFO phenomenon have accumulated important collections. It was with their assistance that we were able to plan our moves into the vast region of forests, jungles, wide meandering rivers, swamps, and hot, dusty, humid plantations Brazilians simply refer to as the Interior, a region as vast as the western United States.

There are maps of the Interior, but they are generally unreliable.

It is bad enough that place names do not correlate with surface features (Brazilian mapmakers, like American ufologists, like to stay in air-conditioned offices in Brasília and Rio, overlaying aerial photographs on older maps bearing location names that are out of date), but political hyperbole sometimes dictates that straight modern highways be drawn over wide stretches of territory when only the *plan* for the highway exists. One drives there expecting to find a magnificent thoroughfare and discovers instead a winding, dusty trail full of potholes and intersected by mountain streams, a road barely wide enough for one car to pass a herd of cows in single file.

It is useful to stop every few miles for a bottle of Guarana (a soft drink made from an Amazonian fruit), and for directions and advice. This makes for slower progress, but it helps in understanding local conditions in this extremely remote part of the world; in the process we met some of the most sincere, honest, and hospitable people we have ever known. When they were told why we had come to their village or their *fazenda*, they opened their minds and their hearts to us. Local police and administrative authorities put four-wheel-drive trucks at our disposal, advised us on places to stay, and took time to answer our inquiries.

The next three chapters summarize our findings. We began with the cluster of cases in the heavily forested area immediately west of the Parnaiba River near Parnarama, where we spent three days and two nights. We made another trip along the valley of the Acarau River in the areas around Santana, where another cluster of medical injury cases was reported. And we concluded our investigation with a trip to São Luís, on the northern coast of Brazil, where the major wave of 1977 had originated; and a two-day visit to the town of Belém, the island of Mosqueiro in the mouth of the Amazon, and the beach of Baia do Sol where the Brazilian military had photographed the UFOs we reproduced in figures 9 and 10.

This two-week investigation, during which we interviewed fifty witnesses at the very site of the events, could never have succeeded without the generous help of several American and Brazilian friends. We are especially grateful to Bill Calvert and Regina Pereira for their hospitality, to Professor Agobar Oliveira of the University

197

of Fortaleza, to former mayor Sr. Barros of Parnarama, to Lt. Giraldo Magela of the military police in São Luís, to Daniel Rebisso Giese of the public health service in Belém, and to several medical doctors and military officers who spoke to us only on condition that their names be withheld from publication.

13

Deer Hunters

If you like New York in July or Houston in August, you would love Parnarama any time of the year. From Fortaleza you reach it by a ten-hour drive to Teresina, one of the hottest points in all of Brazil, followed by a two-hour drive on a smaller road south, until you come to a sandy turnoff that takes you over the embankment to a cluster of huts on the shore of the Parnaiba River. In our case, the whole trip was uneventful but slow because of numerous potholes in the middle of the highway. Other than an encounter with a beautiful, shiny ten-foot cobra sunning himself on the road, we saw nothing unusual.

You have now reached the point at which you say goodbye to your car, because there is no bridge on the Parnaiba, and you transfer your bags to a small motorboat that looks like an overgrown sardine can enthusiastically controlled by a laughing, joking group of teenagers. Fighting the strong current and listing heavily to starboard, this contraption takes you to a muddy sand flat and you find yourself on the main street of Parnarama, population 3,000.

199

Mercifully, the sun was about to set when we arrived there in late July 1988. The local authorities recommended one of the town's two hotels. We were allocated a room where we could hang our hammocks and mosquito nets and where we could be assured of a hearty breakfast, good Brazilian coffee, and solid meals of rice, grilled meat, and tapioca.

We went to the bar next door for a beer, and the first person we engaged in conversation turned out to be a UFO witness. His name was Jorge Pereira and his experience had taken place in the fall of 1984. One dark night, he was hunting near the hamlet of Povoada Saco. He was waiting for game in his hammock strung between two trees. Suddenly, everything was lit up from above.

"I had a good rifle," he told us, "and I thought, well, it's either him or me. But after a few seconds I thought better of it. I climbed down from the tree, making a solemn promise to God: if He allowed me to get out unharmed, I would not kill any more deer. Shortly after I reached the ground, it went away."

"And you don't hunt anymore?" I asked.

"I only hunt during the day now," came the reply. I wondered what God thought of the way this particular sinner kept his promises.

"How big was the light?"

"As big as the moon."

"How large an area did it light up?"

"About a hundred feet in diameter, and I was right at the center of it."

"Did you look at the light?"

"It was too strong for me to look. I only glanced at it."

"What color was it?"

"White, like an incandescent bulb."

"Did you feel anything?"

"Only extreme terror. There was no sound at all."

Many witnesses came to us spontaneously to tell of their experiences. Others reported things they had heard about. None of these sightings had ever been discussed in the press or outside the community. In one case, from September 1987, a group of six hunters were driving on Route 4 in an open truck when a light as bright as an electric arc, coming from a metallic object six feet in diameter, hovered ahead of them. There were three powerful lights underneath, lighting up in sequence: blue, red, orange, with varying intensity.

In another case that took place at 3:30 A.M. in Cajneiro about November 11, 1983, a farm worker was riding his bicycle and suddenly saw a very fat man, glowing with a green shimmering light on the road ahead of him. As he saw this, the bicycle "stalled" and he was unable to make it move forward, no matter how hard he tried. The man walked toward the witness, and as he did so he became tall and skinny instead of short and fat. He stopped and assumed a strange posture, placing his right foot over the left knee, the right hand on the left shoulder, and the right arm straight in the air.

Having done so, he simply vanished into thin air.

The witness was so shaken that he refused to talk to anyone about the incident until a year later, when he agreed to be interviewed. He was still agitated when he gave his testimony and was reluctant to discuss the dreams he has been having since the encounter.

We quickly realized that we had very limited time in which to document the observations that have accumulated in the Parnarama region, which probably number about five hundred. Given these limitations, we decided to concentrate on the specific incidents that involved medical injuries. Thus we spent most of our time on four cases: that of Cosmo the fisherman, the experience of a prospector named Manuel, the death of a county clerk named Ramon, and the death of a hunter, Raimundo Souza.

COSMO, THE FISHERMAN

This experience took place on or about September 23, 1984, between 6:30 P.M. and dawn. José Morais da Silva, forty-eight, nicknamed Zé Cosmo, had gone fishing in the broad Parnaiba River with his ten-year-old-son. At first they were fishing for bait. About 6:30 P.M. they saw a pulsing light, as bright as lightning, far away from them. They went on fishing.

About 8:00 P.M. the same thing happened again, directly over the river this time. Cosmo pulled out his line and scrambled up the steep bank as well as he could to get to his son, who was asleep.

Cosmo had lost the use of one of his knees several years before in an accident that fractured the articulation. The injury was never corrected properly, and he has to walk with a cane. It must have been difficult for him to clamber up the embankment to warn his son of the danger. Once he was there, it started raining and the light went out. Cosmo went back to the river to resume fishing while his son remained on the bank.

As he was in water up to his waist, he suddenly saw that a powerful light was behind him, so that his shadow was projected on the water. The light was about sixty feet above the bank, illuminating a large area. Again, Cosmo went back toward his son, who was at the foot of a tree. They got down low on the ground to watch the object as it periodically expanded and receded, sometimes shrinking to a starlike point. It behaved that way until about 10:00 P.M.; by then they had moved, and they watched it from the shelter of an overhanging rock, at the edge of the water.

At 10:00 P.M. the light moved to a different place on the bank, down the river on the path they would have to follow, and it seemed to wait for them. Then it moved to the other side of the river, where other fishermen were located. It changed to a bright red color and danced, oscillating over the water. Cosmo heard the fishermen yell and saw them run away.

The object remained at the same spot until 4:00 A.M., when it rose about 70° above them, making a sound "like the dynamo that generates current on a bicycle." It passed slowly at that level. "It was raining the whole time," Cosmo told us as we sat in a circle in front of his house. "The thing went back and forth over the river, shining the beam in our direction, but we were still hiding in the stream, under the rock. We had covered ourselves with palm leaves.

It landed in the sand above us. We heard something like a car door slammed shut. We also heard voices, but we could not discern the language. At 6:00 A.M. it went away, and we found large footprints where it had landed."

We asked the fisherman about any sensations or reactions he might have had at the time. His observations were precise and detailed. When the beam of light hit him he couldn't open his eyes, and he felt intense pain. He became dizzy. He has not experienced any eye trouble, or any change in sleep patterns. However, the pain has not gone away in the last four years. It comes over him every day, starting with the head, then the legs and the hips; when this happens he has to stop working. He gets numbness in his fingers, pricklings. He has to massage his hands to make them return to normal. Sometimes he cannot even pick up a spoon.

The above information was obtained and verified over two interviews with Cosmo. Both times we found him working, with the help of his children, to spread a new coat of mud over the walls of his cabin. Neighbors clustered around us while small black pigs roamed and grunted along the unpaved street and the open areas littered with garbage. A young girl walked past us proudly, coming back from the forest, a long gun over her shoulder.

These are people who have never heard of *Close Encounters*, or of Steven Spielberg. They fish and hunt because they are too poor to afford the food they need. At night the countryside is perfectly dark. The only high-tension line runs twenty miles to the west.

We walked over to the river to understand better the circumstances of Cosmo's experience. The bank is practically a vertical drop of fifteen to twenty feet, but in the intervening years the tree under which he sought shelter with his son has been uprooted and carried away by the summer floods.

Cosmo does not drink anything except water. Before we left we tried to make arrangements for him to get in touch with a physician in Fortaleza whom we had briefed on the symptoms of UFO-related injuries, but there are only five telephones for the three thousand people who live in the town, and Fortaleza is very far away. We left his cabin convinced that he was telling the truth and helpless to alleviate his pain.

MANUEL, THE PROSPECTOR

Manuel is a forty-six-year-old prospector, a rugged outdoorsman who stays alone in the wilderness for weeks or months at a time. He was forty at the time of the incident, in the fall of 1982.

He was not in Parnarama when we visited the area, but we were able to speak at length with his wife and his children, who remember vividly the event and its aftermath.

When Manuel announced that he was going out hunting, his wife tried hard to make him change his mind: a man down the street (see the case of Ramon, below) had died in what people thought was an encounter with a chupa. Manuel only laughed at her, claiming with typical Latin machismo that he did not believe in such tales.

Manuel shot and killed a deer early in the night; as he lay in his hammock trying to get some sleep, two objects came over his position and fired a beam at him. He did not hesitate for a minute to take aim and to fire at the lights. Seeing that this had no effect, he jumped down from the tree and started running; one of the objects stayed in hot pursuit, shining the beam in his direction as he staggered through the underbrush. Everytime the light hit him he felt weak and fell. He also smelled a foul odor.

He managed to run to a cave, crawled in, and expected to find shelter there. Instead, the object positioned itself in such a way that it shone straight at him. He came out again, dizzy with the light, his clothes torn by the dense brush, his shoes lost along the way. He ran from 10:00 P.M. to 5:00 A.M., occasionally resting under trees until the light found him again. Eventually he managed to stagger to a house in Lagoa de Dentro, a tiny village in the middle of the forest. The boy who opened the door saw the object that followed Manuel. It was shaped like a refrigerator, with the red light beam coming out of the middle of one side. Manuel attributed his survival to the fact that he had torn off a piece of his shirt to cover his nose, so that he did not breathe the ill-smelling gas expelled by the chupa.

When he came back home after two days of nursing his injuries in Lagoa de Dentro (he had a tear in his leg, numerous scratches and cuts, and infected wounds in his feet), he was reluctant to discuss the ordeal. He had been forced to change his mind about the existence of UFOs, and the experience had scared him out of his wits. He sold his collection of guns and has never gone back to hunt.

Seated in Manuel's spacious house in the middle of town, surrounded by kids and neighbors, I started asking for more details about the incident.

"What happened to the gun?" I asked his wife.

"It stayed there, in the hammock. And the dead deer stayed there too. Local people went and got them."

"How did he describe the light?"

"It was bigger than the moon, mercury-white, so bright he could not look directly at it. It was steady, without pulsations or changes."

"How could he miss when he fired? Evidently he is an experienced hunter."

"The light jumped up suddenly. Also he might have missed out of nervousness."

"What about the color? Why was it described as red?"

"That's the strange thing," she admitted. "The light was not red when he was under it, only a bright white, but from a distance it appeared to be red."

"Did he actually see gas emanating from the object?"

"No, but he assumed it must be sending out bursts of gas because of the smell."

"What did he feel at the time?"

"He felt heat and burns."

"Did you observe any unusual reactions or effects on his body when he returned home?"

"He had marks on his shoulders, arms, neck, and on his back and chest."

"When did they develop?"

"The day following the incident, when he was still at Lagoa de Dentro."

"What did these marks look like?"

"They were red to purple, round; they did not hurt."

"Can you describe the edges?"

"They were sharp, with the contours a deeper shade than the center. They were round, not irregular. One to two inches in diameter."

"Were the marks flat or raised?"

"The skin was raised somewhat."

"Were there any puncture marks?"

"None. I looked closely."

"Could you compare it to a hematoma?"

"No, it looked more like a steam burn."

"What happened if you pressed it?"

"It turned white where my finger touched the skin, then the color came back."

"How did the marks go away?"

"They stayed the same color but got more and more clear until they disappeared in ten days."

"Was there any blister, any peeling of the skin?"

"None whatsoever."

"What about his eyes?"

"They were red the first day he came back. Since then he has only been able to read very close, and his eyes get tired quickly."

In the ensuing discussion, which became very personal, we established that Manuel had suffered no hearing loss as a result of the incident, but started drinking more than usual, a fact that may account for the slight tremor in his hands.

In the whole incident, which Manuel calls "the worst thing in his life," it was the smell that affected him the most. It was penetrating, like burning sulphur, and it made his nose run. It did not impair his breathing, but forced him to clear his throat at frequent intervals. He believes that it was the smell rather than the light that made him fall, and that it was the piece of cloth over his nose that saved him.

RAMON, THE COUNTY WORKER

The case of Ramon (or, more correctly, Romao, whose full name was José Batista Lima) presented us with our first opportunity to interrogate witnesses of a death allegedly due to a chupa. We spoke with the son and the daughter of the victim, with several men who knew him during his life, with the hunting companions who were with him when he died, and with people who saw the body prior to his funeral. But we were not able to definitely tie his demise to the action of a lighted object, so that the cause of death must remain as a possible heart attack until more evidence can be obtained.

The most important testimony is that of Pedro Curto, whom we tracked down in the small village of Jejo, about forty minutes by four-wheel-drive truck from Parnarama on a twisted dirt trail gutted by the summer rains.

Ramon's daughter, who was eleven when her father died, had given us the basic facts: on August 26, 1982, he had left the house early, carrying his hammock and his gun, to pass the night hunting near Cocalinho with three companions who knew the area well.

He killed a deer, then slept in a tree. The next morning at dawn he climbed down, packed his hammock, and went to get the deer. It is at that moment that he felt ill, lay down, and died at 6:00 A.M. He was brought home at noon. Here again, the family had asked him not to go hunting for fear of chupas, and he had laughed at them. One of his companions had seen a very bright light in the sky that night, but it was not known whether it was in the vicinity of Ramon or not.

Pedro Curto gave us more details: the four hunters had dispersed the evening before over an area of several miles, so that they were not in contact visually or by voice during the night. When Pedro walked up to Ramon's location in the morning he found him lying on the ground and obtained no response when he called his name.

Eventually Ramon got up by himself. He was short of breath. He embraced Pedro emotionally.

"What's the problem?" asked Pedro. To this question, Ramon only shook his head. Pedro helped him sit down again.

"Do you have a pill with you?" Pedro asked.

The answer was yes. He took out the pill (which Pedro insists was simply aspirin, not a heart medication) and swallowed it with some water. Ramon seemed to feel better. He told Pedro to go tie up the deer so they could take it away.

Ramon then sat with one leg bent under him, the right leg out straight, his arms folded on his left knee and his head over his arms. He remained in this position until the two other hunters (Ze Zinho and Manuel Eugenio) caught up with them.

"What's wrong with Ramon?" one of them asked.

"He's resting," said Pedro, busy with the deer.

The others looked at him closely.

Ze Zinho examined the eyes. "He is not resting. He is dead."

There had been no agonal movements, no convulsions. He had died about ten minutes after drinking the water. He had not seemed to be in pain. He had not grabbed his chest or any part of his body. He had been able to swallow the pill and the water normally. Prior to taking the pill, as he sat on the ground, according to Pedro, Ramon did pull at the grass repeatedly either in pain or to try to get up.

Pedro stayed with the body while the others went to get the family.

The body was still pliable an hour after death. There was no blood at the mouth. The report of a light in the area came from a man named Velho'Tonio, who was returning to Cocalinho that night, riding a horse. But there was nothing specific about his sighting and we could not tic it to Ramon's experience.

A curious fact in the case concerns the observation made by several people of two round, red marks on either side of the neck, two inches directly below the ear.

Later that day Eugenio, the second witness, came to our hotel. He told us that he disagreed with the idea that Ramon suffered a simple heart attack. He confirmed that Ramon was prostrate and already dead when he arrived on the scene with Ze Zinho. He noticed the round, red-purple, smooth marks on the neck, about one and a quarter inch in diameter. "I have seen many bodies," he told us, "but never anything like this."

He traveled along with the corpse back to town, and on arrival he noticed that the marks had turned a deeper shade of purple. He suggested that an autopsy be performed, but the family did not authorize it. He did examine the whole body carefully and found no other marks.

That night, according to Eugenio, the sky had been illuminated from 10:00 P.M. to midnight by a light that reminded him of the glow of a city.

We returned to Ramon's house armed with this information, and we interviewed his children again. His son, who is twenty, confirmed that Ramon was only forty when he died, that he had never had any problem with his heart, and that he was not taking any medication on a regular basis. When he went hunting he took only a headache pill with him, not aspirin as we had been told but a similar medication called Fontol.

The children and their mother went to the site of Ramon's death two weeks after his funeral. He had placed his hammock in a "very high tree in dense woods." Everything around it was normal, except for some foliage that was torn off where he had grabbed it.

We went through Ramon's health record again: he was muscular but not fat; he had no history of tiredness or of difficult breathing. He did not smoke and his family has no history of heart conditions. In fact, Ramon's own father is still alive and well.

We closely examined photographs of Ramon's face as he lay in his coffin prior to burial. The angle of the pictures was such that we could not verify whether or not there were circular marks on his neck.

Later that night we met with Sr. Barros, the former mayor of Parnarama, who was Ramon's boss at the time. He had been surprised by his death: Ramon was in good shape and had no work problems, he told us.

Had Ramon died of overexertion as he struggled to bring his hammock down from the tree at dawn, on an empty stomach and low blood sugar level? Or was his death precipitated in some way by a chupa encounter during the night? We came away from this case without the key pieces of evidence that would have enabled us to resolve the issue.

SOUZA, THE HUNTER

The case of Raimundo Souza was first published in December 1981 in a sensational U.S. tabloid article entitled "UFOs Murder Four Men." In that piece the former chief of police of Parnarama, Lieutenant Magela, was quoted as saying that he had seen the body, as well as that of another victim, and that the corpses had been "drained of blood."

We flew to São Luís, where he now works, to review the case with Lieutenant Magela, and we quickly established that he had not in fact seen the bodies, contrary to what the tabloid had reported in typically hyperbolic fashion. As for the draining of the blood, he regarded it as a ridiculous suggestion. But he did confirm some important facts.

Magela's experience as police chief during the key period of the wave in 1981 and 1982 is very interesting. He had himself observed flying luminous objects, including red lights rotating around the television installations on the summit of the Serra de Tarantide. At one time an object triggered a failure of the oil-powered diesel generator for the TV station, and he was called to inspect the burned-out motor.

He not only took numerous witness accounts from people who saw the objects, but he himself saw a light as big as the full moon and an object shaped "like the cupola of St. Peter's." In two cases the objects flew over witnesses who panicked and fell. On one occasion he was called to drive to Teresina a woman who had broken her clavicle; there was another case with a broken arm.

According to Lieutenant Magela, Raimundo Souza, forty, was a professional hunter and was in good health. He was waiting for game one night in August 1981 when he struck a match to light a cigarette. His hunting companion, Anastasio Barbosa, believes that the light of the match revealed their position to an object that rapidly came over them and aimed a beam at them. Seeing this, Barbosa dropped from his hammock, crept under the bushes, and watched the object as it circled above before leaving. Scared, he remained in the underbrush until daylight, when he discovered Souza's body. It was lying on the ground where he had fallen from the hammock, breaking one arm, and it bore several purple marks. These marks were on the upper torso, the arms, the whole body, but not on the face. There were no puncture wounds anywhere.

Lieutenant Magela, who was in charge of this criminal investigation, took testimony from Barbosa and a dozen other people who had attended the victim. He is certain of the report's credibility. The marks were circular and smooth like a bruise, ranging in size from one inch to two and a half inches.

No autopsy was done, but the entire body was carefully examined. The marks did not change between the time of death and the time of burial. In the absence of an autopsy, Magela agrees there is no evidence that the light of the UFO inflicted the fatal injuries. Instead, it is possible that Souza died of heart failure when he felt the beam hitting him and panicked, falling from the hammock. The marks on the body are consistent with those observed in other cases in which the victims survived. Given the evidence, Barbosa was not suspected of having killed his companion.

The above is only a selection of the most relevant injury cases among the many firsthand accounts we heard in Parnarama. In many other cases men observed UFOs and were exposed to the light while riding horses. In one incident in 1983 the horse was frightened and fell, but there were no subsequent ill effects. In a remote *fazenda*, workers told us they often saw the light, which made the ground so bright one could see a needle as if it were daylight.

The activity in the Parnarama region has not stopped: The Sunday before our arrival (which would have been July 24, 1988) Antonio José Carvalho, while fishing in the Parnaiba, saw a blue light accompanied by a steady white light. He was not scared by it, until the object flew overhead and disappeared suddenly. He told us that he gave up his fishing activity and hurried home.

Two people gave us testimony about the physical nature of the beam. Luís Silveira, twenty-two at the time of the incident, was walking through the Interior in 1978 when he saw a light shining on him from the sky. He ran back to the house where he collapsed, drained of strength. He had a high fever for two days, but had no marks on his body, not even a sunburn. He said there were "several colors in the same beam," which made him "feel strange and nervous." He had a headache that passed rapidly.

Another witness, Manuel Duarte Pinheiro, gave us a firsthand description of a very recent experience with the beam of light, in an incident that had taken place on Friday, July 15, 1988, eleven days before our arrival.

Pinheiro was outside with his companions at 4:00 A.M., getting ready to go to work, when they saw a light coming from the north, meandering, "looking around," and making a bright spot on the ground. The eight witnesses saw the object shine on one place, turn off, then shine on another spot. When it was off, the witnesses saw nothing at all in the sky. It was as if only the light were real. They ran for cover as the beam, playfully, seemed to chase them around.

At one time Pinheiro was caught in the light and looked straight at it.

"It hurts your eyes," he told us. "It makes them water. It's very hot on the eyes. It is constant in color and intensity, with sharp edges."

It is worth noting that in many of these incidents the victims were hunters who in turn became hunted, struck from above by a

212

beam very much in the manner of their own hunting technique. As we walked along the dirt trails around Parnarama at dark, we could easily understand the ominous feelings of the hunters who had seen the chupa and the panic they experienced when an unexpected light appeared suddenly above them.

14

High Beams

The Acarau River is another stream that flows north from the Interior of Brazil to the wide marshes, salt basins, and swamps at the edge of the Atlantic Ocean. After a four-hour drive west of Fortaleza, the road turns north at Sobral and becomes an interminable dusty trail all the way to Santana, where mud and wood huts covered with broad leaves line up on both sides.

As soon as we arrived there, asking our way to the house of a witness who had recently moved, an old woman volunteered her own observation, just a year ago, on the very road where we stood. A round, moon-size object flew over her, lighting up the ground as it moved.

We started on the trail that leads to the Santa Rita Fazenda, a twisted country road where we spent an hour to cover twelve kilometers, occasionally enjoying the welcome shade of banana, mango, and cashew nut trees. Near the *fazenda* we had to slow down further on the rocky road. After we replaced a tire that did not resist the harsh treatment, we followed in the dust of a herd of cows led by cowboys in typical red leather coat and hat, designed to enable them to move through the heavy brush. They led us to the main house, where a rancher told us that he "had never believed those stories," until one night, as he was fishing in one of the property's numerous lakes, two objects flew over him.

A fifty-two-year-old man named Almundo Marie Araugo told us that during the winter of 1979, around midnight, he and his companions saw three objects behind them, each the size of the full moon, as they hunted armadillos. They turned off their lights and hid in the thick underbrush. The objects flew over them with a yellow to orange light, as bright as daylight. There was no noise. Their dogs were nervous and stayed close to them until the objects flew away.

There is a legend in the Acarau valley about a small being similar to the elves of Celtic folklore. This being is about four feet tall, and is called a Caipora. An old man we interviewed at the Santa Rita Fazenda told us that he knew people who were alive today who had seen the Caipora. Older folks said that one should give him *fumo* (chewing tobacco), and that dogs that meet the Caipora become afraid and unable to hunt any more. The Caipora is humanoid in shape and can go from one point to another instantly, without using his legs, in the manner of modern UFO entities.

Back in the village we spoke to forty-five-year-old Antonio Gomes, who, in July 1987, saw two blinding red lights above him as he was fishing in the Acarau River. He took cover at the foot of a tall tree as the lights moved together above him, apparently connected to a single, solid object.

Aiming his long-barrel gun between the two lights, he fired at the dark rectangular shape and heard a ping sound as the shot hit metal. The object left, evidently unharmed.

We next interviewed the daughter of "Chico" Chiliano, who also saw a UFO over the Acarau River as he was fishing in May 1984. The light was so strong that it illuminated the pebbles in the riverbed. He fled to the shore, but he felt very weak, his body heavy; he sought shelter under a large tree rather than running away. The object flew around and around as if it were looking for him; eventually it went away.

Gathering up his courage, Chiliano walked off toward a fence and began climbing over it to get home, but suddenly the light was there again, and he felt heat "as if walking in front of an oven with an open door." He came home scratched, shaking and gasping, but suffered no lasting effects.

A few months later, in August 1984, his wife, Maria Frota, encountered a similar object at 10:00 P.M. while she was returning from town. It was dark and she was smoking a cigarette when a luminous object flew over her. She hid in the bushes on the river's edge. As soon as the object passed, she went on her way and reached the same fence, where the light caught up with her. It was larger this time, changing from yellow to green before lifting up into the sky. Maria put her arms around the trunk of the tree that sheltered her until the object flew away.

She was afraid and chronically nervous after this, but her daughter told us that she suffered no burns, no marks, and no ill effects. She died of natural causes in September 1986 at the age of forty-six.

We heard of many such UFO cases in the region of Sobral and Santana, but there were no reports of medical injuries—a fact that enabled us to better calibrate the sightings in Parnarama and those we would later investigate in Belém.

What I remember most from our trip there: the hospitality of the people who opened their homes and their minds to us; a flock of parrots flying in the distance while we argued about the Caipora with an old rancher; a brilliant iguana dashing out of the bushes ahead of the car like a multicolored dragon from another age.

And the sincerity with which people told of their experiences! A sincerity, a straightforwardness I had rarely seen in France, in the United States, in the more "advanced" countries. I am used to people saying, "You will think I am crazy, but I saw this object," or simply withholding key information, admitting to paranormal events only as a last resort. I am used to witnesses who have been brain-

TABLE 2
Claims of UFO-Related Deaths*

CASE	DATE	VICTIM	SURVIVAL TIME	SYMPTOMS
1. Aracriguama, Brazil	1946	Joao Prestes	6 hours	Detached Flesh
2. Mount Kenya, Africa	June 1954	Whole Village	N.A.	N.A.
3. Duas Pontes, Brazil	Aug. 20, 1962	Rivalino do Alevia, 54	N.A.	Vanished
4. Niterói, Brazil	Aug. 20, 1966	Miguel Viana, 34	N.A.	None
		Manuel Pereira, 32	N.A.	None
5. Anolaima, Colombia	July 5, 1969	Arcesio Bermudez, 54	7 days	Diarrhea, Vomiting
6. Colares, Brazil	Oct. 1977	Woman	12 hours	Red skin, Punctures
7. Parnarama, Brazil	Oct. 17, 1981	Abel Boro	1 hour	Unknown
8. Parnarama, Brazil	Oct. 19, 1981	Raimundo Souza	N.A.	Unknown
9. Parnarama, Brazil	1981 or 1982	José Vitorio	N.A.	Unknown
10. Parnarama, Brazil	1981 or 1982	Dionizio General	3 days	Unknown
11. Cocalinho, Brazil	Aug. 26, 1982	Ramon	N.A.	Unknown

* Accidental deaths have been excluded.

washed by scientific superstars and television academics into believing that everything in the cosmos can be explained rationally
by modern science.

The people of the Interior are closer to nature than any scientist:
they survive by observing and noticing, by understanding patterns
in wild things and natural phenomena over an area half as big as
the United States, where few scientists have ever set foot.

Nobody has ever ridiculed these people. Their intelligence has

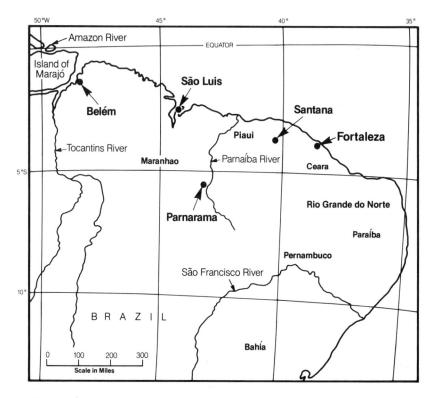

Figure 4. Detail of northeast Brazil

never been insulted by the pundits of the *New York Times* or the arbiters of rationalism of *Le Monde*. They speak in simple, direct ways about what they saw. They admit to being scared, and when they speak about illness and death it is in the same calm, even voice with which one speaks about the reality of all the mysteries around us.

During the long drive back from the valley of the Acarau we tried to come to grips with the nature of the evidence. Was someone testing an exotic weapon over the vast Interior of Brazil, where communications are almost nil and where chances of observation are small? This hypothesis could explain some cases, but it quickly runs into a logical contradiction: what kind of sophisticated weapons

218

system would need to chase an easy target like Manuel for seven hours through the underbrush without once getting a clean shot? We already have helicopters that give off no light and make no sound, and we have many Rambo types who would have nailed Manuel between the eyes with one bullet from a rifle with an infrared scope before he had made a single move to leave his hammock.

The evidence, once again, seems as incontrovertible as it is absurd. And local legends are rising to meet this level of absurdity: some people believe the chupa sucks the blood of its victims to take it to the moon. Or to America, which seems even farther away when the sun comes down from the north and sets behind the massive black hills.

If you look at the map (figure 4) you will see that the region we crisscrossed in our investigations ranges from French Guiana to Natal; in other words, from the European spaceport at Kourou, where new launching pads are being prepared for the Ariane V rocket, to the Brazilian space facility at Barrera do Inferno. But the main concentrations of sightings are in primitive areas, away from the technology centers. There is a single correlation with surface features, and it concerns large bodies of water: the Parnaiba, the Acarau, the vast bays at São Luís. And, of course, as we found out at the end of our trip, the ocean near Belém.

15

Ground Truth

I t is in the islands around Belém, where the waters of the Tarantins and the Amazon majestically come to meet the ocean one degree south of the equator, that the 1977 Brazilian wave culminated; and it is there that for the first time the proof of the reality of the phenomenon was obtained. More specifically, as Daniel Rebisso Giese has revealed, the culmination took place over a three-month period from July to September 1977 on the island of Colares and on the beach of Baia do Sol, on the island of Mosqueiro.[1]

We found fishermen there who had witnessed the objects, and a doctor who had ministered to the medical needs of dozens of people hit by the light from the chupa. She confirmed that one of her patients died after the experience. Several of these witnesses also told us that they had observed two teams of Brazilian military men filming the objects, attempting contact.

Ground truth: there was no denying the wave of 1977. It started in June near Cape Gurupi, north of the town of Vizeu, and it moved in both directions along the coast: toward São Luís to the east and toward Belém to the west during June and July; it reached a peak in September and October.

The reason the phenomenon could not be denied was very simple: every evening the UFOs appeared, coming from the north. In some cases, they flew down from the sky, in others, they emerged out of the ocean. I saw a photograph of an object with a luminous white ring flying right out of the brackish water at dusk.

They came over the islands at low altitude and circled; they descended as if to land; they made loops and accelerated suddenly; they hovered over houses and probed the inside with beams. They even emerged out of larger objects and reentered them. And this happened on schedule, every evening for three months.

The panic on the island of Colares, according to a firsthand witness who lived through the ordeal, was hard to imagine. All the people who were able to leave, including the dentist and the school teachers, abandoned their posts. People who had family on the mainland left. The sheriff fled.

The objects were never alone. On numerous photographs taken by journalists they are seen accompanied by smaller probes. They exhibit a variety of shapes that would drive an aeronautical engineer to insanity. They range in size from starlike objects to things as big as two 737s end to end. The larger objects were more frequent than the smaller ones; and they hovered in the sky, apparently secure in the belief that out there, in the mist and the mud at the mouth of the Amazon, nobody would ever bother them. Perhaps they knew that the Brazilian Air Force had issued confidential orders directing air traffic away from the area.

There was nothing elusive about these objects. They were not the fleeting phenomena so often described in the American literature or the dreamlike manifestations experienced by the contactees, which become even more dreamlike under hypnotic regression. There was a superior technology at work over Colares, and all the observers could do was to film it and watch in awe.

Doctor Wellaide Cecim Carvalho de Oliveira, who had stayed on the island throughout the duration of the wave, agreed to speak with me. As the director of the community health center on the archipelago of Marajo (population: 6,000), she was quoted by Daniel Rebisso Giese in his report. She amplified her earlier testimony about the medical cases in the area.

Ground truth: Dr. Carvalho had worked in Colares eight months when she started to see patients who claimed to have been attacked by strange lights. Until then she had ascribed such stories to hallucinations and drunkenness. She had to revise her conclusions when she found that her patients presented similar symptoms:

1. A feeling of weakness; some could hardly walk
2. Dizziness and headaches
3. Local losses of sensitivity. Numbness and trembling
4. Pallid complexion
5. Low arterial pressure
6. Anemia, with low hemoglobin levels
7. Blackened skin where the light had hit, with several red-purple circles, hot and painful, 1 inch to $1\frac{1}{4}$ inches in diameter (see plates 16 and 17)
8. Two puncture marks inside the red circles resembling mosquito bites, hard to the touch
9. Hair in the blackened area fell out and did not rejuvenate, as if follicles had been destroyed
10. No nausea or diarrhea

The doctor told me that at the time she did not have access to a sophisticated lab for further tests, but she did establish a drop in red blood cells in all patients. She put the victims under observation for four or five days.

About twenty patients between the ages of eighteen and fifty, many of them young men, were treated this way. They all told the same story: They had been resting in their hammocks when the light hit them from above. They were immediately immobilized, as if a heavy weight pushed against their chest. The beam was about three inches in diameter and white in color. It never hunted for them but hit them suddenly.

When they tried to scream, no sound would come out, but their eyes remained open. The beam felt hot, "almost as hot as a cigarette burn," barely tolerable. After a few minutes the column of light would slowly retract and disappear.

The beam never hit the victims on the hands or the arms, always on the neck and torso. The discoloration and the mark appeared immediately. The body hair fell out later. And everything usually returned to normal after seven days.

There were several exceptions; in one case a forty-eight-year-old woman was seriously hurt. She had awakened during the night and had started to crochet to pass the time, when the light suddenly hit her chest. After it withdrew, she went to military doctors, who gave her a simple tranquilizer (Somalium) and five milligrams of Diazepan, which made her sleep. In the morning she came to the health center seeking treatment, but she never fully recovered, and she has continuing symptoms of dizziness and weakness to this day.

In another case, a thirty-two-year-old male victim suffered a similar fate. And one woman, as stated in chapter 9, died the day after her exposure to the light, which seems to have aggravated a preexistent cardiac condition.

Ground truth: when the wave of reports and medical injuries reached the town center, people panicked. They did not sleep for fear of night attacks. Only the priest, the mayor, and the doctor remained behind when the pillars of the community made their getaway. The buses were crammed with people leaving. At night, fishermen refused to go out. Soon there was nothing to eat; the people had to resort to canned food and whatever could be brought over from the mainland.

People drank coffee throughout the night to stay awake. When they saw anything unusual flying overhead, they set off fireworks and beat on pans to scare it away.

The federal government eventually sent a military team with strict orders to observe but not to interfere. One witness to whom we spoke got to know all the team members. They had a base on the beach, another on the road, higher up. They rotated. There were biologists, physicists, medical doctors, chemists—forty men in all with tents, cameras, tape recorders, and telescopes. They were from southern states and had grades up to captain. They had trucks, drugs, thermometers, and blood pressure machines. They treated people during the night when they were up and waiting for the objects.

Ground truth: we asked Dr. Carvalho to tell us about her own sighting, which occurred one day at 6:00 P.M., and she told us it was the most beautiful thing she had ever witnessed. Even today, if she closes her eyes, she can make the image appear again. "I have forgotten a lot of things in ten years," she stated, "but I will never forget this!"

It was a brilliant, large cylinder with a purple light at the top and at the bottom, shining in concentric rings. It flew low over the street, dancing in majestic circles as it moved. There were no doors or windows. Her maid fainted and fell when she saw the object, but Dr. Carvalho ignored her and followed the object in a state she described as "almost ecstatic," so beautiful the vision was. She hoped it would land and take her.

A group of people rushed out from the town, beating on drums and saucepans, shooting fireworks. The object went on dancing, higher and higher, and it flew away.

A few nights later, one of the objects came in very low and landed on the soccer field. The military rushed toward it, hoping to make contact, but the crowd was there first, with drums and noisemakers, and it flew off.

How ironic, that we are hoping to communicate with alien beings when we cannot even communicate among ourselves; that military and civilians cannot agree on the reality of the phenomenon; that data cannot be shared among doctors, among investigators, among countries.

All the medical data we gathered during our trip seems to be consistent with the conclusion that UFOs are able to focus on selected human subjects a beam of radiation that contains, among other things, pulsed microwaves that interfere with the central nervous system. Such a beam could cause the dizziness, headaches, paralysis, pricklings, and numbness reported to us by so many witnesses. It could also create long-term behavioral effects, changes in sleep patterns, even delusionary episodes and hallucinations. It is the entire phenomenology of UFO contact claims that will now have to be revised.

Where is the proof of all this? The reader is entitled to ask, as Janine and I did, when we met with the people who had lived through the experience, along the beach at Baia do Sol.

The answer gave me food for thought. There were not one but two series of photographs, movie films, and tape recordings that were made during this period. The military team, which operated in full view of the population, is known to have compiled a thick report with a wealth of physical measurements attached. The report was sent to higher authorities in Brasília, where it presumably disappeared into a drawer.

The second team was composed of journalists and cameramen who were almost as well equipped as the military. They obtained excellent photos, which can be consulted in the newspaper archives of that period. Unfortunately, as I indicated earlier, only the negatives have scientific potential. And all the negatives taken by the newspaper teams have left Brazil, purchased from the publishers by an unnamed American firm.

Somebody in the United States owns a collection of records that contains the proof of the reality of the phenomenon.

Ground truth: there is a simple reason for the absence of open academic interest in the UFO phenomenon. As we have seen throughout this book, it is not lack of evidence.

On the contrary.

The evidence that has now been obtained by the major powers is so valid and it has such devastating implications for future military systems that the decision has been made to keep it under lock and key, and to entrust its study only to highly specialized teams with selected, compartmented access. In my opinion, the work of these teams is doomed to failure, as it has been since 1953, in spite of all the resources behind it and in spite of the absurd disinformation operation that surrounds it to keep it secure.

The UFO phenomenon cannot be compartmentalized. It is global in nature and it touches every part of human knowledge—from folklore to astrophysics, from ethnology to microwaves, from particles to parapsychology.

Ground truth: what happened at Baia do Sol can happen again anywhere, tomorrow. I detest the thought that it will find us unprepared. Once again.

Conclusion

The material gathered in this book represents only a portion of the cases I have personally investigated and a very small percentage of the data compiled by other researchers and by official agencies. The realization that none of this material has ever been seriously examined by professional scientists is staggering. Strictly in terms of the sociology of science, the refusal to consider the facts of the UFO phenomenon is a remarkable statement about the narrow limits within which our society authorizes the serious pursuit of knowledge. My hope is that, in some small way, this report on my own fieldwork will help change this situation.

What the public learns about the phenomenon comes from that small portion of the facts that has been preselected by believers to promote enthusiastic support for the extraterrestrial theory. I think I have shown that the time has come to take a wider view of the problem and to conduct a new, objective assessment of the accumulated material.

Among the great variety of observations that compose the UFO phenomenon, I believe it is the careful documentation of the physical effects and their medical consequences that can provide new breakthroughs rather than the abduction cases that have become fashionable because of their sensational nature.

Throughout this book the careful documentation of physiological effects and injuries has been my primary objective. I have tried to clarify the extent and the types of these injuries. In these cases, the decision to help the witnesses should not be based on whether we believe in UFOs or reject the idea. Here are human beings who obviously need assistance; they present consistent symptoms that could not be self-inflicted or simulated.

It is remarkable that we found our greatest concentration of injury cases in Brazil, one of the few areas of the world that remains of difficult access for scientists and also combines remoteness, large expanses of uncharted, unpopulated land, and access to immense amounts of water. At one time, in fact, the Brazilian Air Force and Navy Intelligence speculated that actual UFO bases might exist somewhere between the mouth of the Amazon and the São Luís area.

Beyond the evidence of the injuries suffered by many witnesses, a new question is now posed: how should we react against the potentially hostile action of the phenomenon?

Hostility, as I have pointed out, can be taken at two levels. First-order hostility, as manifested in Korea in 1951, or in Parnarama in more recent years, involves direct hits against people, injuries to the nervous system, and occasional deaths. Yet the beam does not seem effective as a weapon. We have noted that silent helicopters equipped with the tools of modern anti-guerrilla warfare could have done away in minutes with the isolated Brazilian hunters. In the Iron Triangle incident, witnesses to the battle against the UFO have survived nearly forty years to talk about it, although they may have suffered debilitating, lingering injuries.

In earlier, innocent days UFO injuries could be called accidental. Dr. J. Allen Hynek compared the effects suffered by Floyd and Michalak to what happens when a child puts two fingers into an

electrical socket: one should not infer from the result, alarming
it is, that the utility company is hostile. These days of innocenc
and rationalization are gone; the witnesses of Parnarama and Colares were deliberately zapped by a superb, advanced technology
that did not care whether its effects were lethal or not.

In recent years the major powers have done much development
of their own in the area of beam weaponry.[1] Microwave technology
is now used under the general acronym HPM (high-power microwave) to jam or burn the electronic hardware of enemy missiles,
aircraft, and tanks.

Generators for the types of beams used in the new weapons include magnetrons and klystrons, as well as newer devices with
names like gyrotron and vircator (virtual cathode oscillator). Vir-
cators are especially relevant here. They operate in pulse mode at
demonstrated powers up to twenty gigawatts.

An obvious biological effect of microwaves is that they heat tissue.
Brain temperature changes of only a few degrees have been shown
to cause convulsions, unconsciousness, and amnesia in rats. Even
weaker microwave pulses, too weak to heat animal tissue, can have
serious effects by disturbing cell membranes. Howard Wachtel and
his colleagues at the University of Colorado have shown that the
activity of nerve cells could be temporarily altered by a single microwave pulse.[2] They have also observed "a brief depression in the
electroencephalograms of rodents exposed to similar pulses," and
they add that "the effects of such pulses on humans is unknown."

In his review of the field, Dr. Keith Florig, an expert on policy
issues involving ionizing and non-ionizing radiation, notes that
"HPM weapons that merely stun the nervous system temporarily
seem, like short-acting chemical agents, to be more humane than
lethal force. . . . HPM weapons that blind, burn or bake people to
death are likely to be viewed as an abhorrent addition to the arsenal."

It seems that the objects observed in Brazil had no such reser-
vations.

Interestingly, Dr. Florig remarks that "the difference between a
disabling and a lethal (force) is largely one of range. So it would be

hard to show that a weapon intended to disable could not be lethal at short range."

The power requirements of beam weapons are such that they will be deployed initially either on land or on large ships. It is difficult to conceive, in our present state of technology, of a pulsed microwave beam carried aloft by anything as small as a chupa. But perhaps a weapon designed only to disable humans on the ground would not need to be heavy and large. Here again, the UFOs seem to represent an alien force that anticipates our own scientific development by decades, mocking our efforts to identify its nature and its long-term intentions. Understandably, the military establishment does not feel comfortable with the disclosure of our weakness any more than the scientific establishment feels inclined to confessing its ignorance.

Future progress will have to come from a few individuals with enough courage to go into the field themselves, to meet the unknown face-to-face.

Appendix

Bringing Order Out of Chaos: Definitions and Classifications

The infinite variety of phenomena that somehow make their way into the UFO literature is so bewildering that the scientist finds few handles to begin a rational study. How could a specialist analyze within the same project reports as diverse as those involving the medical sequelae of Dr. X and the peculiar magnesium from Ubatuba? What can we do when one report describes a strange object flying overhead, creating a whirlwind in its wake, and the next report involves a whirlwind but no flying object at all, as we saw in one of the Valensole cases?

Consider also the abduction reports: in most cases, the witnesses state that they were stopped on a lonely road and that beings took them inside a UFO, where they were examined. Yet this scenario, which has been presented in many recent books, is by no means universal. There are reports of abductions where the body of the abductee never left the car, while his or her consciousness was said to be lifted into a hovering object. There are also many cases of abductions that do not involve a UFO at all. In other words, the witnesses report leaving their body and going to another realm.

In some instances there were people present who can swear that the body of the witness did not leave the earth, although the authenticity of the interaction, as perceived by the subject, must be seriously considered.

In this appendix I propose to try to come up with definitions and classifications that can help us to recognize what we are looking for. By suggesting priorities, and by providing the missing handles, such a system can save us much valuable research time, and it can enable us to exchange data more efficiently in the future. Most significantly, it can also bring to light some unrecognized patterns.

DEFINITIONS

Despite the massive interest in UFO sightings, there have been few attempts at defining the phenomenon itself. For the enthusiasts, such definitions are not needed since they already know what UFOs are: they are . . . well, flying saucers! When you see one you recognize it, because it's round and it has lights on it. What if the night is dark and you see only some lights? Well, you just have to assume there is a round shape in the dark somewhere behind the lights. What if the lights are so elusive that you can't really say whether they belong to a UFO or not? Well, you use your intuition! I have seen some UFO celebrities pointing at distant street lamps, passing headlights, and flickering fireflies as evidence of alien craft observing them.

For those scientists who have not been completely nauseated by this exercise and have had the patience to apply their critical abilities to the phenomenon, the UFO is simply "any sighting that is puzzling to the observer," as the Condon Report put it. But this definition errs in the opposite direction; it is much too vague and too broad, because anything will sooner or later be puzzling to somebody. That does not make it a topic fit for scientific research.

In his thoughtful book *The UFO Experience*, J. Allen Hynek took a more careful approach, insisting that we should be interested only in those cases that remain unexplained after study by competent scientists. He wrote that we could "simply"(?) define the UFO as

the reported perception of an object or light seen in the sky or upon the land, the appearance, trajectory or general dynamics and luminescent behavior of which do not suggest a logical, conventional explanation and which is not only mystifying to the original percipients but remains unidentified after close scrutiny of all available evidence by persons who are technically capable of making a common sense identification, if one is possible.[1]

We may have to live with this type of definition until we know more about the phenomenon, but it presents certain bothersome problems. It is not operational, since it relies on an arbitrary group of "technically capable persons" to do the screening. As people in the legal profession know well, for every expert who is willing to assert in court that $A + B = C$, one can produce an expert with equally impeccable credentials who will testify that $A + B \neq C$, or even that A and B should never have been added together in the first place.

Hynek's definition of a UFO is insufficient because it assumes that there is a group of wise, technically capable people somewhere who can always reach a consensus to decide, for example, whether a particular light in the sky could, or could not, be a reflection from the wings of a distant aircraft.

Another problem with the definition is that it leaves out many phenomena that most ufologists find relevant to their work. For example, it does not leave room for reports of beings seen by themselves, independent of "an object or light," and it does not encompass cases in which a pattern of unusual physical effects was observed, suggesting a UFO phenomenon, although no "object or light" was seen.

Although this situation is frustrating, it is not unique in science. Similar problems are found in pure mathematics. An excellent example is provided by prime numbers. For many centuries the finest minds in mathematics have tried to come up with a direct characterization of prime numbers: there is no formula that will automatically generate the nth prime number, or all the prime numbers, to the same extent that we have formulas that will generate all the even numbers and all the odd numbers. We know that five is a prime number because it can be divided only by one and by itself, but what about 21,637? The only way to find out is to try all possible prime factors.

We do know that even numbers like 232 cannot be prime because we can always divide them by two. Some odd numbers cannot be prime either; for example, those ending with five. In such cases, mathematicians give a two-part definition: (1) prime numbers are to be found among a set that includes one, two, three, five, and those odd integers greater than five that do not end in five; and (2) an empirical "recipe" is provided to test whether or not a given member of this set is prime or not.

Twenty-five years ago, in *Anatomy of a Phenomenon*, I proposed to apply the same construct to a definition of UFOs. The first part of an updated definition would state:

> UFO phenomena *are to be found* among reports of objects, lights, beings, or physical effects that are regarded by the witnesses as anomalies because of their appearance or behavior.

The second part of the definition would be an empirical recipe that could be used to determine if a given report of such an anomaly belongs to the UFO phenomenon or not. But aren't we right back to Hynek's problem? Since we can test the genuineness of a UFO only by eliminating what it is *not* (not a helicopter, not a plane, nor a bird, etc.), where are we going to find the group of wise experts who can be relied upon to apply the same body of specialized knowledge to all the cases? Fortunately, there is now a good answer to this question, an answer that did not exist twenty-five years ago.

THE SCREENING PROBLEM

Assume that we now face the following situation: we are in charge of an operational center for the monitoring of unusual aerial phenomena, and we must separate UFO reports from ordinary effects. Furthermore, we are concerned with the frequency of UFO reports. In quiet periods a screening center may not get more than two or three UFO reports a day. But the situation is very different during a wave. At the height of the 1952 flap in the United States, the Air Force was getting two hundred reports a day.

Given this background, how would our monitoring center function? Clearly it is out of the question to dispatch field investigators to interview witnesses of two hundred reported sightings every day. We need to eliminate marginal cases that have a high probability of having conventional explanations, and to assign priorities to the few potentially significant cases—those that can teach us something new about the phenomenon.

Our second problem is the acute need for highly specialized expertise, which makes it unlikely that any single scientist can be knowledgeable about the entire range of conventional phenomena that can explain UFOs. Although I have spent enough hours tracking things in the sky to be familiar with any astronomical phenomenon, I remember being utterly shocked the first time I witnessed an Air Force refueling operation. I also remember being on a radio panel with a respected space scientist who seriously thought UFOs could all be explained by the floating material in the liquid medium of the eye.

What we need is a uniform, standard system of knowledge that contains all the rules for the recognition of everything from refueling operations to flotsam in the cornea, and which will consider *all* hypotheses to make an impartial judgment.

O V N I B A S E : A SCREENING SYSTEM

Over the past ten years computer science has evolved rapidly in the representation of human knowledge and of complex decision making. Some of the resulting developments are directly applicable to our problem of screening UFO reports among all other potential anomalies. During 1985 and 1986 I developed an expert system called OVNIBASE (*OVNI* is the initialism for *UFO* in French) that has many of the desired characteristics. The program, which was presented before the American Institute of Aeronautics and Astronautics and the Society for Scientific Exploration, is an expert system that contains the rules of recognition of the phenomena most commonly mistaken as UFOs.

Such a system can integrate the contributions made by specialists of many disciplines into a single whole. It presents the added advantage of being portable (my version can work on the Macintosh or the IBM PC-AT and compatibles) and usable by people such as a clerk or a secretary who are untrained in the relevant specialties. All the user has to do is to fill out a very simple form that includes the year of the sighting, whether it was daylight or night, the duration in minutes, the number of objects, and a true/false answer to the question "Was the trajectory continuous?" (*Unknown* is an acceptable answer.)

Based on these simple pieces of data, OVNIBASE will make inferences, looking through its list of hypotheses to find out which rules apply and asking specific questions to guide its reasoning.

Because the system functions in real time, it can be used to screen reports while the witness is on the telephone. Future versions could be made available to the public through communication networks using home terminals, such as the MINITEL network in France.

In spite of the current progress in artificial intelligence, most computer scientists agree that no expert system can replace human judgment. A program like OVNIBASE should eliminate at least 50% of all UFO reports, otherwise it is not very useful as a screening tool, but it should not eliminate more than 75% of them, or it will enter an area where human judgment should be able to intervene.

The most useful products of OVNIBASE are a printed report of all "rejected cases" *with the reason for the rejection* in the form of a list of recognition rules that were true and corresponded to a natural explanation, and a report of all possible or probable UFOs with the list of all the patterns of natural phenomena that are contradicted by the data. It is then up to the analyst to override the system's judgment if it is felt that special circumstances make some of the rules irrelevant.

We have now improved on the earlier definitions of the UFO phenomenon by (1) stating where instances of it could be found, and (2) providing an automaton that embodies the empirical knowledge necessary to separate possible and probable UFOs from conventional phenomena.

It is this residue of genuine UFO reports that we now have to classify.

EARLY CLASSIFICATION SYSTEMS FOR U F O PHENOMENA

To my knowledge, the first classification system for UFO phenomena grew out of my work in 1961 and 1962 with Aimé Michel and with Dr. Pierre Guerin in Paris. I proposed to separate the massive collections of French sightings into four major categories. Briefly summarized, they encompassed the following:

Type I, which was divided into three subgroups, gathered all the landing reports that Allen Hynek would later call close encounters. It may be hard for the modern reader to realize that until the late Sixties American ufology did not admit that such reports even existed. Among the major civilian organizations, only APRO, headed up by Jim and Coral Lorenzen, recognized their significance. The Air Force's Project Blue Book automatically sent landing reports into the psychological category.

Type II reports were observations of the cloud cigars so prevalent in France in 1954, and whose role in the development of major waves had been discovered by Aimé Michel. It is a source of puzzlement to me that these reports have practically disappeared from the scene. I am unable to speculate about a reason for this change. But the fact is that this category is no longer justified.

Type III were those sightings of objects that had a discontinuity in their trajectory; either they stopped and hovered, or they came toward the earth with a falling leaf motion before resuming their flight, or they performed some maneuver that identified a specific point in space and time. This was important to me since I was compiling a case catalogue in which I wanted to include precise longitudes and latitudes.

Type IV, by contrast, gathered all cases of objects in uninterrupted flight.

This classification served its purpose for many years. It enabled us to discover specific patterns for various types of UFO behavior, notably the law of the times for the landing reports.

In 1972 Allen Hynek built upon this first classification when he proposed in *The UFO Experience* to divide all reports into two groups: the short-range sightings that corresponded to my Type I and which he called close encounters, a term later immortalized by Steven Spielberg; and the objects observed "at some distance," which he further divided into three categories:

1. Nocturnal lights for objects seen at night (NL)
2. Daylight disks for those seen in daytime (DD)
3. Radar-visual for those detected on radar (RV)

Hynek was well aware that this division was arbitrary, and he remarked himself that the categories "may not be mutually exclusive."

The major contribution in Hynek's classification was the clarity with which landings were now defined:

CE1 was the class of objects seen on the ground or at short distance to the observer.

CE2 was the class of close encounters in which physical effects or traces were present.

CE3 was the class of close encounters that involve "entities" or "occupants," a category from which he excluded repeated contact.

237

These categories have withstood the test of time and continue to be useful today. In recent years a fourth category has been added. Called CE4, it encompasses the abduction reports in which the witness has not only seen the occupants but claims to have extensively interacted with them inside their craft.

Serious problems arise, however, when one tries to use Hynek's categories of nocturnal lights, daylight disks, and radar-visual cases, especially when the screening process works from a computerized database, as it will need to do in any sophisticated effort to attack the UFO problem in the future. Not only do those categories overlap, as Hynek had noted, but many reports cannot be placed within any of the classes.

Examples of the former problem are provided by the numerous cases of disks seen in daylight and tracked on radar at the same time. If they are placed into the RV category, the statistics on DD cases are amputated by one potentially important data point, and vice versa.

An example of the latter deficiency is Whitley Strieber's observation of a dark disk flying between him and the field of the stars at night: this was neither a daylight disk nor a nocturnal light.

Other problems arise with daylight objects that are not disks, like the flying hexagon seen by Mr. Dillon in 1928, and with the cases that are observed at dusk or at dawn, and which could conceivably belong to several categories.

The work we have done with computer-based expert systems in the last three years has suggested new, more practical, solutions to these remaining problems, although it must be recognized that no classification system is perfect.

A NEW CLASSIFICATION SYSTEM: ANOMALIES, CLOSE ENCOUNTERS, MANEUVERS, AND FLYBYS

In order to encompass the full range of phenomena one finds in the modern literature, it is important to acknowledge that UFOs are related in significant ways to other anomalies. It is the rule, rather than the exception, to find significant UFO sightings preceded or followed by other anomalies, notably of the poltergeist variety.

For that reason, I have found it useful to begin with a classification of anomalies into four groups that parallel Hynek's close encounter categories:

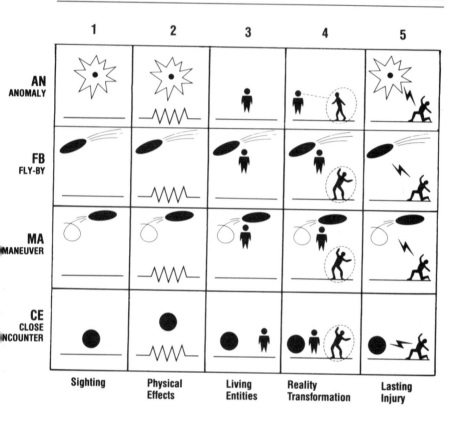

Figure 5. Classification of anomalies related to UFOs

AN1 are anomalies that do not have lasting physical effects, such as amorphous lights or unexplained explosions.

AN2 are anomalies with lasting physical effects, such as some poltergeist phenomena, *apports* (materialized objects), and areas of flattened grass.

AN3 are anomalies with associated entities. This class could include reports of ghosts, yetis, and other instances of cryptozoology as well as elves and spirits.

AN4 are those anomalous reports in which witnesses experienced personal interaction with entities in the reality of the entities themselves. They include near-death experiences, religious miracles and visions, and many cases of out-of-body experiences.

Finally, I place under the AN5 category the cases of anomalous injuries or deaths, such as spontaneous combustion or unexplained wounds. I also place here the cases of permanent healing often described in the literature of the paranormal. The unexplained beating of Mrs. Victor described in chapter 6 belongs in the AN5 category.

We now come to the UFO reports themselves, which I will divide, following Allen Hynek, into close encounters and distant sightings.

I see no reason to change anything to the classification of close encounters which is in current use, from CE1 to CE4, although Hynek himself was not responsible for creating the CE4 category and was not especially happy with it. In recent years the need has become acute for a new category, CE5, which will encompass cases of close encounters in which the witnesses have suffered permanent injuries or other physiological effects.

The distant sightings, in my view, are best classified according to the apparent behavior of the object rather than circumstances independent of it, such as daylight or night, or radar rather than visual observation. Accordingly, I have found it useful to introduce two general categories called MA for "maneuvers" and FB for "flyby." Within these categories I have tried to give definitions that were parallel to those of close encounters:

MA1 gathers those UFO observations that involve an object with a discontinuous trajectory (such as a drop, a maneuver, or a loop).

MA2 includes those cases that give rise to physical effects in addition to a discontinuous trajectory: the episode in Arcachon, described in chapter 1, in which an object triggered the photocell for the whole city, fits in the MA2 category.

MA3 contains the cases of objects with discontinuous trajectories when beings are observed on board. Some of the "airship" cases of the late nineteenth century were in this category, as well as the famous 1959 sighting by Father Gill in New Guinea.

MA4 covers instances of maneuvers accompanied by a sense of transformation of reality for the percipient.

MA5 is a maneuver as a result of which the witnesses suffer permanent injury or death. Part five of this book gives several detailed examples of this category. The reader will note in the index beginning on page 242 that I have also placed under MA5 the case of Dr. X, in which we do not have permanent injuries but permanent healing.

FB1 is a simple sighting of a UFO "flying by" in the sky, the category most frequently reported.

FB2 is a flyby accompanied by physical evidence.

FB3 is a flyby of an object accompanied by the observation of beings on board. Although rare, this type of observation is reported occasionally.

FB4 is a flyby where the witness experienced a transformation of his or her reality into the reality of the object or its occupants.

FB5 would be a flyby as a result of which the witnesses would suffer permanent injuries, as in the celebrated Cash-Landrum case in Texas, which can be found in the literature. In that case, two women and a boy were hurt by the effects of a bright object that flew above them without landing or stopping.

THE S V P CREDIBILITY RATING

No classification system is complete without a way of assigning credibility or "weight" to an observation. While such a procedure is an integral part of any intelligence evaluation task, UFO researchers have rarely bothered to apply it in support of their own work. One exception is the "quality index" proposed by Spanish researchers Ballester and Guasp, but it is so detailed that I have found it difficult to apply in practice.[2] While acknowledging such efforts, it is important to implement a system that is simple enough to be applied quickly and with enough mnemonic value that it does not require constant reference to a user's manual or a set of tables.

In my own work I now use a three-digit code to indicate the weight of a UFO case. Each of the three digits has a value from zero to four, as follows:

FIRST DIGIT: SOURCE RELIABILITY (S)

   0 Unknown source or unreliable source

   1 Report attributed to a known source of uncalibrated reliability

   2 Reliable source, secondhand

   3 Reliable source, firsthand

4 Firsthand personal interview with the witness by a source of proven reliability

SECOND DIGIT: SITE VISIT (V)

0 No site visit, or answer unknown

1 Site visit by a casual person not familiar with such phenomena

2 Site visit by persons familiar with such phenomena

3 Site visit by a reliable investigator with some experience

4 Site visit by a skilled analyst

THIRD DIGIT: POSSIBLE EXPLANATIONS (P)

0 Data consistent with one or more natural causes

1 Natural explanation requires only slight modification of the data

2 Natural explanation requires gross alteration of one parameter

3 Natural explanation requires gross alteration of several parameters

4 No natural explanation possible, given the evidence

In the present book, seventy-one out of the one hundred cases cited have a rating of 222 or better (meaning that each of the three digits is two or higher), indicating *events reported through a reliable source in which a site visit has been made and where a natural explanation would require the gross alteration of at least one parameter*. Fifty-four percent of the cases have a rating of 333 or higher, and 47% have a rating of 443 or even the top weight of 444.

A complete alphabetical case index for all the phenomena mentioned in the book with their classification and credibility rating follows.

Case Index

LOCATION	TYPE	SVP	DATE	TIME	REGION	WITNESSES	PAGE
Anolaima	CE5	444	5-Jul-69	20:30	Colomb	Bermudez	130
Aracriguama	CE5	334	-46	19:00	Brazil	Prestes	124
Arcachon	FB1	443	19-Jun-78	01:30	France	Bachere	35
Arenal	FB1	443	4-Sep-71	08:25	C.Rica	Sergio L.V.	58
Arenal	CE1	443	25-Oct-86	09:00	C.Rica	U.A., L.A.	60
Ashland	CE4	444	3-Dec-67	02:30	Nebrsk	Schirmer	159
Atafona	AN1	430	13-Jun-66	day	Brazil	Elcio, Valdir	9
Aulnat	FB1	442	5-Nov-76	22:00	France	Withheld	31
Aurora	CE3	042	17-Apr-97	day	Texas	Unknown	45
Baia do Sol	CE5	444	Sep-77	night	Brazil	Multiple	220

Case Index

LOCATION	TYPE	SVP	DATE	TIME	REGION	WITNESSES	PAGE
Bogota	MA2	201	-75	04:00	Colomb	Unknown	43
Bolton	CE5	233	23-Jan-76	17:15	U.K.	McLenaghan	122
Bonham	CE1	112	1873		Texas		126
Cajneiro	AN3	323	11-Nov-83	3:30	Brazil	Withheld	201
Campinas	MA2	242	14-Dec-54		Brazil	Withheld	49
Cocalinho	AN5	431	26-Aug-82	06:00	Brazil	Ramon, Curto	207
Cocalinho	MA1	414	15-Jul-88	04:00	Brazil	Pinheiro	212
Colares	CE5	444	Sep-77	night	Brazil	Multiple	136
Colusa	CE3	443	Oct-77	night	Calif	Amos	149
Colusa	FB1	443	18-Oct-77	01:30	Calif	Withheld	167
Council Bluff	MA2	442	17-Dec-77	19:45	Iowa	Withheld	48
Crab Island	AN5	442	-77	night	Brazil		136
Duas Pontes	CE3	444	17-Aug-62	eve	Brazil	Aleuia	125
Duas Pontes	AN3	442	19-Aug-62		Brazil	Aleuia	125
Duas Pontes	CE5	444	20-Aug-62		Brazil	Aleuia	126
Everglades	CE5	444	15-Mar-65	01:00	Florid	Flynn	113
Falcon Lake	CE5	334	20-May-67	12:13	Canada	Michalak	113
Falcone	CE1	203	27-Sep-78	18:40	Italy	Withheld	61
Fort de France	MA1	443	Sep-65	21:15	Martin	Michel F.	27
France SE	MA5	444	2-Nov-68	04:00	France	Dr. "X"	113
French Gulch	CE2	444	30-Oct-69	10:30	Calif	Chapin	183
French Gulch	CE5	443	27-Dec-76	11:00	Calif	Chapin	183
French Gulch	AN1	441	13-Oct-77	day	Calif	Chapin	184
French Gulch	CE3	443	4-Apr-80	day	Calif	Chapin	184
Gilroy	CE1	443	10-Aug-75	23:00	Calif	"Victor"	88
Gilroy	AN5	404	15-May-78		Calif	"Victor"	90
Grumari Beach	AN5	441	Mar-86		Brazil	Barreta	128
Gujan	MA2	444	19-Jun-78	01:30	France	Pavia, Guitard	35
Happy Camp	CE1	443	25-Oct-75	19:00	Calif	Harris, Gayer	164
Happy Camp	AN3	443	27-Oct-75	19:00	Calif	Harris, Gayer	165
Happy Camp	MA3	443	27-Oct-75	20:00	Calif	White et al.	165
Happy Camp	CE4	443	2-Nov-75	eve	Calif	White et al.	165
Happy Camp	MA1	443	8-Feb-76	night	Calif	Gates, Cerny	166
Happy Camp	CE2	443	Fall-77	eve	Calif.	Withheld	166
Happy Camp	FB1	442	6-Sep-77	eve	Calif	Lorraine	167
Happy Camp	AN2	442	17-Jul-77	night	Calif	Pat	167
Happy Camp	AN1	442	24-Jun-78	23:15	Calif	Vallee et al.	169
Happy Camp	AN3	441	Winter-76	eve	Calif	Pat et al.	170
Haynesville	CE2	443	30-Dec-66	20:15	Louisn	Dr. G.	37
Healdsburg	CE3	442	30-Aug-77	20:30	Calif	"Gray"	71
Industrial City	CE4	401	15-Sep-75	night	Calif	"Victor"	92
Iona	AN5	441	-30		U.K.	Fornario	129
Iron Triangle	MA5	404	Spring-51	night	Korea	Wall	122
Japan NE	MA5	444	Spring-59		Japan		127
Kiana	AN2	021			Alaska	Unknown	49

Case Index

244

Notes

Prologue

1. Numerous articles on the Morro do Vintem case were written; in particular, Charles Bowen, "The Mystery of the Morro do Vintem," *Flying Saucer Review* 13, no. 2 (March–April 1967): 11; and Charles Bowen, "No Easy Solution to the Morro Mystery," *FSR* 14, no. 4 (July–August 1968): 36.
2. On the confession of Hamilton Bezani, see Gordon Creighton, "Follow-up on the Morro do Vintem Mystery," *FSR* 17, no. 4 (July–August 1971): 6.

Introduction

1. Jacques Vallee, *Dimensions: A Casebook of Alien Contact* (Chicago: Contemporary Books, 1988; Ballantine Books, 1989).
2. Regarding these hearings, see Subcommittee of Investigations, Committee on Science and Technology, "Information Technology for Emergency Management," 98th Cong., 9 October 1984.

PART ONE

Introduction

1. Among the numerous studies of physical effects of UFOs that have been published by civilian groups are: Gordon Lore, *Strange Effects from UFOs* (NICAP Special Report, 1969); Mark Rodeghier, "Summary of Vehicle Interference Reports" in *The Spectrum of UFO Research*, ed. Mimi Hynek (Chicago: CUFOS, 1988) 153; and Ted Phillips, *Physical Traces Associated with UFO Sightings* (Chicago: CUFOS, 1975).

Chapter 1

1. A landscape illuminated by the full moon receives 0.318 lux, or 1.8 10^{-3} watts per square meter. Since there is agreement among the observers that the object had approximately the same brightness as the full moon and was situated about 10 kilometers away, we can compute its total light emitting energy as:

$$L = 1.8 \times 10^{-3} \times 4 \times (10{,}000)^2$$

which gives $L = 2.3$ MW (megawatts).
2. The Grenoble observation is GEPAN Case No. 76305441.
3. The Gujan-Mestras investigation was conducted on behalf of GEPAN by Messrs. Dorrer, Mauroy, and Mouilhayrat.
4. The diameter of the disk was about 5 meters, or 15 feet. The minimum luminosity of the object had to be 10 mW/m^2 (10 milliwatts per square meter) in order to trigger the photocell. Since the energy is given in this case by the formula

$$E = R \left(\frac{r}{d}\right)^2$$

where R = radiance, r = radius of the disk, and d = distance, we compute the minimum and maximum radiance as follows:

$$E_1 = R_1 \left(\frac{2.5}{135}\right)^2 = 100 \text{ mW/m}^2 \text{ hence } R_1 = 29 \text{ W/m}^2$$

$$E_2 = R_2 \left(\frac{15}{480}\right)^2 = 10 \text{ mW/m}^2 \text{ hence } R_2 = 21 \text{ W/m}^2$$

246

leading to a range of total energy (black body radiation) between 160 kW and 5 MW.

5. The Condon report, which reprinted Dr. G.'s calculations, gives the very simple formula

$$E = 150 \, d^2$$

where d = distance between the car and the object. See E. Condon, *Scientific Study of Unidentified Flying Objects* (New York: Bantam, 1969).

Chapter 2

1. The Aurora case was first described in the literature by Hanlon and Vallee in "Airships over Texas," *Flying Saucer Review* 13, no. 1 (January–February 1967): 20. In the same issue, see also the letter on page 27.
2. The Maury Island case will be found in numerous UFO books and magazines, notably Ronald Story, *The Encyclopedia of UFOs* (Garden City, NY: Doubleday, 1980).
3. Frank Edwards mentions the Campinas incident in his book *Flying Saucers—Serious Business* (New York: Bantam, 1966), 42.
4. P. Sturrock, personal communication with author, 1987. Also J. C. Lorin and A. Havette, "Isotopic and Elemental Characterization of a Magnesium Sample of Unknown Origin Collected in Brazil in 1957," (unpublished paper) 1986.
5. J. R. Bumby, *Superconducting Rotating Electrical Machines* (Oxford: Clarendon Press, 1983).
6. K. R. Behrendt, "Understanding Metal-Ejecting UFOs," *Annals of Ufological Research Advances* 1, no. 4 (November 1985).

Chapter 3

1. Analysis by Dr. Richard Haines published in the *Journal of Scientific Exploration* 1, no. 2 (1987).
2. The camera type was RMK 15/23, the film was Kodak Plus X, ASA 80, the exposure time was 1/500 second and the f-stop was 5.6. The disk is located at longitude 84.916° west and latitude 10.583° north. Lake level is at altitude 640 meters.
3. Dr. Richard Haines, personal communication with author, 26 February 1988. Quoted with permission.

4. A report on the phenomenon, along with other cases of submerged objects, was published in the February 1979 edition of *Notiziario UFO*, the excellent journal of Italy's Centro Ufologico Nazionale.

PART TWO

Chapter 4

1. *Santa Rosa Press Democrat*, Wednesday, 31 August 1977.

Chapter 5

1. To protect the privacy of the witnesses, most of the names have been changed, even when the individuals had been quoted in the press at the time. UFO witnesses have been subjected to so much harassment and vandalism that such a procedure seems to be the only ethical way to deal with the cases.

Chapter 6

1. Pierre Giscard, *Mystique ou Hysterie?* (Paris: La Colombe, 1953).

PART THREE

Chapter 7

1. Report by Antonio Chiumiento published in the *Italian UFO Reporter*, June 1987.
2. Technical Note No. 16: "Enquete 81/01–Analyse d'une Trace," Document CT/GEPAN-00013. GEPAN is the Groupe d'Etudes des Phenomenes Aeriens Non-Identifies, located at the Toulouse facility of the French Space Research Agency. In 1988 GEPAN became SEPRA (Service d' Expertise Phénomènes de afdes Rentrée Atmosphérique).
3. Aimé Michel and Charles Bowen, "A Visit to Valensole," *FSR* 14, no. 1 (January–February 1968): 6.; and J. Lemaitre, "A Plan for Valensole," *FSR* 15, no. 4 (July–August 1969): 8.

Chapter 8

1. Lore, *Strange Effects*.
2. On the Michalak case, see Story, *Encylopedia of UFOs*; also E. Barker, letter to the editor, *IUR* (CUFOS) 13, no. 2 (March–April 1988): 21.
3. The Dr. X episode was first published by Aimé Michel in *Flying Saucer*

Review (Special Issue no. 3, September 1969): 3, with a follow-up in *FSR* 17, no. 6 (November–December 1971): 3.

4. Jean-Yves Casgha published his observations in *Le Monde Inconnu*, 1986.
5. Whitley Strieber, *Communion* (New York: William Morrow, 1987).
6. As defined in Garner-Delamare, *Dictionnaire des termes techniques de medecine* (Paris: Maloine, 1978).
7. Daniel Mavrakis, "Du mécanisme d'une akinésie physiologique éventuelle touchant des témoins d'observations rapprochées d'OVNI," personal communication with author.
8. Cells produce K+ ions when releasing energy, while they absorb Na+ ions from the surrounding medium.
9. M. Guiot, Centre de Physiologie du Travail (Paris, France) No. 38, 1958. Reissued in 1962.
10. James McCampbell, "UFO Effects upon People" in *UFOs 1947–1987: The Forty-Year Search for an Explanation*, ed. Hilary Evans (London: Fortean Tomes, 1987): 200–210.
11. Article by Peter Hough in *Australasian Post*, 30 July 1987.
12. The Iron Triangle case of 1951 came to light when the witness reported his observation in 1988 to the Center for UFO Studies.

Chapter 9

1. *UFO Report*, December 1977, p. 30.
2. Richard Haines, *Melbourne Episode* (Los Altos, CA: LDA Press, 1985).
3. The death of Laverne Landis was documented in an Associated Press dispatch, quoted in "Woman Waiting for UFO Dies in Wilderness," *San Francisco Chronicle*, December 1982.
4. Alan Richardson, *Priestess* (London: Aquarian Press, 1987).
5. Ibid.
6. The area in question lies at longitude 40.20° west and latitude 3.45° south.
7. Robert Pratt, "Letter from Brazil," MUFON *Journal* (August 1987): 14.
8. Daniel Rebisso Giese, *OVNI no Para*, personal communication with author.

PART FOUR

Chapter 10

1. Leo Sprinkle, "Impressions of the February 13, 1968 Interview with Sergeant Herbert Schirmer," personal communication with author.

2. Bertrand Meheust has summarized his extensive work on UFOs, folklore, and science fiction in two well-researched books, both published in Paris by Mercure de France: *Science-fiction et soucoupes volantes* (1978) and *Soucoupes volantes et folklore* (1985).

Chapter 11

1. The town's altitude is 1,100 feet, and it is surrounded by small mountains like Cade Mountain, Slater Butte (4,685 feet), China Peak, and Baldy Mountain (5,745 feet), all of which figure prominently in the UFO events.
2. The extensive use of CB radios as a communications medium led to some misunderstandings that initially tended to discredit the entire case. For instance, conversation on the air about road crews using a survey laser called "Satellite" led to rumors that an artificial satellite had crashed in the hills.
3. Rev. 21: 18, 21.
4. I took the samples for analysis (at my expense) to the criminalistics laboratory of the Institute of Forensic Science, in Oakland, California. They were examined using microscopic, chemical, and heating techniques. The report concluded: "The fibers are straight and of uniform diameter (9–10 microns) and cross-section. They show no birefringence when examined with cross-polarizing filters and show a high melting point. They are chemically very inert, being unaffected by hot concentrated sulfuric acid. This combination of properties is characteristic of glass fibers and no other type of fiber."
5. Stuart Holroyd, *Prelude to the Landing on Planet Earth* (London: W. H. Allen, 1977).
6. Thomas Bullard, "Comparative Analysis of UFO Abduction Reports" (Washington: FUFOR, 1987).
7. Streiber, *Communion*; and *Transformation* (New York: William Morrow, 1988).
8. Alvin Lawson, "A Touchstone for Fallacious Abductions: Birth Trauma Imagery in CE3 Narratives," in *The Spectrum of UFO Research*, 71.
9. Martin T. Orne, "The Use and Misuse of Hypnosis in Court," *International Journal of Clinical and Experimental Hypnosis* (October 1979).
10. Philip Klass, *UFO Abductions—A Dangerous Game* (Buffalo: Prometheus Books, 1987).
11. About Sprinkle's statements regarding hypnosis and his own UFO experiences, see: "Some Uses of Hypnosis in UFO Research," *FSR* (Spe-

cial Issue no. 3, September 1969): 17; and "Psychologist Recalls Space Ride," *Fort Collins Coloradan*, 10 July 1988.

12. Joost Meerloo, *Hidden Communion*, New York: Helix Press, 1964.

13. J. Dywan and K. Bowers, "The Use of Hypnosis to Enhance Recall," *Science* 222 (October 14, 1983): 184–185. A clear summary of this research was published in the *Wall Street Journal*, Wednesday, 2 March 1988 under the headline "Memory on Trial. Witnesses of crimes are being challenged as frequently fallible; Courts allow Defense to give psychologists' testimony about unreliable recall; the effect of Personal Biases." Another relevant article, entitled "Flashbulb Memories: The Picture Fades," appeared in *Science News* 133, 4 June 1988.

14. "Do Lie Detectors Really Detect Lies?" UC-Berkeley *Wellness Letter* 4, issue 6.

Chapter 12

1. William E. Clark, "Gold Districts of California," California Department of Mines *Bulletin No. 193* (1970): 136–137.

2. William Murphy, who worked with me throughout the case, drove to Weaverville to find the original claim description. He discovered that it was known locally under various names (Little Brown Bear, Black Bear, Ferrett Mine; Mary Hazel was the official name). The claim had been recorded April 19, 1955, in Book 54, page 493, Mining Claims, Trinity County.

PART FIVE

Introduction

1. Jacques Vallee and Janine Vallee, *Challenge to Science: The UFO Enigma* (Chicago: Henry Regnery, 1966; New York: Ballantine).

Chapter 15

1. Rebisso Giese, *OVNI no Para*.

Conclusion

1. H. Keith Florig, "The Future Battlefield: A Blast of Gigawatts," IEEE *Spectrum* (March 1988).

2. R. Jacobsen and H. Wachtel, in the *Proceedings* of the 6th Annual Meeting of the Bioelectromagnetics Society, Atlanta, 15–19 July 1984.

Appendix

1. Allen J. Hynek, *The UFO Experience* (Chicago: Henry Regnery, 1972), page 10.
2. V. J. Ballester and M. Guasp, "Standards in the Evaluation of UFO Reports," in *The Spectrum of UFO Research,* ed. Mimi Hynek (Chicago, CUFOS, 1988), 175.

Index

ABOUT THE AUTHOR

Born in France, Dr. Jacques Vallee trained in astrophysics. He moved to the United States in 1962, obtained his doctorate in computer science in 1967, and now lives in California with his wife and two children.

A former principal investigator on Department of Defense computer-networking projects and the author of many articles on high technology, Dr. Vallee first became interested in the subject of UFOs when he witnessed the destruction at a major observatory of tracking tapes of unknown objects. His research into the phenomenon has taken him around the world.

In *CONFRONTATIONS* he presents a series of firsthand case investigations conducted in several countries. His analyses support the conclusion that UFOs are neither imaginary nor extraterrestrial. Instead, argues Vallee, they represent a complex technology with potentially harmful effects.